Clifton Fadiman : Sinclair Lewis : Carl Van Doren

THE THREE READERS

DEDICATED TO THE MEMORY OF

Alexander Woollcott

The Contents

SECTION I: Selected by CLIFTON FADIMAN

SECTION II: Selected by SINCLAIR LEWIS

SECTION III: Selected by CARL VAN DOREN

Acknowledgments

Acknowledgment for permission to reprint selections in this volume is gratefully given to the following: GEORGE ADE, for *The Fable of the Foozle & the Successful Approach.* JOHN BAINBRIDGE and THE NEW YORKER, for *Hu Shih's Musketeer* by John Bainbridge; copyright, 1942, by *The New Yorker.* BRANDT & BRANDT, for *The Pelican's Shadow* by Marjorie Kinnan Rawlings; copyright, 1940, by *The New Yorker.* JOHN COLLIER and THE NEW YORKER, for *Back for Christmas* by John Collier; copyright, 1939, by *The New Yorker.* DOUBLEDAY, DORAN AND COMPANY, for *The Hill* by Eleanor Green; copyright, 1936, by Doubleday, Doran and Company. ESQUIRE, INC., for *The Death of Arrowsmith* by Sinclair Lewis; copyright, 1941, by Esquire, Inc., 919 North Michigan Avenue, Chicago (*Coronet,* July 1941). FARRAR & RINEHART, INC., publishers, for *Country People* by Ruth Suckow; copyright, 1924, by Ruth Suckow. HARPER & BROTHERS, for the excerpt from *Three Worlds* by Carl Van Doren; copyright, 1936, by Carl Van Doren. HENRY HOLT AND COMPANY, for *Daybreak,* reprinted from *Thirteen by Corwin;* copyright, 1942, by Norman Corwin. HENRY HOLT AND COMPANY, for *A Winter Diary,* reprinted from *Collected Poems* by Mark Van Doren; copyright, 1939, by Mark Van Doren. B. R. JOHNSTONE and THE HISTORICAL SOCIETY OF PENNSYLVANIA, for material from the *Indian Treaties Printed by Benjamin Franklin.* ALFRED A. KNOPF, INC., for *The Celestial Omnibus,* reprinted from *The Celestial Omnibus and Other Stories* by E. M. Forster, by permission of and special arrangement with Alfred A. Knopf, Inc. THE MACMILLAN COMPANY, for *Zuleika in Cambridge* by S. C. Roberts. MAJOR ST. CLAIR MCKELWAY and THE NEW YORKER for *Benzoin for the Turbinates* by St. Clair McKelway; copyright, 1941, by *The New Yorker.* W. W. NORTON & COMPANY, INC., for *Sea Raider,* reprinted from *My Name Is Frank* by Frank Laskier, published by W. W. Norton & Company, Inc., 70 Fifth Avenue, New York. OXFORD UNIVERSITY PRESS, for *The Struggle for North America,* reprinted from *A Study of History,* Vol. II, by Arnold J. Toynbee. RANDOM HOUSE, for *September 1, 1939,* reprinted from *Another Time: Poems* by W. H. Auden; copyright, 1940, by W. H. Auden. CHARLES SCRIBNER'S SONS, for George Santayana's Preface to his *Poems;* copyright, 1901, 1923, by Charles Scribner's Sons. LIONEL TRILLING and the PARTISAN REVIEW, for *Of this Time, of that Place* by Lionel Trilling; originally published in the *Partisan Review,* January-February, 1943. THE VIKING PRESS, INC., for *Bats,* reprinted from *Animal Treasure* by Ivan T. Sanderson; copyright, 1937, by Ivan T. Sanderson. THE VIKING PRESS, INC., for the excerpt from *Sea of Cortez* by John Steinbeck and E. F. Ricketts; copyright, 1941, by John Steinbeck and E. F. Ricketts.

A Preface: Three Letters to George

IN WHICH THE EDITORS OF THIS VOLUME RESPOND TO THE REQUEST THAT THEY COMMENT UPON THE LITERARY TASTES SHOWN IN THE CONTENTS

1. FROM MR. FADIMAN:

DEAR GEORGE: I am grateful for the chance to explain to the patient members of The Readers Club the handicaps under which I labor in my pitiful attempt to work in harmony with two such literary Pooh-Bahs as Carl Van Doren and Sinclair Lewis.

In the first place, both Van Doren and Lewis have read at least twenty times as many books as I have. This in itself would not be so bad were it not that neither Van Doren nor Lewis has learned to conceal his knowledge one-tenth as expertly as I have learned to conceal my ignorance. When, in the course of one of our conferences in the book-lined living room of the mellow Macy menage, Van Doren and Lewis loftily bat back and forth the titles of volumes I have never even heard of, what is a short-memoried junior like myself—born only yesterday in 1904—to do? Obviously, one thing only: make up my own book-titles, authors, plots, and what have you. The result is that our conference is apt to consist of two-thirds erudition (Van Doren, Lewis) and one-third sheer invention (Fadiman). The strain on my creative faculty is slowly becoming unbearable. So far I have been saved from a breakdown only by the gullibility of Van Doren and Lewis. But I cannot assume that this is inexhaustible.

Now, George, this is not the only handicap under which you make me labor. There is that matter of photographs. Under the terms of my contract—which, as you recollect, I signed after you had applied an acetylene torch for an hour and a half to the soles of my feet—you are entitled to use my picture in those coy advertisements of yours. This not only shows inept business judgment on your part, but causes me acute distress. The fact is that Van Doren looks exactly like the sort of fellow he is—a wise, serene galoot of almost intolerable charm, with a ruggedly handsome face irresistible to any woman over the age of four. As for Lewis, while he is no Victor Mature, he also looks like what he is—one of those irritating geniuses who can penetrate your soul with half a glance, and sum up your entire character in a confounded immortal phrase. Now, next to these unforgettable visages is placed my own. Lewis once said of me (he didn't even have the grace to say it behind my back) that I looked like an amiable floorwalker—and, by God, the man, as usual, was right! Of what avail are all my moral and mental virtues when my photograph reveals the placid countenance of a slightly overfed, slightly bald young man who looks as if he had never encountered an idea in his life? Me, with all that wild poetry pent up beneath the vest which one of these days I will yet constrain to meet the top of my trousers.

Now, George, one more thing. These two world-celebrated colleagues of mine are disturbing my sleep. It so happens that in his salad days Lewis wrote a novel called *Free Air* which, I am reluctantly compelled to admit, is a very fetching book. It did not, however, enjoy the sale that those other trifles—some oddments called *Main Street* and *Arrowsmith* and *Babbitt*—achieved. By the same token, Van Doren a few years ago wrote a study of Jonathan Swift which by some accident happens to be the best book on Swift in English. It, too, never became a best-seller.

Well, you'd think these two literary tycoons would be willing to let sleeping books lie. Not on your life. Naturally, they haven't the nerve, the cravens, to try to bring pressure on me directly. They've worked out something much subtler. About once a week, Van Doren floats into my dreams and apropos of nothing at all, seems to say, "By the way, you know Lewis' early novel *Free Air*? Damn fine book. Seems a shame we can't issue it as a Readers Club choice, just because Lewis is a member of the Editorial Committee." Then the next night the wraith of Lewis will uncoil itself, interrupt my sound sleep, and give me the same selling talk about Van Doren's *Swift*.

George, I warn you that if these two conniving politicians continue to spoil my well-earned rest, if they succeed in working on my subconscious so as to force me to join them in their nefarious schemes to unload their early books on our innocent membership, I shall in turn force you (on pain of letting your ration board know about those three cans of asparagus in your cellar) to print some extraordinary love poems I once wrote. It's true, I was only twelve at the time. But did you ever hear of Chatterton? CLIFTON FADIMAN

2. FROM MR. LEWIS:

DEAR GEORGE: There is a foolish sort of notion that, to start off this first anthology edited by the Three Readers with fireworks and pleasant agony, we are each of us to write you a letter belittling and bedeviling the other two. I am to be humorous and pretty derogatory about Clifton Fadiman and Carl Van Doren, and to hint that personally I am a very dependable judge of books but I have had to put up with their bad judgment and psychopathic unpunctuality.

But I can't do anything of the sort because, possibly leaving out certain encounters with girls, I have never had more fun, along with no inconsiderable reverence, than in working with Van Doren and Fadiman.

They are large, bland, handsome gents, quiet, witty, and amazingly punctual. For the dozens of meetings that the Editorial Committee of The Readers Club has held over the past two years, the latest that any one has ever been was three minutes—and that was Kip Fadiman, and he was appalled at himself. (By the way, that is literal.) Business men are supposed to be so much more efficient than scholars; yet I have never known any business man so precise about appointments, so quick to make up his mind and so dependable in carrying out his promises, as these two.

Dragging for complaints about them, all I can bring up is this: Van Doren is so much the historical scholar, and Fadiman is, under the tinfoil of his radio glitter, so much the liberal humanitarian, that I have never been able to convince them about any of the novels that, just as stories with no soggy ethical import, delight me as a rival fictioneer.

They are serious fellows, these two cultural pathologists who look so much like infantry officers. To them, a book must "mean something." They would prefer a ponderous bad funeral march to a good gay sonata. For two years I have been trying to persuade them that The Readers Club ought to publish *Night Over Fitch's Pond* by Cora Jarrett, *Four Frightened People* by Arnot Robertson, *Vile*

Bodies and *Decline and Fall* by Evelyn Waugh, any of the crime masterpieces of Joseph Shearing, particularly *The Spider in the Cup* and *The Golden Violet;* and this year I have been trumpeting for *In the Forests of the Night* by Kenneth Davis. But the best I could ever get out of these major generals was a condescending "Ye-es, it's a fairly good *story,* but——"

To quote myself, George, "Fadiman prefers the brief epilogue that Leo Tolstoy has added to Clifton Fadiman's *Introduction to War and Peace,*" while Van Doren, to quote myself again, would rather possess a thousand-word treatise on the uniforms of the Seventh New Hampshire Militia at the Battle of Saratoga than a newly-discovered story by Saki illustrated by Leonardo da Vinci and published by the Elzevirs or even by your Limited Editions Club (adv.).

But I hope to endure them both for the next twenty years.

SINCLAIR LEWIS

3. FROM MR. VAN DOREN:

DEAR GEORGE: It will be up to me, I suppose, to get some poetry and history into THE THREE READERS. Fadiman and Lewis talk about William Butler Yeats from time to time, but they seldom mention a poet in our discussions. Lewis is a renegade from verse, who began his writing life at nineteen with tender poems like A Song of Prince Hal, Puck to Queen Mab, A May Time Carol, The Coward Minstrel, but now only improvises rhymes when the fit hits him. Do you remember the day we went to visit Woollcott on what Fadiman would call the Lake Isle of Bomoseen; and Lewis on the way back suddenly burst out with

Why should Alex
Live in a palex?

and then settled back into another year of prose? As to Fadiman, who was born with a steel trap in his mouth, I suspect him of never having had his fling—like wilder young men—at verse at all. He lisped in *bon-mots,* for the *bon-mots* came. Still, he has gone on liking Yeats through all his changes.

As to history, Fadiman prefers theories about it—provided they are not by Spengler—to histories themselves. And Lewis, though he is a principal historian of our times, gets his history through his skin. Mention something that happened farther back than Lewis can remember, and he may look skeptical. Mention something that F. P. A. or John Kieran might not remember, and Fadiman may regard it as irrelevant. Fadiman and Lewis, active as grasshoppers, may jump in any direction, but they are, like grasshoppers, not likely to jump backwards. This is a fine way to keep from being dull in your writing, but it is also a fine way to miss a good deal of substance and flavor in your reading. I mean to slip into my section of THE THREE READERS some things that have never been referred to in any Lewis novel and will never come up as questions for Information Please.

And I mean, too, to allow more space to love—verse and prose—in my section than we have in general allowed it in The Readers Club selections. Lewis is disposed to straight-arm love when he meets it in literature, and Fadiman to high-hat it. I look on it as a force of nature and study it, observing or reading, with respect. After all, without some such force in nature there would be no Lewis, no Fadiman.

Perhaps in the prefatory letters you have asked for, the Three Readers of your Committee have revealed some secrets about each other's tastes that it might have been wiser to keep private. But in fact nobody can reveal secrets about an editor like the editor himself. His selections tell as much about his mind as a poet's sonnets tell about his heart. My guess is that Lewis's part of this volume will be full of stories. After fifty years of reading novels and thirty years of writing them, he still has an appetite for fiction, like an ageless man who has never lost the sweet-tooth of his greedy boyhood. Fadiman's part will be boiling with ideas, explicit in argument or implicit in forms of art; and there will probably be a pun in his preface.

CARL VAN DOREN

THE THREE READERS

Section I: Selected by Clifton Fadiman

Introductory Remarks

Mr. George Macy, in that airy publisher's manner of his, suggested that I heap together sixty or seventy thousand words of reading that I would like to persuade other people to read. I dove at once into my files (consisting of a bad memory that is not improving with age) and emerged with the treasures, as I think, displayed in the pages that follow.

I have been trying to figure out what principle of unity can possibly govern this baker's dozen of oddments: a shivery trick of a tale, some popular natural science, a masterpiece of classic French literature, a *New Yorker* report on the sniffles, a grave poem by a young Englishman, a long short story by an American newcomer, a British mariner's true yarn, a diaphanous literary burlesque, an essay drawn from the work of the greatest living theorist of history, a stray piece of comic verse, an allegorical fantasy, a few pages of diversion from the hand of a famous American novelist, and some seventeenth-century rules for judicial conduct.

There is no principle of unity observable, except the trivial circumstance that all of these morsels of prose or verse have at one time or another aroused my admiration to a pitch of fervency sufficient to turn me into a literary evangelist. I do not know why professional readers like myself are so lacking in self-control that we must perforce try to convert others to our own enthusiasms. Perhaps we read so much, so quickly, with such excessive catholicity, that we grow unsure of our own taste, and timidly solicit the agreement of others.

In any case, I believe that each of these selections is sound writing of its kind; that only two (those by Toynbee and Flaubert) have any claim to permanence; that one (by Lionel Trilling) is a discovery; and that I would give a good deal to have written any of them and am sadly aware of my total incapacity to do so.

Like many good things, John Collier's "Back for Christmas" originally appeared in the pages of *The New Yorker,* in the issue of October 7, 1939. It is a piece of pure, devilishly ingenious manipulation, and I suppose sardonic is the word for its special atmosphere. Mr. Collier has inherited the mantle of Saki, but he adds to that minor master's cynical wit and infernal fancy an extraordinary faculty of invention. I hope to be able to persuade my colleagues that The Readers Club owes its membership an omnibus John Collier. If you enjoy this murderous trifle, you might drop me a card, and tell me so, and help along my Collier campaign.

Mr. Ivan T. Sanderson is also in my good books. He is a brilliant young English zoologist and naturalist who above all things prefers to poke about in nasty places observing unpleasant animals. Out of this lunatic activity he somehow concocts fascinating volumes. From one of them, *Animal Treasure,* published in 1937, I have drawn a long account of some bats Mr. Sanderson made friends with in West Africa. To my mind it is as good as anything William Beebe ever wrote, almost as good as W. H. Hudson.

If you haven't read *Animal Treasure,* perhaps Mr. Sanderson's bats may impel you to do so. In Nigeria he encountered not only these odd and to me obsessively interesting creatures, but also rats with yellow spots and spiral tails, belching baboons, a green-and-orange frog that blows sky-blue bubbles, a lizard with a demountable tail, squirrels that make booming noises, and skinks that bellow like foghorns. He tells you about giant water-shrews and leering whip scorpions and supercilious toads; gives you the low-down on how to skin, cut up, and preserve a quarter-ton gorilla; how to find out what's going on inside a hollow tree; how to amuse the natives with swing music recorded by the Washboard Rhythm Kings. He is admirable on hippos, terrifying on spiders, epic on rats. As for these rats, I am pleased to pass along the information that the family in general is called *Rattus;* that there is a species known as *Rattus rattus;* and that, finally, there is a sub-species, *Rattus rattus rattus.*

Of Gustave Flaubert's "A Simple Heart" there is little to say. I think it is the most beautiful thing he ever wrote, and it is generally considered one of the greatest stories of the world. "A Simple Heart" has been reprinted, but not often enough, and my hope is that even among the extremely well-read members of this Club there may be several to whom it will come as something new. It is very simple, very quiet, apparently without any pretension; like the Psalms, like the Sermon on the Mount. I think a comment by Edward J. O'Brien expresses its quality perfectly. He said, "This story is the greatest act of faith made by any story teller I know."

St. Clair McKelway's hilarious piece of research on the Common

Cold appeared in the March 22, 1941, issue of *The New Yorker.* Since that date, I am assured by Mr.—now Major—McKelway, nothing much has occurred to diminish the commonness of the Common Cold. Like the weather (with which it is connected—or is it?) a cold remains something everybody discusses and nobody does anything about. In addition to being a brilliant job of writing in itself, "Benzoin for the Turbinates" pulls the leg of the great god Science in a manner to gladden the heart of anyone who has ever visited a doctor.

I am no judge of modern poetry, a defect which, some of my friends tell me, saves me much painful reading. For example, though I admire the English poet W. H. Auden, I do not always understand him, and still less often enjoy him. By some strange chance, however, I enjoy, understand, and admire the curiously haunting poem you will find below. It is titled with a fatal date, but applies as justly in 1943 as it did in 1939.

Lionel Trilling, a young professor of literature who teaches at Columbia, is of Mr. Auden's generation, but is making his mark more slowly. He has written some of the most thoughtful literary criticism of our time, work that deserves collection. "Of this Time, of that Place" seems to me the work of a man now ready to write fine fiction. (It appeared in the January-February 1943 issue of the *Partisan Review.*) In Mr. Trilling's story I am not certain what he means to convey by the girl with the camera, but the rest of the tale seems to me beautifully balanced, poised, sensitive. Its material is of the sort that in coarser hands would lend itself to easy satire; Mr. Trilling apparently was not even aware of the temptation. "Of this Time, of that Place" is subtle, but not obscure. It merits careful reading.

A great deal of literature, of course, is never written down—the forecastle yarn, for instance. Sailors are among the least inarticulate of men, but very few of us ever get a chance to listen to them. In the spring and summer of 1941 a British merchant mariner named Frank Laskier was induced to tell some true stories of his wartime experiences, ad libbing them into the microphone of the British Broadcasting Corporation. He was a great success simply because he proved a natural spinner of yarns. I've chosen one of his tales, "Sea Raider" (this was the *Von Scheer,* by the way), because I consider it an extraordinary piece of legitimate rhetoric. Also because I hope it will help people to hate to the death—and beyond it—those self-declared enemies of, and traitors to, the human race—the Germans.

As a contrast to Frank's tale I sought something dulcet and artificial, and in *Zuleika in Cambridge* I think I have found it. Readers of that now slightly faded classic, *Zuleika Dobson* by Sir Max Beerbohm, will recall that after the brash and bewitching Zuleika had worked havoc among the students of Oxford, she decided to leave the scene of carnage and attempt the hearts of the Cantabrigians. On the note of this resolve the book ends.

And so it was that until recently the Zuleika's Cambridge adventures ranked with the song the sirens sang and the name Achilles assumed when he hid himself among women. But at last the great Dobson mystery has been unlocked by Mr. S. C. Roberts, of whom I know nothing but suspect of being a don. The creator of Zuleika himself has seen fit to approve Mr. Roberts' ingenious guesses. Says Sir Max, "I had often wondered what happened when Zuleika went to Cambridge. And now I know beyond any shadow of a doubt."

Everyone is aware that Oxford and Cambridge exist on separate planets and have no common center. It is with their differences, often of an extremely rarefied quality, that this toothsome piece of preciosity deals. Its humor, I grant you, is of the mildest and most donnish and most English and even most eighteen-ninetyish; but true humor nonetheless. The inclusion in THE THREE READERS of this pastiche of a pastiche is a miniature scoop, for there are but a few hundred copies of the paper-covered English edition (1941) available in this country. I do not suppose many of our members can have run across them.

From the diverting triviality of Mr. Roberts' *jeu d'esprit* I invite our members to turn their attention to a few characteristic pages drawn from a work which I consider the most magnificent intellectual structure of our time, six enormous volumes of whose projected nine or ten have already been published. They are familiar to most historical students and to a few laymen, such as myself, who have been fortunate enough to come upon them.

A Study of History by Arnold J. Toynbee, Research Professor of International History in the University of London, is the book which during the last decade has made the deepest impression on my own mind. It is a difficult and incredibly learned discussion of the birth, growth, breakdowns and disintegrations of civilizations. I do not claim the ability to follow all of Dr. Toynbee's sweeping arguments and I am certainly completely disqualified to comment on his all-time, all-space embracing scholarship. Yet I am certain that this book (or rather series of books) reduces to relative unimportance the much-touted theses of Spengler and Pareto.

Toynbee's style is dense, grave, measured, with occasional glints of ceremonious humor. In his sanity, his objectivity (he is a universal, not a British historian), his unswerving appeal to experience, he represents the finest tradition of English historical writing. Inspiring as are the intellectual vistas his multifarious new theses open up, it is the quality of his mind that even more powerfully arouses one's admiration—so clean, pure, courageous, and truly religious is it.

His great work was composed during the troubled and uncertain thirties; it is still being composed; it was being written as bombs crashed on London. Like Flaubert's "A Simple Heart," but far more dramatically, it is a superb act of faith and a gesture of courage. The Western Civilization, which is ours, and which is one of the many Toynbee discusses, may be passing into a new, perhaps a darker phase; but Toynbee, like a great doctor charting the course of his own disease, proceeds to analyze it with a calm and a power given only to minds that live, like the observer in Lucretius' *De Rerum Natura,* upon a mountain top. The quality of his mind is perhaps indicated by the four wonderful lines from the old Anglo-Saxon *Lay of the Battle of Maldon,* which appears on the title-page of Volume I:

"Thought shall be the harder,
Heart the keener,
Mood shall be the more,
As our might lessens."

In his preface to Parts IV and V, Toynbee has a final paragraph that I find masterful in its combination of modesty, stoic dignity, and true authority. I quote it:

"Though the original sketch of Parts IV and V was worked out, like that of all the parts that precede and follow, in the summers of 1927 and 1928, the actual writing of Part IV was not begun before the summer of 1933, and the last proofs were sent to press, at a moment of public anxiety and private grief, in March 1939. It will be seen from the dates that the contemporary atmosphere in which the present three volumes were produced was painfully appropriate to the themes of "breakdown" and "disintegration" which these volumes have for their subjects. There were moments when it almost seemed like tempting Fate and wasting effort to go on writing a book that must be the work of many years, when a catastrophe might overtake the writer's world within the next few weeks or days. At such moments the writer has often fortified his will by calling to mind the dates of writing of another book with which this book is comparable only on the single point of length. Saint Augustine did not begin writing *De Civitate Dei* before the sack of Rome by Alaric in A.D.

410; yet he finished the work within the next twenty years, and, although, at the moment of his death in A.D. 430 in his episcopal see of Hippo, a Vandal war-band was beleaguering the city-walls, the book survived to inform the minds and inspire the souls of Christians from that day to this, in times and places that were far beyond the fifth-century African Father's mundane horizon. Of course the author of this tale of two cities had a supramundane range of vision in comparison with which no appreciable difference is made by a few thousand terrestrial miles or years more or less; and a glimpse of this vision is the boon for which the present writer is the most deeply grateful to the writer of *De Civitate Dei.*"

To choose among the thousands of pages that comprise what is so far published of *A Study of History* is a task of almost insuperable difficulty. I have selected from Volume II a short section, comprehensible, I hope, in itself, entitled "The Struggle for North America." This is one of the many examples Toynbee uses to make clear what he calls "the stimulus of hard countries." One of his major arguments revolves around his conception of "challenge-and-response," the notion that certain high forms of civilization arise as a direct result of a challenge, a difficulty, a set of obstacles. One of these challenges is often that posed by a hard terrain, an unpromising physical environment. In "The Struggle for North America" Toynbee works out this idea with extraordinary cogency, inventiveness, and even humor.

Now, to descend from the cosmic to the miniature: Many years ago, in a faded Victorian compilation called *Ballades and Rondeaus,* selected and edited by Gleeson White, I came across some verses called "Monologue d'Outre Tombe." For twenty years I have considered them a wondrous merger of the laughable and the gruesome. The odd form of the "Monologue" is such that when you have read it three or four times it is hard to get its lines out of your head. It is also an excellent versified illustration of the law of the transmutation of energy.

The curious reiterative pattern in which it is composed is called a *pantoum.* The *pantoum,* not a French verse form but of Malay invention, is oddly suited to the securing of one of the rarest of (conscious) literary effects—that of monotony. In this case the effect of humor is secured at the same time.

I would be grateful to our members for any clue to the author of this soliloquy of a corpse. I have never seen it included in any anthology of verse, except the little out-of-print Gleeson White collection. I hope it will amuse you as much as it has amused me. Funnybones, however, differ.

Following this piece of *macabric-à-brac* the reader will come upon "The Celestial Omnibus." I suppose in a sense all the writings of E. M. Forster, the still widely unrecognized dean of English novelists, deal with a single theme: the collision, quiet and often fatal, between the claims of the imagination and the claims of reality. It is of this ancient war that "The Celestial Omnibus" is a fantastic record, charming and chilling. It is a fairy-tale about poetry which, as the terrible-faced driver of the Celestial Omnibus reminds his strangely assorted passengers, "is a spirit; and they that would worship it must worship in spirit and in truth." Like all Mr. Forster's tales, this is a very moral one; and fragile; and beautiful. I fear it has been rather widely reprinted. Should some of our members find it over-familiar, I hope they will not nurse against me too obstinate a grudge.

Just two more, and we're through. In a brilliant essay, Edmund Wilson has interpreted John Steinbeck as a biological novelist, one whose vision of life flows from his sensitivity to its animal manifestations. This would explain why Steinbeck writes even better about beasts than about men. It also explains why, despite the warmth of his social sympathies, he seems so curiously detached.

Sea of Cortez, written a couple of years ago in collaboration with E. F. Ricketts, one of Mr. Steinbeck's biologist friends, would seem to drive home Wilson's thesis to the hilt. It was obviously composed not merely to tell us—and interestingly, too—about how the marine invertebrates of the Panamic faunal province are killed, preserved, labeled, and classified. Nor was it written as a simple narrative of the small adventures, many of them quite comical, that befell the crew on the expedition. It was written primarily to explain Steinbeck's view of life and mode of thinking.

Steinbeck is an intellectual anti-isolationist. He is interested in interrelationships. His aim, whether as novelist in *The Grapes of Wrath* or as amateur philosopher in *Sea of Cortez,* is to arrive at the total pattern—he calls it the "design"—of any experience. Anyone interested in total pattern is apt to be amoral in his judgments, for all moral judgments proceed out of the isolation of experience, the statement *"This* is more important or more valuable than *that."* Thus, Steinbeck is anti-teleological in his thinking, as all good biologists should be; his eye is on the thing as it is, not on the thing as it should be. This is-thinking, as Steinbeck calls it, means to him what the killing of large animals does to Hemingway. It has religious, even mystical overtones for him, overtones that may be inaudible to other ears. It makes him aware not only of the ecological but of the evolutionary relationship between man and the Lightfoot crab. His mind is attuned to the survivals in us of previous existences. He believes in biological memory (more than a trace of Jung here), and some of the finest passages in the book have to do with atavism in man.

I transcribe herewith a few pages from this "leisurely journal of travel and research." As a matter of fact, they are not particularly characteristic of *Sea of Cortez* nor of Steinbeck generally. I commend them to the attention of our members because I find them highly amusing and, also, for the more solemn reason that they are a first-rate example of how the lingo of science can be manipulated by a subtle mind to yield rich humor.

For a tail-piece I have turned to a British Lord Justice, dead for some centuries. I once visited the pleasant chambers of United States District Court Judge John M. Woolsey, author of the famous *Ulysses* decision which lifted the ban on that classic. On the wall I noticed a broadside, beautifully printed by the Merrymount Press of Boston, and was struck by its sharp wit and sound, nutty seventeenth-century prose. I reproduce it here because Justice is a matter that concerns not Justices alone, but all of us.

Back for Christmas

BY JOHN COLLIER

"DOCTOR," SAID Major Sinclair, "we certainly must have you with us for Christmas." It was afternoon and the Carpenters' living room was filled with friends who had come to say last-minute farewells to the Doctor and his wife.

"He shall be back," said Mrs. Carpenter. "I promise you."

"It's hardly certain," said Dr. Carpenter. "I'd like nothing better, of course."

"After all," said Mr. Hewitt, "you've contracted to lecture only for three months."

"Anything may happen," said Dr. Carpenter.

"Whatever happens," said Mrs. Carpenter, beaming at them, "he shall be back in England for Christmas. You may all believe me."

They all believed her. The Doctor himself almost believed her. For ten years she had been promising him for dinner parties, garden parties, committees, heaven knows what, and the promises had always been kept.

The farewells began. There was a fluting of compliments on dear Hermione's marvellous arrangements. She and her husband would drive to Southampton that evening. They would embark the following day. No trains, no bustle, no last-minute worries. Certainly the Doctor was marvellously looked after. He would be a great success in America. Especially with Hermione to see to everything. She would have a wonderful time, too. She would see the skyscrapers. Nothing like that in Little Godwearing. But she must be very sure to bring him back. "Yes, I will bring him back. You may rely upon it." He mustn't be persuaded. No extensions. No wonderful post at some super-American hospital. Our infirmary needs him. And he must be back by Christmas. "Yes," Mrs. Carpenter called to the last departing guest, "I shall see to it. He shall be back by Christmas."

The final arrangements for closing the house were very well managed. The maids soon had the tea things washed up; they came in, said goodbye, and were in time to catch the afternoon bus to Devizes.

Nothing remained but odds and ends, locking doors, seeing that everything was tidy. "Go upstairs," said Hermione, "and change into your brown tweeds. Empty the pockets of that suit before you put it in your bag. I'll see to everything else. All you have to do is not to get in the way."

The Doctor went upstairs and took off the suit he was wearing, but instead of the brown tweeds, he put on an old, dirty bath gown, which he took from the back of his wardrobe. Then, after making one or two little arrangements, he leaned over the head of the stairs and called to his wife, "Hermione! Have you a moment to spare?"

"Of course, dear. I'm just finished."

"Just come up here for a moment. There's something rather extraordinary up here."

Hermione immediately came up. "Good heavens, my dear man!" she said when she saw her husband. "What are you lounging about in that filthy old thing for? I told you to have it burned long ago."

"Who in the world," said the Doctor, "has dropped a gold chain down the bathtub drain?"

"Nobody has, of course," said Hermione. "Nobody wears such a thing."

"Then what is it doing there?" said the Doctor. "Take this flashlight. If you lean right over, you can see it shining, deep down."

"Some Woolworth's bangle off one of the maids," said Hermione. "It can be nothing else." However, she took the flashlight and leaned over, squinting into the drain. The Doctor, raising a short length of lead pipe, struck two or three times with great force and precision, and tilting the body by the knees, tumbled it into the tub.

He then slipped off the bathrobe and, standing completely naked, unwrapped a towel full of implements and put them into the washbasin. He spread several sheets of newspaper on the floor and turned once more to his victim.

She was dead, of course—horribly doubled up, like a somersaulter, at one end of the tub. He stood looking at her for a very long time, thinking of absolutely nothing at all. Then he saw how much blood there was and his mind began to move again.

First he pushed and pulled until she lay straight in the bath, then he removed her clothing. In a narrow bathtub this was an extremely clumsy business, but he managed it at last and then turned on the taps. The water rushed into the tub, then dwindled, then died away, and the last of it gurgled down the drain.

"Good God!" he said. "She turned it off at the main."

There was only one thing to do: the Doctor hastily wiped his hands on a towel, opened the bathroom door with a clean corner of the towel, threw it back onto the bath stool, and ran downstairs, barefoot, light as a cat. The cellar door was in a corner of the entrance hall, under the stairs. He knew just where the cut-off was. He had reason to: he had been pottering about down there for some time past—trying to scrape out a bin for wine, he had told Hermione. He pushed open the cellar door, went down the steep steps, and just before the closing door plunged the cellar into pitch darkness, he put his hand on the tap and turned it on. Then he felt his way back along the grimy wall till he came to the steps. He was about to ascend them when the bell rang.

The Doctor was scarcely aware of the ringing as a sound. It was like a spike of iron pushed slowly up through his stomach. It went on until it reached his brain. Then something broke. He threw himself down in the coal dust on the floor and said, "I'm through. I'm through."

"They've got no right to come. Fools!" he said. Then he heard himself panting. "None of this," he said to himself. "None of this."

He began to revive. He got to his feet, and when the bell rang again the sound passed through him almost painlessly. "Let them go away," he said. Then he heard the front door open. He said, "I don't care." His shoulder came up, like that of a boxer, to shield his face. "I give up," he said.

He heard people calling. "Herbert!" "Hermione!" It was the Wallingfords. "Damn them! They come butting in. People anxious to get off. All naked! And blood and coal dust! I'm done! I'm through! I can't do it."

"Herbert!"

"Hermione!"

"Where the dickens can they be?"

"The car's there."

"Maybe they've popped round to Mrs. Liddell's."

"We must see them."

"Or to the shops, maybe. Something at the last minute."

"Not Hermione. I say, listen! Isn't that someone having a bath? Shall I shout? What about whanging on the door?"

"Sh-h-h! Don't. It might not be tactful."

"No harm in a shout."

"Look, dear. Let's come in on our way back. Hermione said they wouldn't be leaving before seven. They're dining on the way, in Salisbury."

"Think so? All right. Only I want a last drink with old Herbert. He'd be hurt."

"Let's hurry. We can be back by half past six."

The Doctor heard them walk out and the front door close quietly behind them. He thought, "Half past six. I can do it."

He crossed the hall, sprang the latch of the front door, went upstairs, and taking his instruments from the washbasin, finished what he had to do. He came down again, clad in his bath gown, carrying parcel after parcel of towelling or newspaper neatly secured with safety pins. These he packed carefully into the narrow, deep hole he had made in the corner of the cellar, shovelled in the soil, spread coal dust over all, satisfied himself that everything was in order, and went upstairs again. He then thoroughly cleansed the bath, and himself, and the bath again, dressed, and took his wife's clothing and his bath gown to the incinerator.

One or two more little touches and everything was in order. It was only quarter past six. The Wallingfords were always late; he had only to get into the car and drive off. It was a pity he couldn't wait till after dusk, but he could make a detour to avoid passing through the main street, and even if he was seen driving alone, people would only think Hermione had gone on ahead for some reason and they would forget about it.

Still, he was glad when he had finally got away, entirely unobserved, on the open road, driving into the gathering dusk. He had to drive very carefully; he found himself unable to judge distances, his reactions were abnormally delayed, but that was a detail. When it was quite dark he allowed himself to stop the car on the top of the downs, in order to think.

The stars were superb. He could see the lights of one or two little towns far away on the plain below him. He was exultant. Everything that was to follow was perfectly simple. Marion was waiting in Chicago. She already believed him to be a widower. The lecture people could be put off with a word. He had nothing to do but establish himself in some thriving out-of-the-way town in America and he was safe forever. There were Hermione's clothes, of course, in the suitcases: they could be disposed of through the porthole. Thank heaven she wrote her letters on the typewriter—a little thing like handwriting might have prevented everything. "But there you are," he said. "She was up-to-date, efficient all along the line. Managed everything. Managed herself to death, damn her!"

"There's no reason to get excited," he thought. "I'll write a few letters for her, then fewer and fewer. Write myself—always expecting to get back, never quite able to. Keep the house one year, then another, then another; they'll get used to it. Might even come back alone in a year or two and clear it up properly. Nothing easier. But not for Christmas!" He started up the engine and was off.

In New York he felt free at last, really free. He was safe. He could look back with pleasure—at least, after a meal, lighting his cigarette, he could look back with a sort of pleasure—to the minute he had passed in the cellar listening to the bell, the door, and the voices. He could look forward to Marion.

As he strolled through the lobby of his hotel, the clerk, smiling, held up letters for him. It was the first batch from England. Well, what did that matter? It would be fun dashing off the typewritten sheets in Hermione's downright style, signing them with her squiggle, telling everyone what a success his first lecture had been, how thrilled he was with America but how certainly she'd bring him back for Christmas. Doubts could creep in later.

He glanced over the letters. Most were for Hermione. From the Sinclairs, the Wallingfords, the vicar, and a business letter from Holt & Sons, Builders and Decorators.

He stood in the lounge, people brushing by him. He opened the letters with his thumb, reading here and there, smiling. They all seemed very confident he would be back for Christmas. They relied on Hermione. "That's where they make their big mistake," said the Doctor, who had taken to American phrases. The builder's letter he kept to the last. Some bill, probably. It was:

"DEAR MADAM,

We are in receipt of your kind acceptance of estimate as below, and also of key.

We beg to repeat you may have every confidence in same being ready in ample time for Christmas present as stated. We are setting men to work this week.

We are, Madam,

Yours faithfully,

PAUL HOLT & SONS

To excavating, building up, suitably lining one sunken wine bin in cellar as indicated, using best materials, making good, etc.

£18/0/0"

Bats

BY IVAN T. SANDERSON

Everybody is at least vaguely aware of the existence of bats. Even the town dweller may, if he care to, notice their little phantom forms flitting around the houses. Believe it or not, there are bats sleeping in the Albert Memorial in Kensington Gardens every day of the year. Still, probably less than one person in every five hundred thousand could describe accurately what any bat really looks like.

In Africa, as in other tropical countries where bats are even more numerous, it is much the same. These strange creatures are one of the most diverse and numerically predominant groups of animals in existence, yet they live around and among us like ghosts, unnoticed and unknown.

What is the reason, or what are the reasons?

This was a question that we asked ourselves as soon as we got to Africa. The answer was fairly simple—bats fly by night. But it is how and where they fly that are the vital points; these lead us into a number of problems that have so far been confined to the realms of pure science. Nevertheless, they proved to be so interesting to us, as we investigated each problem in turn, that I feel our troubles may be shared with you.

Scientists divide the bats into two classes—the *Megacheiroptera* and the *Microcheiroptera*—which only mean the "large bats" and the "small bats." The former are vegetarians, the latter mostly carnivorous, eating insects or sucking blood. We soon discovered, however, that from the point of view of the collector this division was not quite satisfactory. The habits of the two groups overlap somewhat.

We noticed, in fact, that the bats fell into the following two classes: those that fly in the open air away from trees and obstructions when they first appear every evening and, secondly, those that do not. Nearly all the large frugivorous bats belong to the first class, almost all the small insectivorous ones to the second; but, still from the point of view of the collector, there is another vast difference between them. The first can be shot, the second cannot, except in unusual circumstances.

When the sun begins to set, the first group of bats leaves its hide-outs and soars into the air. They ascend to a very great height, more-over, primarily because the insects are still flying in the warm upper atmosphere or, in the case of fruit bats, because they have to travel some distance to their feeding grounds. Also, this first lot of bats descends towards the earth only by degrees, and all the time it is getting darker every second. By the time they are within gun-shot range, it is far too dark to sight them; they are an almost impossible target at the best of times.

The second type of bat—those that do not fly in the open—has even more irritating habits. As dusk comes rapidly in this country of forests, woods, and endless vegetation, deep shadows are cast across the whole landscape, so that little patches of ever-extending night mottle the whole countryside. The bats—all the small ones—emerge as soon as these shadows are black enough, and content themselves with flashing back and forth from the gloomy depths of one patch of forest to another, always keeping in the darkest shadows in their flight.

Both groups are therefore from the outset well out of range of any designing human. These facts we quickly appreciated. Had we realized that our troubles were really only just beginning, I believe we should have given up the attempt to collect these animals right away. In our ignorance, we believed that we would be able to shoot them none the less, and also eventually discover them in their re-treats during the daylight hours. In both these things we had made serious miscalculations.

Nobody seems to appreciate just what a bat's flight consists of. Practically all birds behave in the air in much the same manner as an airplane, or at least as a helicopter, but a bat—words fail me en-tirely! To support the body in the air during flight the wings, which are formed, as everybody knows, by the elongated fingers with a thin membrane stretched between them, are moved up and down and, what is more important, backwards and forwards. The wing is, in fact, used exactly like a hand clawing at the air to gain a grip. Since this hand is a multitude of joints bent in a score of different direc-tions, and because the whole animal is constructed to facilitate the capture of minute, swift-flying insects, the so-called flight becomes a jumble of the most fantastic motions imaginable. Flight consists of a series of collapses, jerks, spurts, headlong drops, side-slips, and indiscriminate tumbles that defy description, all known laws of dynamics, and the swiftest aim with a gun.

The species that fly in the open air are not such bad offenders in this respect as those that do not, but apart from the fruit bats, which have a steadier flight, they are nevertheless best described as tortured animated springs let loose in the clear air.

Now if you will just consider the following facts, you may be able to appreciate the difficulties that we were up against. The body of a bat may be taken as, on an average, about one-fifteenth of the area of the whole animal when the wings are fully extended. The flight of some species is so swift that when they are proceeding in a straight line—which is rare—they cannot be photographed with an ordinary film-camera. There is no given direction for a bat's flight—it depends solely on the spatio-temporal relation of the next insect! Lastly, the animal is either at the very limit of gun range or makes its appearance only for a second in a deep shadow among dense vegetation. I may add that a bat frequently closes its wings entirely in mid-air during flight to increase the speed of its descent upon a crisp mouthful.

Will you place yourself on a plot of rough ground covered with fallen trees, ant-hills, and tangled ground creepers, and imagine yourself gazing up into the rapidly darkening sky (a thing you have already been doing for twenty minutes, to the discomfort of your neck)? Suddenly a tiny flitting thing skids out of the invisible beyond and you imagine it is within the range of your gun, now that the latter seems to weigh half a ton. You stumble backwards trying to take aim at the dot above. First it is to your right side, now above you, then to the front, now right behind. At last you are roughly covering it with your sight—then suddenly something happens, in a flash it has become only one-fifteenth its former size. You blaze away—or perhaps you don't—only to see the wretched creature streak off in the least expected direction just slowly enough for the eye to follow. Disgusted with this encounter, you repair to the adjacent forest and take up your position in a silent narrow glade.

An endless stream of small flashes is projected out of the trees from one side to the other. You raise your gun, determined to fire at the very next to appear. At first they are too quick for you. Since it is almost dark, you determine to press the trigger as soon as one flies by your aim. Not one comes out. The stream has ceased, but presently commences again in the opposite direction, the vanguard passing between your legs and between your nose and the end of the gun. Exasperated, you wheel about, but as you do so the whole ground bursts into eddies of practically invisible flitting forms. You fire at random but there is nothing there.

It is now so dark that you light your torch, affix it to your forehead, and stand with your gun to your shoulder facing down the beam of light which is cast into the glade. Bats rocket from everywhere. All at once a flopping, fluttering entity appears, coming straight down the beam of the bright light. Overjoyed at this unexpected chance, you try to take aim, but the bat is now here, now there, and always advancing directly at you.

You fire. Bang! Out of the smoke appears the bat. With a sideslip it skids past the muzzle of your gun and is gone over your left shoulder.

I ask you—what are you to do with tangible ghosts?

Our base camp at Mamfe was housed in a structure known locally as a rest house. These abodes are thoughtfully provided by the government at all the "stations" and in most of the more important villages on the main forest pathways between them. They vary greatly in size, shape, and development. The most primitive are little better or even worse than the meanest local native houses; the best, in big towns where many white officials and traders are domiciled, are truly palatial dwellings with verandas, gardens, ice-boxes, and electric light. The village rest houses are mere mud and wattle structures built on the native plan. The worst station rest houses are glorified editions of these, but the better ones are stone-built structures with "pan" (corrugated-iron) roofs.

Mamfe provided just such a one. It consisted of two square rooms, each with two doors and two windows, built on a raised concrete platform which formed a veranda all round. A conical tin roof covered the whole. The underside of the roof over the veranda was neatly covered in with match-boarding brought at great expense from Europe; the rooms were similarly roofed, though here the boarding was horizontal, so that a small "un-get-at-able" attic was sealed above to catch the dust, the dead rats, and the heat.

We slept and bathed in one room, worked in another, and fed on the veranda on the leeward side. Simple though perfect domestic arrangements that should content the most élite.

A few days after our arrival at Mamfe, George and I were contentedly browsing on platefuls of rice and chicken with groundnuts, and gazing out at the night between the cascade of miniature waterfalls streaming from the pan roof above. It wasn't raining; it was pouring as it can do only in the tropics. It was, to be precise, the seventy-third hour that the elements had been giving vent to their pent-up emotions in this unmistakable manner. We were so pleased to have reached our destination and got unpacked without a single loss, that not even all this water could dispel our satisfaction.

The rice stowed neatly away in its appointed place, we leant back preparatory to a period of groaning. Then we noticed that several bats were silently flitting round the veranda in the angle formed by the match-board lining to the roof and the outside walls of the central living rooms. A multitude of insects had congregated there, attracted by the bright light.

We watched these bats flying round and round the house with such regularity that we could time their exact appearance round the corner. There were about half a dozen of them. This seemed to be a direct challenge which we groaningly accepted despite the rice and groundnuts.

Butterfly nets were lashed to long light poles and raised up to the angle of the roof. The bats continued to circle round and round the house. We waited half-way along a wall facing the corner around which they appeared. As they flashed by above us, we endeavoured to pop the net up at the psychological moment. Though some practice was required before we could judge their speed, soon we were very near the mark.

It then became apparent that the bats could slip through between the rim of the net (which was circular) and the roof-wall angle. We therefore lowered the nets and constructed angles in their rims to coincide with the corner of the roof. Assured of a capture, we again raised the nets.

Now the bats flew straight at the net, partly entered the mouth, then backslid out again; by a couple of deft stallings, like an airplane in an air-pocket, they squirmed round the bottom edge of the net and proceeded on their way round the house. It was obvious that whatever we put in their path they would be able to avoid with comparative ease. Exasperated, I loaded a shotgun, seated myself by the dinner table, and, to the great amazement of the kitchen staff and the detriment of the government's valuable roofing, fired both barrels at the further corner of the roof as soon as I saw a bat appear. Perhaps it is unnecessary to mention that I did not hit the bat, but blew an eight-inch hole clean through the match-boarding.

Two bats, however, were close enough to be thoroughly dazed by my performance. These were scooped into the nets as they fluttered amazedly about above us. Our first two bats were brought to earth, where they promptly fixed their needle-sharp teeth on my and George's fingers respectively.

Since we were guests of the government, we could not continue blowing the roof of the rest house away, a square foot at a time. It therefore became imperative to devise some other method of capturing our nightly visitors. This led to most interesting discoveries.

I had heard that bats had some marvellous mechanism by which they find their way through the air, and more particularly those parts that are cluttered up with obstructions. All the microcheiroptera have minute eyes, some even are totally blind, their eyes being reduced to pin-point dimensions and covered by skin. The ones we captured at our first attempt (*Hipposideros caffer* and *Nycteris arge*) had the smallest black beads totally concealed in the thick fur. Bats have been released in a confined space across and throughout which up to four hundred piano wires were stretched at all angles. The bats continued to fly indefinitely among them without ever so much as touching a wire with their wing tips either in bright light or in total darkness, even when what eyes they had were completely sealed over. By what method is this performed?

If a bat is caught, look at its face. This will probably give you quite a shock, but it is nevertheless worth an inspection. Bats' faces vary enormously, probably more so than any other animals'; few of them are straightforward visages and many are beyond the wildest nightmares of a deranged liver or fancies of the grotesque. The nose is often developed into a whole series of leaf-like structures one on top of another, and there are wrinkles, folds, and feelers of naked skin. One bat we found had a fleshy crucifix surrounded by a dozen complicated leaves spreading from its nose all over its face.

No less remarkable than the endless variety of noses are the extremes to which the ears go. These are, in the first place, often immense in proportion to the animal—I know one bat whose ears are very much larger than the whole animal itself. Inside the main ear there may be another pinna or false ear of almost any form. Some are exact replicas of the big ear, and the whole thing may be multiplied so that there appears to be a series of ears of diminishing size, one within the other. The eyes, as I have mentioned, are negligible quantities.

Those peculiar people who take an interest in bats have debated for many years as to whether these wonderful structures are the means by which the bat directs itself through the maze of piano wires or natural obstructions to its aerial passage. They seem to have decided that not only are the nose-leaves and ears the centre of a kind of super-tactile sensitivity but that the wing-membranes also serve this purpose. This sixth sense must in some way be connected with a power of touch so acute that the animal can feel objects before it actually comes in contact with them. This is not nearly so strange as it seems, if we do not judge all senses by our own, which are feebly developed to say the least. It is possible that in the case of the bats this sense is effected by minute increases in air pressure, or responds to electro-magnetic waves propagated by matter.

George and I had debated these interesting facts from every angle during the days that followed our first captures, having had such clear proof of their potentialities. As I lay in bed at night, the problem assumed gigantic proportions, until one night when, just after the light had been extinguished, I was galvanized into action by a material example of my mental speculations.

From within my mosquito net I saw a phantom form flutter momentarily across the rectangle of moonlight cast by the window opposite my bed. There was definitely a bat in the room. We held a rapid conference in the dark. The torch was unearthed and lighted, and disclosed not one but half a dozen bats flying round the room. As soon as the light came on, they streamed out of the window. This gave us the idea.

The bright paraffin lamp was set blazing near the window. Long pieces of string were attached to both doors. Members of the staff were crowded into the room, the window was closed, and the light extinguished. We then sat patiently in the dark; sure enough, bats began to enter almost at once, presumably in search of the insects that had been attracted by the light. We pulled the strings, which closed the doors with a bang. We were now sealed up with the bats. The lamp was relighted and our troubles began.

The room was approximately twenty feet square and fourteen feet high. There were five of us, all supplied with nets, and four bats. After twenty minutes, we had caught only one, although all four followed each other round and round the room in a wide figure eight, never deviating from their course except to avoid our nets, which feat they accomplished with maddening regularity. The whole business made one feel quite impotent. People have given me glowing accounts of capturing bats in butterfly nets over ponds or around a house in the open air; they must either be blatant liars or have operated in some other part of the world, because the average West African bat seems to be something of a flying ace.

These bats provided us with golden opportunities for observing the way in which they can avoid almost any object while on the wing. When we had at last captured them all, which was only accomplished by their becoming tired and hanging to the wall upside down, we tried the experiment of sealing over their eyes with tiny pieces of adhesive tape. This had not the least effect on their efficiency, but when we folded one of the ears downwards and attached its tip to the face, they all behaved in a most ludicrous and far from competent manner. The right ear caused them to gyrate in an anticlockwise or left-handed direction with ever-increasing velocity, so that they eventually went into a violent spin in mid-air and slowly descended to earth like a whirling helicopter. The sealing of the left ear had an exactly contrary effect. Moreover, when the ears were released, the effects were still apparent for some time.

Other experiments affecting the nose-leaves and parts of the ears had very strange results, all of which seemed to prove conclusively that these organs are the centre of their balance- and direction-finding mechanism and that they function quite involuntarily. If the right ear be sealed, one would have supposed that the constant pressure on it would have been construed by the bat's nervous system as implying that an obstruction lay constantly to its right front. The animal would therefore keep veering to the left, exactly what we observed the little animals to do.

One evening lingers in my memory as being the first which I consciously realized was dry as opposed to wet. We had been in Africa for more than two months, during which time it had rained every day and often during the whole day. There had been weeks together without sunshine, so that animals skinned and stuffed had remained limp and damp as on the day when they were first prepared. It had been a most trying time. We had waited patiently for the rains to cease so that we could move out into the uncharted forests under canvas. We had so far been contenting ourselves with a detailed investigation of the commoner animals and those that have survived or taken up their abode among the semi-cultivated land and secondary forest around the settlements of man.

Sitting at work on the veranda facing the clearing of Mamfe station, I had an uninterrupted view of a great expanse of sky to the west. The sun began to set, flaming like a furnace behind a false skyline of dense, black clouds whose pillars and towers stood motionless, like a monstrous, shadowy mirage of New York's stately skyline. Above, the air was crystal-clear and depthless. Towards the disappearing day it remained delicately blue between great horizontal zones of pale, soft gold. As it towered above, the blue melted to glowing heliotrope, lilac, violet, and thence, to the east, into the indigos and the mysteries of the oncoming tropical night.

Work under these conditions was impossible and sacrilegious. The Africans, who had already discovered this, had melted away into the twilight without permission and without a sound. I followed suit and drifted out across the soft green grass, gazing up into the immensity of the sky with that hopeless yearning that all mortals feel when confronted with the immense calm of the evening heavens. I found Ben perched on a termites' nest facing the setting sun, his chocolate skin burnished with the reflection of the flaming glory. He just sat and stared and I was happy.

Here was an example of that much scorned type—the white man's African servant—who had, in addition, been subjected to the indignity and stifling stupor of a mission school. And yet, although he was born of a race that we are incessantly told can only be lazy or sensuous when not asleep, here he was sitting quietly enraptured by a sight that must after all have been as commonplace to him as a blaze of electric signs is to us.

"T'ick-ehn, it's very fine" was all he said. Then very mysteriously he spoke in his own language, enlarging upon the beauty of the scene, as I later discovered. I could almost feel a European "used to managing natives" at my elbow, whispering: "Damn it, boy, what infernal insolence!"

Under the dome of the sky we sat together in silence, watching and mentally recording the ever-changing flush of colours. The air was still except for a very distant drum throbbing in unison with the blood coursing through our veins, and an occasional croak issuing from a near-by, frog-infested ditch.

Yet, was that all? Every now and then I felt rather than heard an infinitesimally faint noise. Slowly these indescribable sounds became more pronounced until I could ascertain that they came from the sky above. Looking up, I could see nothing. Every so often, and ever more plainly now, rang out a faint, high-pitched "tit-trrrr." Then, all at once, Ben looked up and pointed out a black speck, fluttering and tumbling hither and thither. Bats!

As the night came on, the air became filled with "tit-trrrrs." The busy little animals circled slowly towards the earth. It was not until several days later that we obtained our first specimens of these bats, and then we received a great surprise.

They were large, powerfully built animals with relatively small wings, simple, rather pig-like faces, and almost naked bodies. The whole skin glistened with a pungent-smelling oil, while the flesh, which was dense and excessively heavy, oozed a similar substance for hours after death. Most strange of all were pocket-like pouches under the chin and directed forwards. On the skin at the back of these pouches (that is to say, on the throat) a nipple connected with a gland was situated and, clinging to this, we found on several occasions a peculiar parasitic fly which has no wings.

These bats (*Saccolaimus peli*) belonged to that aggravating class that flies in the open air. They were the first we encountered.

After several weeks' intensive trapping around the camp, we appeared to have more or less cleared up or frightened away all the animals. Trap lines were thus being moved to another locality, because, with that particular method of collecting, a practice known as "completing a circle" is employed. This means that one selects a circle and works inwards from it to the camp, so that all animals, to get away, must either pass through the ring of traps, or congregate in the end around the camp. When the traps reach the borders of the camp, a final swarm of animals appears. After they are collected or have escaped, the whole area is played out.

With a view to selecting a new ground I left camp for a day's outing by myself, in order to cover a wide area and quietly investigate its possibilities to the best of my knowledge and ability. These days alone were most profitable, as we had discovered, not because we wanted in any way to be away from each other, but because the absence of conversation and freedom to wander wherever the spirit moved one brought to one's notice an extraordinary number of new facts and phenomena.

On this particular occasion I set out towards a large "lake" of grass that had been reported to me as existing to the south-east of the camp. I chose this as a starting point, since I was rather keen not to get lost in the forest again as I had done only a short time before.

Entering the dense forest beyond this open grass area, I was rather surprised to find that the ground descended very abruptly. Before I had gone far, I saw at a distance below me the glimmer of sun reflected from water. By some exigencies of local geological structure, the Mainyu River that we knew so well elsewhere had got twisted up into a knot and meandered off into the jungle, to appear here flowing in an exactly contrary direction to its main course. This we discovered later by following it downstream. I at once decided that this was to be our future happy hunting ground and the site of our next camp.

The whole structure of this gorge will one day prove of the greatest interest to geologists. It is a natural model of the great Rift Valley of East Africa. Following a subsidence or a great release of pressure, the land surface has simply collapsed along a central line now occupied by the river. The "country" rock, as it is called, has fractured all along into gargantuan cubes which, with the general subsidence, have shifted about so that they may be likened to the lumps of sugar in a bowl. Between them and under them are almost endless narrow clefts and passages leading into the side of the gorge, along its face, and out again into the open air.

The whole area was covered with dense forest. As I began exploring the level, sandy floors of the street-like passageways between the great chunks of rock, the light became fainter and fainter. There was practically no bare rock at all, every inch of its surface where there was any light being covered with smooth, soft, bright-green moss. The place was like a buried city, silent, mysterious, and eerie.

Turning an abrupt corner, I came upon a wide sunken arena overhung by a tall cliff. In the very dim light under this natural arch I saw an endless stream of bats passing to and fro from the mouth of a cave at one end to a monstrous horizontal crack at the other. The whole roof of this archway was a dense mass of sleeping bats, suspended upside down in serried ranks. The ground below was covered to a depth of more than a foot with their excrement, which had disintegrated under the influence of the weather and resulted in a mass of broken remains of uncountable millions of insects.

In this stratum of bat guano, I found a number of peculiar insects and a small bright-red millepede that I have never seen anywhere else.

By a mere fluke I had a torch in my collecting bag; with its aid I entered the cave. Though the mouth was just wide enough to permit my squeezing through, it expanded somewhat within and rose to a great height above. On both walls, as far as the light of the torch penetrated, bats were hanging or crawling about. The air was literally filled with them. The floor here was covered with guano to such a depth that I could not reach the earth below even by digging with a trapper's friend!

I was so amazed at the whole place and its denizens that I forgot all time and scrambled onwards into the depths, following the endless streams of bats that hurried along and round the corners just as busy traffic does in the streets of a great city.

Turning a corner, I was confronted by a blank wall. The bats were all passing upwards and disappearing over the top of a miniature cliff. I clambered up with some difficulty, to find that I was on top of one of the great blocks of rock. The next one above it was held away by a third block's edge far to the right. This left a horizontal gallery that stretched far ahead, beyond which I could see a large chamber. Into this I eventually emerged complete with gun and all other equipment, after a few uncomfortable minutes of wriggling through, all the time obsessed with that ridiculous but persistent impression that the roof would suddenly cave in and pin me in a not quite dead condition where nobody would ever in any circumstances find me.

The place I now found myself in was much larger than any that I had previously passed through. It was nearly the size of one whole block and almost exactly cubic in shape. The air was as dry as a desert sandstorm; whether it was due to this or the pungent smell of the bats I do not know, but my lips became hard and cracked in a surprisingly short time and my eyes began to water. The roof was altogether free from resting bats, but on the walls were what I at first supposed to be a great number of them. Some being very low down, I put down my collecting bag and gun, and advanced with the torch and a net only, to try to effect a capture.

As I approached the side, however, these things that I had supposed to be bats vanished as if by magic. One minute they were there; the next they were gone. By the time that I was close enough to the rock face to be able to see what they were, had they still been there, there was not one in sight. This was most perplexing.

Deciding that the light must disturb them, if they were not mere shadows, I put out the torch and crept forward to another wall. When I judged that I was close enough, I suddenly flashed on the torch again. A perfectly horrible vision met my eyes. The whole wall was covered with enormous whip-scorpions, crouching and leering at me. Only for a second did they remain, then, like a flash, they all shot out and away in all directions, disappearing into paper-thick crevices with a loathsome rustle.

Their behaviour and appearance are, as I have remarked before, revolting in the extreme, but they were of such unusual size and colour that for the sake of science I steeled myself to a systematic hunt with all the low cunning of a cave man in search of food. Eventually I captured a few after many misses, once being subjected to the nerve-shattering odiousness of having one of them scuttle over my bare arm in escaping from the net.

After this experience I deemed science had sufficient material to gloat over, and I devoted my attention to an examination of the ground for other invertebrates. The bats were entering by the same route as I had done. After crossing the gallery diagonally, they disappeared through one of three vertical fissures, though most of them streamed into and out of the left-hand one, which was the widest. Across the floor below the line of their flight stretched a ridge of their droppings, showing that they excrete while on the wing. Elsewhere the floor was covered with silver sand and spotlessly clean. Only in one corner of the room, remote from the bat highway, was there a pile of small, pellet-like dung.

Examining this, I at once noticed that it was not composed of the crushed remains of insects as was that of the other bats. It resembled more the droppings of a rabbit, although there seemed to be a few small bones projecting from it. This prompted me to search the ceiling above to ascertain where this might be descending from. All I could see, however, was a small cleft above; so, taking the shotgun, I managed by degrees to lever myself up the sharp angle of the corner and eventually peered over the brink into the cleft.

As I switched on the torch, I went cold all over and felt as if my skin were wrinkling up everywhere preparatory to splitting and falling off in one piece. The only alternative to looking into the crevice a second time was falling down backwards. Therefore, after summoning up courage, I switched on the torch again and took a second look. The result was just as bad.

In the mouth of the hole not eighteen inches from my face, four large greenish-yellow eyes stared unblinkingly at me. They were so large that I thought involuntarily of some dead human thing, but the face that projected in front of them soon dispelled this impression. That face is indescribable. In addition there were clammy groping fingers all muddled up with endless flaps of wrinkled naked skin. I pushed in the net and made a random scoop; then I slipped and crashed to the bottom of the cave.

The gun, luckily, fell in the soft sand, and I retained hold of the net in which a huge hammer-headed bat (*Hypsignathus monstrosus*) was struggling. My left leg was emitting piercing pains and both wrists were quite numbed. There followed an awful period during which I tried to kill the bat in the net and nursed my leg and arms, making, I am afraid, a great deal of noise about it. At last I got the animal under control and chloroformed in the "killer," and then set about gathering together the wreckage. When I came to the gun, my wrists were still numb, but being anxious to make sure that there was no sand choking the barrel, I foolishly tried to open the breech. I am not exactly certain what happened; anyway, both barrels went off almost at once and the gun shot partly out of my hand.

At the same moment the light went out.

There was a period of tremendous echoing, then the whole of this eerie subterranean world seemed to give way, starting with a gentle "swussssh" and culminating in a rattling roar. Things fell down on all sides; choking dust filled the air; while I groped for the torch, hundreds of bats wheeled around my head screaming and twittering.

The torch would not light; for some maddening reason it was not forming a proper contact. I had to sit down and take the batteries out in the dark. I pulled out the metal strips on the ends and procured a flash of light by holding on the screw cap at the back of the container. In my excitement I could not for the life of me get this screw onto the thread. Finally I had to light a match, but before I could see anything, the flame went greenish-blue and quickly died. Other matches did the same.

I had just discovered that they burnt better at a higher level when, with an awful crash, a shower of earth cascaded down from my right side and covered my feet and most of my equipment, which was lying on the floor. There was a wild scramble to retrieve all my possessions and move to a bit of clearer ground, but every time I bent down, the match went out. There was obviously some gas or lack of gas that killed a flame near the floor. I therefore concentrated on fixing the torch. At long last it lit up.

It was less use than a car headlight in a dense mist, because the air was filled with clouds of billowing dust from which a very much startled bat periodically emerged. Groping forward, festooned with gun, collecting bag, net, and torch, I tried to locate the wall with the cleft through which I had gained an entrance, but I soon lost my sense of direction. Then I stumbled across the ridge of bats' dung. This I followed up until it disappeared under a great scree of fine dry earth which was still being added to from above. After further fumbling I found the cleft; the dust was so dense that I could not see more than a few feet into it. This was, however, quite sufficient really to disturb me.

The cleft was choked with earth and rubble. Slowly it dawned on me that the percussion of the shots had released all kinds of pent-up things and perhaps even shifted the roof, as I had imagined might happen through natural causes.

By this time the dust had begun to clear considerably and the rumblings and droppings had ceased. I trekked back to the other side of the cave and tried each of the three exits. The largest, upon which I based my hopes, narrowed quickly, then plunged downward into a low, uninviting crevice. One of the others was too narrow to permit the passage of my head, while the third, although very small, seemed to continue endlessly. Its floor descended rapidly, however, and I soon discovered that the air was very bad a few feet down—matches hardly lit at all. I had therefore to return to the central cave from which I felt almost certain there were no other exits. As the dust was by now less thick, I determined to go all round and make certain.

There proved to be a hopeful-looking chimney in one corner, but try as I would, my left leg steadfastly refused to assist me to climb! This was rendered even more exasperating by the fact that a piece of burning paper thrown upwards to its mouth was instantly sucked up out of sight never to return, which all went to show that the passage had some connexion with the outer world. Burning bits of note-book were then applied to the three exits. In one the flame promptly went out, in another it just wilted, and only in the narrowest one did it sail away into the distance, burning merrily. Such a result might, of course, have been predicted!

It then struck me that the choked entrance might not be all choked, so, scrambling along the ledge formed by the long horizontal mouth of this, I peered among the piles of earth that now clogged it, pushing small pieces of burning paper into any gaps or hole that remained. About two-thirds of the way down to the right the paper left my hand and blew straight into my face. I could feel a small draught. The hole was very low and descended towards the right, whereas the part of this gigantic crack through which I had come further up had distinctly sloped upwards out of the square chamber. There was fresh air coming in, so, provided it was not too small, it seemed the only feasible exit. I accordingly packed everything into the collecting bag, including the stock of the gun, wrapped the gun-barrel in the muslin bag of the net to prevent its getting scratched, crammed my felt hat onto my head for the same reason, and, holding the torch in my right hand, committed myself to the depths and the will of Allah.

Progress was slow and at one period extremely painful, for the ceiling—being the flat underside of a giant tilted cube—gradually descended until there was room for me to squeeze through only with the greatest difficulty. This effort I had to make, because I could reach for and feel the angular edge of the ceiling cube just beyond. This edge was as sharp as the angle on a small pack of cigarettes, though the block of rock above must have weighed thousands of tons. Through this slit I must get, and it was a struggle in no way made easier by having a now more or less useless left leg and also having to get the collecting bag over my head in order to push it through before me. How I envied those beastly *Amblypygi!*

Once through, I found myself in a long wide corridor again immaculately carpeted with silver sand. Having by now lost all sense of direction, I set off to the left, where I was soon involved in a tumbled mass of immense angular boulders. To climb over them was a little more than I felt prepared to attempt, so I dived in and tried to find a way through. This led me into a tunnel that smelt strongly and vaguely familiar. Before I had time to think what the cause of it could be, a rasping grunt echoed out from its depths; realizing at once that I had walked voluntarily into a leopard's private quarters, I lost absolutely no time at all in passing back through those boulders as if I were a sandworm brought up to perform such feats. The only course now was to try the other way, as I had no desire to meet a leopard, and even less to fire at one with a shotgun in the depths of the earth, considering what had occurred after the last cannonade.

The other end was a perfectly smooth blank wall. I began to feel rather desperate, a thing one should not do in well-regulated adventures. The feeling was nevertheless sufficiently insistent to call for a cigarette. How I thanked everything, not least myself, that I had cigarettes!

While seated on the sand smoking, feeling sorry for myself, and recounting a lot of things I should like to have done, I played my torch hither and thither over the opposite wall. It was only after a long time that it dawned on me that I was gazing at great patches of green moss. Even after this it was a long time, during which I repacked my equipment, bandaged a knee, and smoked another cigarette, before my idiot brain put two and two together and arrived at the simple fact that green moss meant sunlight. Then all at once this fact penetrated my silly head and I realized that I had never yet looked at the roof. I flashed my torch upwards and saw a line of green branches dangling down into the cleft. During my subterranean meanderings night had come—I was actually standing in the open air.

Putting the gun together and loading it against a chance encounter with the inhabitant of the boulders, I advanced on his domain. After some exertion I managed to climb up over the boulders to arrive among the roots of the trees near the bottom of the gorge.

Two hours later I was back in camp, sore, temporarily crippled, and very thirsty.

I have mentioned so far our introduction to five West African bats. We collected during our stay around Mamfe no less than twenty-five species, though most of these were represented by only one or two specimens.

Whenever we smoked trees in the high forest, the first things to come out were bats. They emerged around the summit, fluttering about and trying to regain an entrance, until they decided it was too warm and rocketed off into the surrounding forest. When we did eventually reach some of these with the guns, they turned out to be of three species, two of which were closely allied to the two species we had caught in the rest house at Mamfe. The third (*Hipposideros cyclops*) was something entirely new.

This was a stout animal of moderate dimensions covered with thick, long, rather woolly hair of brindled silver-grey and dark brownish-grey colour. The eyes, set in a most saturnine face, were large for a bat, the nose-leaf was a flat, more or less simple circle, and the lips were rather taut, so that the sharp teeth were visible. But the ears gave the whole face a very startling appearance. Almost as long as the body, they tapered to fine points, besides being corrugated throughout their length.

We kept alive several of these that had fallen upon the wire netting dazed by the smoke. During the day they hung upside down as all good bats should; in the evening they began to stir and climbed down the side of the cage. They then walked about the floor on their wings, supported by the fingers, pointing backwards and upwards. When they prepared to take to the air either from the ground or the side of the cage, they thrust their heads forward and flapped their great ears just as if they were an accessory pair of wings. The arms then took up the motion in rhythm and the animal was on the wing.

These bats, which slept in trees by day, came to us with greater ease than any of the others, provided they were within the range of the gun. As almost every tree housed a few, we gradually accumulated quite a number.

One of the two species that we obtained in the Mamfe rest house (*Hipposideros caffer*) was small and grey in colour, with small, rather pointed ears. Another variety of this species made up the swarms that inhabited the caves in the Mainyu Gorge, and another variety came from hollow trees in the forest. When staying at Ikom further down the river, we again converted the house into a bat trap and obtained another variety of this common type. This was an exceptionally beautiful little animal having bluish-black wing- and tail-membranes and ears. The fur covering the rest of the body was long, silky, and of a rich reddish-orange colour. This is the only bat I have ever handled that emitted a long-drawn-out whistle, a noise to which I can find no reference in any literature upon the subject.

There was still another form of this bat that we met with in a rather odd manner.

Mamfe Division, which has an area almost exactly equal to that of the whole island of Jamaica, has only one road. This is about twenty miles in length and extends from the station towards the east, where it terminates at a fine steel bridge of three spans which abuts at its farther end onto a solid wall of virgin jungle without so much as a native path leading from it. This road and bridge were constructed by the public works department as the commencement of a projected trade route to carry motor traffic from the hinterland of Bamenda down to the British ports of southern Nigeria. The financial depression, yellow fever, which accounted for a dozen Europeans, and the fact that a score of large rivers flowing from north to south were overlooked when drawing up plans, killed the project, which had, in any case, been started in the middle. Its main use, therefore, is that two Ford trucks, and occasionally the remains of an Austin-7 that have been brought up the river on a "launch" during the rainy season, can be employed for the first day's trek to the east of Mamfe. This was the one direction in which we never had cause to go, so our acquaintance with it was confined to strolls in the evening and an occasional joy ride in the Ford truck with the hospitable district commissioner.

We had noticed that this man-made canyon through the forest was a great place for bats. Towards dusk they appeared either flying high in the air, as they must do all over the forest, although they cannot be seen elsewhere, or darting back and forth from the shadow of the trees on one side of the road to that of the trees on the other. Closer investigation disclosed the fact that bats came out along this road in the evening at a much earlier hour than elsewhere. The apparent reason for this was the presence of a number of large drains or culverts running under the road at intervals. The bats used these as a dark passage between the gloom of the trees on both sides of the road.

Having ascertained this fact, we laid plans for catching them. As we had been away working very hard in the less accessible parts of the forest for some time, and the birthday of one of our number was approaching, we reckoned that there was ample excuse for a little harmless frivolity. Into this scheme the only other two European inhabitants of Mamfe (at that time) entered heartily. We organized a fancy-dress bat shoot.

After tea the Ford truck came to the door of the district officer's house. The party foregathered in the most amazing assortment of improvised fancy dress: "le sportsman très gallique"; "the Yankee in the tropics"; a valiant edition of General Göring clad to chase the Polish boar; and a "not-very-sporting English squire." The African truck-driver wore a sky-blue cap and a shirt, so that we were not quite certain whether he was entering into the spirit of the thing, being simply chic according to local custom, or behaving in a manner that called for reprimand on the grounds of incivility. The only truly normal members of the party were our five skinners, who came in their ordinary uniforms of grey shirts and white shorts, bearing guns and nets.

The party set out for the road some three miles into the forest and there deployed, taking up positions over the various drains. Quite soon the bats began to appear. A fusillade was let loose, but the tiny animals are so swift that one saw only a vague flash as they shot across the space separating the entrance to the culverts from the neighbouring wall of the forest. Nobody secured a direct hit, but Mr. Gorges, the district officer, who was an extremely good shot, on two occasions aimed sufficiently close to upset the bats' sense of direction. As animals fluttered around in a circle, Bassi, who was stationed at one end of his drain, dived in with a net and made a capture of the first. On the second occasion, however, the bat managed to flutter into the drain and Bassi went in after it. As he did so, a perfect flight of bats came out of the other end, and I joined Mr. Gorges in an attempt to pot them. This we continued to do quite merrily until all of a sudden Bassi's nut-brown head appeared amid the flying targets. By some fluke we were not firing at that instant. He had crawled right through the drain.

This gave us a new idea. We climbed down into the ditch and lay in position to look down the drains. As soon as the number of bats had entered from the other end, flown towards us, and sensed our presence, we fired a shot. We never once hit a bat, but they were so bewildered by the percussion of the shot that they came to rest on the roof of the drain and we sent the Africans in to collect them alive.

This resulted in the capture of a great number of bats which turned out to be this other variety of *Hipposideros caffer*. They were all some shade of brown and much smaller than the types we had collected elsewhere.

This method of collecting was indeed child's play compared to the highly technical skill and great patience which George devoted to the shooting of another species. These were the smallest bats I have ever seen; in actual bulk they must be the smallest of all mammals, despite the claims of the pygmy squirrel (*Nannosciurus*) to that distinction. The trunk of this animal when skinned was about the size of a bumble bee and a good deal smaller than the last joint of a small woman's little finger.

As I have already mentioned, George, when in the deep forest, adopted the method of sitting in concealment and waiting for the passing of the animals. When thus employed one evening, he noticed far up in the sky above the trees some very small bats flying about in a manner quite unknown among these animals, so that at first he mistook them for swallows. Deciding that he must discover what they were, with more than praiseworthy ambition he set himself the task of shooting some, a problem which I should have judged quite hopeless. However, he eventually found a place where the ground rose sufficiently for him to gain a clear view over some trees. There he patiently waited for several evenings until one of the bats happened to fly low enough to be within gun-shot range. By this painstaking method he obtained two specimens of this extremely rare species (*Glauconycteris beatrix*).

These animals were dark steel-grey in colour with long slender wings and simple noses like a dog's.

Another bat, *Rhinolophus landeri,* which we collected and which also proves to be very rare, was represented by four specimens. When living with the friendly peoples of the northern mountains we had a kind of working contract with the hunter named Afa, as I have already mentioned. One day I asked him for bats, indicating my wishes by exhibiting a stuffed specimen.

"Ah," he said in his own language, "I know where one sleeps."

This was such an astonishing remark that I was not sure that my rather sketchy knowledge of the language combined with the interpreter were not letting me down. However, Afa disappeared and did not return until just before dusk. When he did so, he extracted a live bat from his gun-powder wallet. It was this species, covered in silky grey hair, with a tuft of red bristles in each armpit, and bearing a small fleshy crucifix on its nose.

Apparently he had walked, or rather climbed, about nine miles to a tiny cave which I afterwards visited, where he had seen this animal hanging asleep some days previously when sheltering there from a storm.

Two other rare species, one new to science, came to us quite by chance. They could not be distinguished apart by colour and size alone, both being bluish-grey and small. Only their nose-leaves and ears showed them to be quite different. One, a new species of *Hipposideros,* was shot by the district officer in his house; the other, named *Rhinolophus alcyone,* landed at my feet after I had shot at a squirrel in a tree near a plantation. One pellet had passed right through the head. I had never seen this bat before.

Just before returning home, we paid a visit to N'ko, a large village lower down the Cross River. Here we met with extraordinary hospitality at the hands of the local inhabitants. They had never seen more than one white man at a time before, never heard a gramophone, and, I believe, never imagined that such a thing as a bug-hunter existed, especially attended by nearly forty retainers, to which number our staff of skinners, trappers, collectors, and household servants had by that time swelled.

When we announced that we required local animal life and would pay for it, the whole populace disappeared into the neighbouring bush and was soon returning in an endless stream bearing every imaginable kind of animal.

Later that evening a tribal dance was organized for our entertainment. In the headdresses of the various ju-ju figures I spotted the dried remains of a species of bat that I did not know. I inquired of the chief whether he could procure for me some live specimens of this animal. He seemed morose. After some effort I discovered that the animal was regarded with considerable veneration from the point of view of a fertility ju-ju. A monetary contribution to the privy purse, however, combined with the fact, soon observed by the chief, that I had almost as virulent a dislike of Christians as he had, prompted him to dispatch a number of small boys into the jungle.

They returned some time later with handfuls of fluttering little bats (a species of the genus known as *Eptesicus*), among which was an albino. I subsequently stumbled upon the "mine" from which these bats had been obtained. It was a small ju-ju tabernacle not more than two hundred yards behind the hut where we were living. Under the eaves of the tabernacle countless bats were sleeping, covering the altar with their guano, which had been cleared away except within an area that had an outline representing a gigantic bat with outstretched wings.

The frugivorous bats or megacheiroptera are mostly larger animals, some in the Oriental region having a wing span exceeding four feet. We obtained eight species of this group, four of which were, however, of very small size. They do not have nose-leaves and their ears are usually simple, like those of other animals. Their heads, nevertheless, show an amazing variety of form; one was exactly like a calf's, another like a mastiff's, and the hammer-headed bat's more like a horse's than anything one could imagine.

In the mountains of Assumbo we pitched a camp on one occasion in a little tongue of grass that descended into a patch of mountain forest. This was Camp III, from which we carried out most of our investigations upon the wild life of these weird grass-covered mountains. It was a desolate place miles from anywhere in the clear still air, raised far above the teeming life of the tropical forests, and completely cut off from the rest of the world. As far as the eye could see, long grass waved in the sighing wind as shimmering flushes crossed and recrossed it like surf on a wide beach. Our little encampment nestled in a hollow backed by the peculiar tangled trees found at this altitude, through which rippled and tinkled a broad, crystal-clear brook.

There were only two ways of penetrating this mountain forest: first, by following strange little paths made by large buck, or, secondly, by wading along the beds of rivers and streams. We passed by both these ways, though usually along the main stream in the evening.

This was a somewhat difficult feat as I will endeavour to explain. The clear water swirled along a bed, now deep and narrow, now wide and shallow, but everywhere strewn and piled with boulders both great and small. Only occasionally were there deep, still pools between perpendicular rock walls where the cold water lay oily and brown. There were endless rapids where cascades gushed between boulders the size of a house, and beyond them great, wide, boulder-strewn fields where the water all but disappeared, being subdivided into a hundred thousand tiny trickles. This made a passage down the bed of the little river rather difficult. Nevertheless, it remained the lesser evil, because the banks were both impenetrable masses of vegetation. Even those who know the tropical forests and mangroves of the great tropical deltas would be confounded by the true mountain forest. It is a growth found nowhere else but on elevated areas in the equatorial regions.

It seems that in these regions there is a constant battle between the trees and the high altitude for mastery. The altitude usually wins, and the trees are replaced by grass, giant heather, or some other growth. Occasionally the reverse is the result, and then the trees make up for lost ground. They grow in all directions—upward, outward, and downward—into one solid, tangled, matted conglomeration. A man might force his way through a gorse bush but never through this African plexus. It was impossible to follow the river along its banks.

During the first few days at this camp, I had been employed throughout the twenty-four hours in and around the camp. The ground was uneven; tornadoes blew up; houses for the staff took an excessive time to construct in the absence of sufficient straight bush-sticks; hunters kept calling; I nursed a bad foot; and all the time the "office" work piled up. The Duke had been sent back to the base camp, his legs covered with festering, two-inch sores, called "tropical ulcers." A skinner and one of the household staff had had to go with him to minister to his wants, not to mention half a dozen of the Munchi carriers—backbone of our little empire.

We were short-staffed, overloaded with work, unable to obtain food, and in the throes of pitching a new camp. I therefore had little time to inspect the countryside.

Perhaps George was more efficient with his half of the work on hand, or perhaps it was because his department was the frogs and reptiles, expeditions to collect which we were naturally unable to organize at this juncture; at any rate, he alone was able to get away during the first few evenings and inspect the neighbourhood with a gun.

He came back with ever more remarkable accounts of what he had seen, including details about some fruit bats that sounded like fish stories. As soon as our house was in order, I put myself in George's hands and he conducted me to the bed of the river which I had not previously seen.

It was a peculiar evening. The sky was neither overcast nor clear. The sun shone somewhere to the west behind the mountains, but the sky above did not reflect any of its glory, remaining a pallid, colourless sheet above our heads. The light was bad even before true dusk began to fall.

We entered the archway formed by the trees over the river where it was narrow, and waded downstream for some minutes. The water here was waist-deep, the boulders no larger than a man's head. Eventually we emerged into the open. The river widened and huge rocks appeared out of its ruffled surface. Upon these George advised we should take up our positions.

No sooner had we done so, than a number of large fruit bats commenced a series of reconnaissance flights from above the trees on either side. One had the impression that they were flying there just out of sight all the time and merely came to peep over and see what we were up to. Near at hand were some singularly inedible-looking trees that proved, however, to be a source of unaccountable attraction to the bats. Into these they slipped from the far side. The first that we knew of their arrival was a loud lip-smacking and munching noise which drifted down to us. As we remained quiet, others came flying up the fairway over the river to join their kind.

We fired at them, spraying the shot in their paths. One landed on a patch of dry stream bed. When retrieved, it turned out to be a very large specimen of the hammer-headed bat, the species that I had previously encountered sleeping in the caves by the Mainyu River. A second one was quite different. This animal would probably have been termed a flying fox, though its fur was thin and like polished brass, stiff and shining. A third fell in the water almost at my feet.

Leaving my gun on the rock, I stepped down to try to catch it before it drifted into the main current and was carried away. I stepped on something hard and firm, but before I knew where I was, this thing suddenly came to life and lunged forward. I was flung sideways into the main stream. Here the water, though quiet, was deep and very swift under the surface. Since there could not have been crocodiles in this river, all I could think was that I had trodden on a tortoise. Swept forward by the current, I was soon involved in the rapids among great boulders. The bat disappeared. I had to concentrate on half swimming, half floundering back to my perch.

Suddenly George let out a shout: "Look out!" and I looked.

Then I let out a shout also and instantly bobbed down under the water, because, coming straight at me only a few feet above the water was a black thing the size of an eagle. I had only a glimpse of its face, yet that was quite sufficient, for its lower jaw hung open and bore a semicircle of pointed white teeth set about their own width apart from each other.

When I emerged, it was gone. George was facing the other way blazing off his second barrel. I arrived dripping on my rock and we looked at each other.

"Will it come back?" we chorused.

And just before it became too dark to see, it came again, hurtling back down the river, its teeth chattering, the air "shss-shssing" as it was cleft by the great, black, dracula-like wings. We were both off our guard, my gun was unloaded, and the brute made straight for George. He ducked. The animal soared over him and was at once swallowed up in the night.

We scrambled back into the river and waded home to camp, where we found a number of local hunters waiting with their catches laid out for sale. They had walked miles from their hunting grounds to do business.

"What kind of a bat is it," I asked, "that has wings like this (opening my arms) and is all black?"

"Olitiau!" somebody almost screamed, and there was a hurried conference in the Assumbo tongue.

"Where you see this beef?" one old hunter inquired amid dead silence.

"There," I told the interpreter, pointing to the river.

With one accord the hunters grabbed up their guns and ran out of camp, straight across country towards the village, leaving their hard-earned goods behind them.

Next day the old chief suddenly appeared in camp with the whole village council. He had walked miles from the village capital. He was concerned. Shyly he asked whether we needed to stay just there; wouldn't the hills beyond interest us, he wanted to know.

No, nothing but here exactly would suit us, we explained.

The chief was sad; the elders were uneasy. They went back to the village. We stayed at Camp III, but we never saw the bat again and never received the spoils of any more hunters' trips.

A Simple Heart

BY GUSTAVE FLAUBERT

For fifty years the good ladies of Pont-L'Évêque had longed for Madame Aubin's servant Félicité.

She received four pounds a year. For this she did the cooking and the general housework, the sewing, the washing, and the ironing. She could bridle a horse, fatten poultry, and churn butter, and she was ever faithful to her mistress, who was far from amiable.

Madame Aubin had married a light-hearted young bachelor without any money who died at the beginning of 1809, leaving her with two small children and a mass of debts. She then sold all her property except the farms of Toucques and Geffosses which brought her in five thousand francs a year at most, and she left her house in Saint-Melaine for a less costly one, which had belonged to her ancestors and was situated behind the market.

This house had a slate roof, and stood between an archway and a narrow lane which went down to the river. There was an unevenness in the level of the floors which made you stumble. A narrow front hall divided the kitchen from the sitting room in which Madame Aubin sat all day long in a wicker armchair beside the window. Eight mahogany chairs stood in a row against the white-painted panels. On an old piano which stood under a barometer were heaped wooden and cardboard boxes like a pyramid. A stuffed armchair was placed on either side of the yellow marble Louis Quinze chimney-piece, which had a clock in the middle in the shape of a Temple of Vesta. The whole room was rather musty, because the floor was below the garden level.

"Madame's" room was on the first floor. It was very large, with a faded flowery wallpaper and a portrait of "Monsieur" dressed up as a dandy of the period. It let into a smaller room, which had two cots without mattresses. Next to it was the drawing room, which was always shut up and filled with furniture covered with dustsheets. A corridor led to a study. Books and odd papers filled the shelves of a large bookcase, and inside its three wings was a wide writing table of dark wood. The two panels at the end of the room were covered with pen and ink drawings, landscapes in water colours, and engravings by Audran, relics of better days and departed glory. On the second floor a dormer window, which looked out over the fields, let light into Félicité's attic.

She rose at dawn so as not to be late for Mass, and worked until evening without stopping. Then, when dinner was over, the plates and dishes put away, and the door tightly fastened, she thrust a log in the dying embers and went to sleep in front of the hearth with her rosary in her hand. She was the most obstinate bargainer in the town, and as for cleanliness, the shine on her pots and pans was the despair of other servants. Thrifty in everything, she ate slowly, gathering up from the table the crumbs of her loaf, a twelve-pound loaf specially baked for her, which lasted three weeks. From year's end to year's end she wore a print cotton handkerchief, fastened with a pin behind, a bonnet that concealed her hair, grey stockings, a red skirt, and a bibbed apron, such as hospital nurses wear, over her jacket. Her voice was harsh and her face was thin. At twenty-five she looked forty. After fifty she looked any age. Silent, straight, and wasting no gestures, she was like a wooden woman who went by clockwork.

II

She had had her love story like others.

Her father, a mason, was killed by falling off a scaffold. Then her mother died, her sisters went off here and there, and a farmer took her in while she was a little girl, and gave her charge of the cows in his fields. She was ragged and shivered; she laid flat on the ground and lapped water up from the pools; was beaten for nothing; and finally turned out of the house for stealing thirty sous which she hadn't stolen. She went to another farm, and looked after the hens; and because her employers liked her, the others were jealous.

One evening in August—she was then eighteen—they took her to a feast at Colleville. She was dazed and bewildered by the stir of the fiddlers, the lamps in the trees, the laces and gold crosses in the dresses, and the crowd of folk all dancing together. She was standing aside shyly when a comfortable looking young chap, who was leaning on the shaft of a cart and smoking his pipe, came up to her and asked her to dance. He treated her to cider, coffee, and cakes, and bought her a silk handkerchief, and imagining that she understood what he wanted, offered to see her home. When they came to a cornfield, he threw her down roughly. She was terrified and cried out for help. And he got out of the way.

One evening after this, she was on the Beaumont road, and a great haycart was moving along slowly in front of her. She wanted to pass it, and as she brushed by the wheel she recognised Théodore. He spoke to her quite coolly, telling her that she must forgive him, because it was all the fault of the drink. She could not think what to say and longed to run away.

He began at once to talk about the crops and the important people of the commune, saying that his father had left Colleville for his farm at Les Ecots, so now they were neighbours. "Well, well!" she said. He added that his people wanted him to settle down, but he was in no hurry and would please himself in finding a wife. She dropped her eyes. Then he asked her if she thought of getting married. She answered with a smile that it wasn't fair to make fun of her.

"But I'm not, I swear it!" And he passed his left arm round her waist. She walked on supported by his clasp, and their pace slackened. The wind was soft, the stars twinkled, the huge haycart swung on in front of them, and the four weary horses raised the dust with their dragging feet. Then, without a word from Théodore they turned to the right. He embraced her once more, and she disappeared in the night.

Next week she consented to meet him sometimes.

They used to meet in farmyards, behind a wall, or under some solitary tree. She was not innocent as young ladies are—the ways of animals had taught her something—but her good sense and the instinct of her honour saved her from falling. Her resistance inflamed Théodore's passion so much that, to satisfy it, or, perhaps for more innocent reasons, he proposed marriage to her. She hesitated to believe him, but he swore ardent oaths of faithfulness.

Presently he confessed that he had something awkward to tell her. A year ago his parents had bought him a substitute for the army, but he might be taken again any day now, and the idea of military service terrified him. His cowardice seemed to Félicité a proof of his affection, and it redoubled hers. She stole off at night to meet him, and when she came to him Théodore worried her with his fears and entreaties.

At last he told her that he would go himself to the Prefecture to find out, and that he would let her know the result between eleven and twelve on the following Sunday night.

She hurried to meet him at the appointed hour. She found one of his friends instead at the meeting place.

He told her that she must not see Théodore any more. To save himself from conscription, he had married Madame Lehoussais, a wealthy old woman of Toucques.

There was a wild outburst of grief. She flung herself down on the ground, screamed and appealed to Almighty God, and lay moaning all alone in the field till daybreak. Then she returned to the farm and told them she was leaving at the end of the month. She received her wages, tied up all her little belongings in a handkerchief, and went to Pont-L'Évêque.

In front of the inn there, she asked questions of a woman in a widow's cap, who, as luck would have it, was looking for a cook. The girl had no experience, but she seemed so willing and modest in her demands that Madame Aubin ended by saying: "Very well, I will engage you."

A quarter of an hour later Félicité took up her quarters in this woman's house.

At first she lived there in terror at "the style of the house" and the memory of "Monsieur" hovering over it all. Paul and Virginie, the former seven and the latter just four, seemed to her creatures of a precious substance. She carried them pick-a-back, and it distressed her that Madame Aubin ordered her not to kiss them every minute. However, she was happy there. Her sorrow thawed in the pleasantness of her surroundings.

Every Thursday some regular visitors came in for a game of boston, and Félicité laid out the cards and foot-warmers beforehand. They arrived sharply on the stroke of eight, and left before the clock struck eleven.

Every Monday morning the old scrap dealer, who lived under the archway, spread out his iron. Then the town buzzed with voices, horses neighed, lambs bleated, pigs grunted, and carts rattled sharply on the pavement.

About noon, when the market had got thoroughly busy, you would see a tall, hook-nosed old farmer with his cap on the back of his head come to the door. It was Robelin, the farmer of Geffosses. Soon afterward came Lièbard, the farmer of Toucques, short, flushed and podgy, in a grey jacket and spurred gaiters.

Both had chickens or cheeses to offer their landlady. Félicité was always up to their tricks, and they would go away filled with respect for her.

At uncertain intervals Madame Aubin would have a call from one of her uncles, the Marquis de Gremanville, who had ruined himself by hard living and now lived on the last scrap of his land at Falaise.

He always came at lunchtime with a nasty poodle whose paws left dirty marks all over the furniture. In spite of all his efforts to seem a gentleman,—he even went so far as to lift his hat every time he said "my late father,"—habit got the better of him. He would pour out glass after glass and indulge in pothouse conversation. Félicité used to coax him out of the house. "You've had enough, Monsieur de Gremanville! That's enough till next time!" And she shut the door on him.

She would open it with pleasure for Monsieur Bourais, a retired lawyer. His bald head, white stock, frilled shirt front, and loose brown coat, his way of curving his arm when he took snuff, his whole personality, in fact, gave you that special feeling we have whenever we see an extraordinary man.

As he looked after "Madame's" property, he would stay shut up with her for hours in "Monsieur's" study, though all the time he was afraid of being compromised. He had great respect for the law, and claimed to know Latin.

To join instruction and pleasure, he gave the children a geography full of pictures. They showed scenes in all parts of the world: cannibals with feathers in their hair, a monkey carrying off a young lady, Bedouins in the desert, harpooning a whale, and so on. Paul would explain these pictures to Félicité, and that was all the education she ever had. The children's education was undertaken by Guyot, a humble creature employed in the town hall, who was well known for his beautiful handwriting and used to sharpen his penknife on his boots.

When the weather was fine, the household used to start off early sometimes for a day at the Geffosses farm.

Its courtyard was on a slope, with the farmhouse in the middle, and the sea looked like a far off grey streak on the horizon.

Félicité would take slices of cold meat out of her basket, and they would have lunch in a room beside the dairy. It was the last relic of a country house which was no more. The wallpaper was in tatters and rattled in a draught. Madame Aubin would sit with bowed head, overcome by her memories of the past. The children were afraid to speak. "Why don't you go off and play?" she would say, and they would hurry off.

Paul climbed up into the barn, caught birds, played ducks and drakes on the pond, or hammered with his stick on the great casks which echoed like drums. Virginie fed the rabbits or ran off to pick cornflowers, her scampering legs showing her little embroidered drawers.

One autumn evening they went home by the fields. The moon was in its first quarter and lit up part of the sky. A mist floated like a scarf over the winding Toucques. Cattle, lying out in the meadow, looked placidly at these four as they passed by. In the third meadow some of them got up and made a half circle in front of them. "There's nothing to be afraid of," said Félicité, stroking the back of the nearest animal while she crooned softly. He wheeled round and the others did the same. But as they crossed the next field, they heard a dreadful bellow. It was a bull, which was hidden by the mist. Madame Aubin started to run. "No! no! don't go so fast!" They hurried on, all the same, hearing a loud breathing behind them which kept coming nearer and nearer. His hoofs thudded on the turf like hammer-strokes. Now he was galloping! Félicité turned round and tore up some clods which she threw into his eyes with both hands. The bull lowered his muzzle, shook his horns, and bellowed with fury terribly. Madame Aubin, who had reached the end of the field with her two children, was looking distractedly for a place to climb over the high bank. Félicité kept retreating, always facing the bull, showering clods at his face which blinded him, and crying out, "Be quick! be quick!"

Madame Aubin got down into the ditch, pushed Virginie first and then Paul, fell several times trying to climb the steep bank, and finally managed it with a courageous effort.

The bull had driven Félicité back against a fence, his slaver was blowing in her face, and in an instant he would have gored her. She had just time to slip between the rails, and the hulking brute stopped short in amazement.

This adventure was discussed in Pont-L'Évêque for many a year. Félicité took no special pride in what she had done, and it never occurred to her for an instant that she had been heroic.

Virginie was her sole object of care, for, as a result of her fright, the child had become very nervous, and Monsieur Paupart, the doctor, advised sea bathing at Trouville. The place had few visitors in those days. Madame Aubin gathered information, consulted Bourais, and prepared as if she were going on a long journey.

She sent off her luggage in Lièbard's cart the day before. Next day he brought round two horses, one of which had a lady's saddle with a velvet back, while on the back of the other he had made a kind of pillion out of a rolled-up coat. Madame Aubin rode on this horse behind the farmer, while Félicité took care of Virginie, and Paul rode on Monsieur Lechaptois' ass, which had been lent on condition that great care was taken of it.

The road was so bad that it took them two hours to go five miles.

The horses sank in the mud up to their pasterns, and their rumps floundered about as they tried to get out. Sometimes they stumbled in the ruts, or else had to jump. In some places Lièbard's mare stopped dead. He waited patiently until she went on again, talking about the people who owned property along the road, and adding moral reflections to their stories. And so, when they were in the middle of Toucques, as they passed by some windows smothered with nasturtiums, he shrugged his shoulders and said: "Madame Lehoussais lives there. Instead of taking a young man, she . . ." Félicité did not hear the rest. The horses trotted on and the donkey galloped. They all turned down a side lane. A gate swung open, two boys appeared, and they all dismounted in front of a manure heap just outside the farmhouse door.

When Madame Lièbard saw her mistress, her generosity expressed her joy. She served them a lunch with a sirloin of beef, tripe, black pudding, a fricassee of chicken, sparkling cider, fruit pie and brandied plums, seasoning it with compliments to Madame, who seemed in better health; to Mademoiselle, who was now "splendid"; and to Monsieur Paul, who "was filling out wonderfully." Nor did she forget their departed grandparents, whom the Lièbards had known well, as they had been in the family's service for several generations. The farm, like them, had the hallmark of antiquity. The beams on the ceiling were worm-eaten, the walls black with smoke, the window panes grey with dust. All sorts of useful objects were set out on an oak dresser—jugs, plates, pewter bowls, wolf-traps, sheep-shears, and a huge syringe which made the children laugh. Every tree in the three courtyards had mushrooms growing at the foot of it and a sprig of mistletoe in its branches. Several of them had been thrown down by the wind, and had taken root again in the middle. All were bending under their wealth of apples. The thatched roofs, like brown velvet and varying in thickness, withstood the heaviest gales, but the cart shed was tumbling down. Madame Aubin said that she would see about it, and ordered the animals to be saddled again.

After another half hour they reached Trouville. The little troop dismounted to pass Ecores, an overhanging cliff with boats on the sea beneath it, and three minutes later they reached the end of the quay and entered the courtyard of the Golden Lamb, kept by worthy Madame David.

From the first day of their stay, Virginie began to grow stronger, thanks to the change of air and the sea baths. These she took in her chemise for want of a bathing suit, and Félicité used to dress her afterwards in a coastguard's cabin which was used by the bathers.

In the afternoons they used to take the donkey and wander off beyond the black rocks beyond Hennequeville. At first the path went up hill and down dale through a green sward like a park. Then it came out on a plateau, where green fields and arable land were lying side by side. Holly rose stiffly out of masses of briar at the side of the road, and here and there the branches of a great withered tree zigzagged against the blue sky.

They nearly always rested in a meadow, with Deauville on their left, Havre on their right, and the open sea in front of them. It gleamed in the sunshine, smooth as a mirror, and it was so still that its murmur could scarcely be heard. Hidden sparrows chirped and the great sky arched over all. Madame Aubin would do needlework, Virginie plaited rushes beside her, Félicité gathered lavender, and Paul was bored and wanted to go home.

On other days they crossed the Toucques in a boat and hunted for shells. When the tide had gone out, sea-urchins, starfish, and jelly fish were left stranded, and the children scurried after the flakes of foam which scudded along the wind. The sleepy waves broke on the sand and rolled all along the beach, which stretched far out of sight, bounded on the land by the dunes between it and the Marsh, a broad meadow shaped like an arena. As they came home that way, Trouville, on the hill behind, grew larger at every step, and its varied huddle of houses seemed to break into bright disorder.

When the weather was too hot, they did not leave their room. Bars of light from the dazzling outside fell through the lattices. There was no sound in the village, and not a soul on the pavement outside. This silence made the quiet profound. In the distance, men were caulking, and you could hear the tap of their hammers as they plugged the hulls of their boats, and a heavy breeze wafted up the smell of tar.

The chief amusement was watching the return of the fishing boats. They began to tack as soon as they had passed the buoys. The sails were lowered on two of the three masts, and they glided along through the ripple of the waves, with the foresails bellying out like balloons, till they reached the middle of the harbour, when they suddenly dropped anchor. Then the boats were drawn up against the quay, and the fishermen began to throw their quivering fish over the side. A line of carts was waiting, and women in cotton bonnets darted out to take the baskets and kiss their men.

One of these women came up to Félicité one day, and she went home a little later in a state of happiness. She had found a sister. Nastasie Barette, "Leroux's wife," showed up behind her, with a baby at her breast and another child in her right hand, and on her left walked a little cabin boy with arms akimbo and his cap on one ear.

After a quarter of an hour Madame Aubin sent them away, but they were always to be seen around the kitchen, or met whenever they went for a walk. The husband never appeared.

Félicité grew very fond of them. She bought them a blanket, some shirts, and a stove. Evidently they were doing quite well out of her. Madame Aubin was annoyed by this weakness, and she did not like the nephew's familiarity when he said "thee" and "thou" to Paul. And so, as Virginie was coughing and the weather had broken, they returned to Pont-L'Évêque.

Monsieur Bourais gave her advice about a boys' school. Caen was supposed to be the best, and so Paul was sent there. He said goodbye bravely, glad enough to go and live where he would have playmates.

Madame Aubin resigned herself to the boy's absence. It had to be. Virginie soon forgot all about it. Félicité missed his noisiness about the house. But she found an occupation to distract her. After Christmas she took the little girl to catechism every day.

III

After making a genuflection at the door she walked up between the double row of chairs in the lofty nave, opened Madame Aubin's pew, sat down, and began to look around. The choir stalls were filled with boys on the right and girls at the left, and the curé stood at the lectern. From a stained glass window in the apse the Holy Ghost looked down at the Blessed Virgin. In another window she was kneeling before the Infant Jesus, and behind the shrine on the altar a carved wooden group showed St. Michael overcoming the dragon.

The priest began with an outline of sacred history. The Garden of Eden, the Flood, the Tower of Babel, cities in flames, dying nations, idols overthrown, passed in a vision before her eyes, and the bewildering dream left her clinging reverently to the Most High in fear of His wrath. Then she wept at the story of the Passion. Why had they crucified Him, He who loved children, fed the multitudes, healed the blind, and had chosen, in His meekness, to be born among the poor on the dungheap of a stable? The sowings, the harvests, the wine-presses, all the familiar things of which the Gospels speak, were an ordinary part of her life. God's passing had made them holy, and she loved the lambs more tenderly for her love of the Lamb, and the doves because of the Holy Ghost.

She could hardly imagine Him in person, for not only was He a bird, but He was a flame as well, and even a breath some times. Perhaps it is His Light, she would think, which flits over the edge of the marshes at night, His Breath which makes the clouds run across the sky, His Voice which gives clear music to the bells; and she would sit lost in adoration, enjoying the coolness and stillness of the church.

Of dogma she understood nothing, and made no effort to understand it. The curé discoursed, the children said their lessons, and finally she went to sleep, waking up startled by their wooden shoes clattering on the flagstones as they went out of the church.

So Félicité, whose religious education had been neglected in her youth, learned her catechism by being obliged to listen to it. From that day she imitated Virginie in all her religious practices, fasting when she fasted and going to confession when she did. On the feast of Corpus Christi they made a repository together.

Virginie's first communion lay anxiously before her. Félicité worried over her shoes, her rosary, her book, and her gloves. And how she trembled as she helped the little girl's mother to dress her up for the occasion!

All through Mass she was feverish with anxiety. Monsieur Bourais hid one side of the choir from her, but straight in front was the flock of maidens, with their white crowns above their drooping veils, making a field of snow; and she knew her dear little one at a distance by her dainty neck and reverent air. The bell tinkled. All heads bowed, and there was silence. The organ pealed, and choir and congregation joined in the *Agnus Dei*. Then the procession of the boys began, and the girls rose after them. Step by step, with their hands clasped in prayer, they drew near the lighted altar, knelt on the first step, each received the Blessed Sacrament in turn, and they came back to their seats in the same order. When Virginie's turn came, Félicité leaned forward to see her; and with the imagination of tender affection it seemed to her as if she were that child. Virginie's face became hers. She was wearing the child's crown, the little girl's heart beat in her breast. When it was time to open her mouth, she closed her eyes and nearly fainted. Next morning she went to the sacristy to receive Communion from Monsieur the Curé. She received it with devotion, but did not feel the same delight.

Madame Aubin was anxious to give her daughter the best education possible, and as Guyot could not teach her music or English, decided to put her in the Ursuline Convent at Honfleur as a boarder. The child made no complaint. Félicité sighed and thought that Madame was hard-hearted. Then she considered that no doubt her mistress was right. These affairs were beyond her.

So one day an old cart drew up at their door, and a nun stepped out of it who was come to fetch the young lady. Félicité set the luggage on top of the cart, gave special orders to the driver, and placed six pots of jam, a dozen pears, and a bunch of violets under the child's seat.

At the last moment Virginie sobbed bitterly, and threw her arms round the neck of her mother, who kissed her on the forehead and kept saying: "Come now, be brave! be really brave!" The steps were raised and the cart drove off.

Then Madame Aubin's strength broke down. In the evening all her friends, the Lormeaus, Madame Lechaptois, the Rochefeuille girls, Monsieur de Houppeville, and Bourais, came in to comfort her.

At first life was very painful to her without her daughter, but she heard from her three times a week, wrote to her on the other days, walked in her garden, and so passed the weary time away.

Félicité went into Virginie's room in the morning as usual and stared at the walls. It was dull for her not to have the child's hair to comb, her boots to lace, and her body to tuck into bed, not to see her dear face all the time and to hold her hand when they went out together. To fill up her idleness she tried to make lace, but her fingers were too clumsy and she kept breaking the threads. She could not settle down to anything, lost sleep, and, as she said, was "ruined."

To amuse herself, she asked permission for her nephew Victor to visit her.

He would come on Sundays after Mass with rosy cheeks and bare chest, and country air all about him from his walk. She set the table for him promptly and they lunched together face to face. She ate as little as possible herself to save money, but she would stuff him till he fell asleep. When the bell first sounded for Vespers, she would wake him up, brush his trousers, fasten his tie, and set off for church leaning on his arm with a mother's pride.

His parents always told Victor to get something out of her, a damp packet of sugar, perhaps, or a cake of soap, some brandy, or even money now and then. He brought her his clothes to mend, and she gladly undertook this task, grateful for anything that would bring him back to her.

In August his father took him away for a sea trip along the coast. It was holiday time for the children, and their arrival consoled her. But Paul was getting selfish and Virginie too old to say "thee" and "thou" to her any longer. This made things stiff and created a barrier between them.

Victor went to Morlaix, Dunkirk, and Brighton in succession, and brought Félicité a present after each trip. First he brought her a box made out of shells, then a coffee cup, and finally a big gingerbread man. He was growing handsome with his fine figure, his hint of a moustache, his honest clear eyes, and a little leather cap clinging to the back of his head like a pilot's. He amused her with stories adorned with nautical terms.

It was on a Monday, the 14th of July, 1819 (she never forgot that date), that he told her how he had signed on for a long voyage, and two nights later was to go on board the boat for Honfleur, where he was to join his schooner which was weighing anchor shortly from Havre. He might be gone two years.

The thought of this long absence plunged Félicité in distress. She must say goodbye once more, and so, on Wednesday evening after Madame had finished her dinner, she put on her wooden shoes and soon covered the twelve miles between Pont-L'Évêque and Honfleur.

When she came to the Calvary, she turned to the right instead of the left, went astray in the timber yard, and had to retrace her steps. Some people to whom she spoke told her to hurry. She went all round the harbour, which was full of shipping, and kept tripping over hawsers. Then the ground fell away, lights flashed across each other, and she thought she was losing her wits, for she saw horses way up in the sky. Others were neighing beside the quay afraid of the sea. They were hoisted up with tackle and lowered in a boat, in which passengers were bumping into each other amid cider casks, hampers of cheese, and sacks of corn. Hens were cackling, the captain swore, and a cabin boy was leaning over the bow, indifferent to it all. Félicité, who had not recognised him, cried "Victor!" He raised his head. Just as she was rushing forward, the gangway was pulled back.

The Honfleur packet, with women singing as they hauled, went out of the harbour, its ribs creaking and heavy waves slapping against the bows. The sails swung round, and no one could be seen now on board. The boat was a black speck on the sea which shimmered with silver in the moonlight. It faded away little by little, dipped, and was gone.

As Félicité passed the Calvary, she had an impulse to commend to God what she cherished most, and she stood praying for a long time with her face bathed in tears and her eyes staring at the clouds. The town was asleep, coastguards were walking to and fro, and water poured incessantly through the holes in the sluice with the noise of a torrent. The clocks struck two.

The convent parlour would not be open before dawn. If Félicité were late, Madame would be sure to be annoyed. In spite of her wish to kiss the other child, she went home. The maids at the inn were just waking up when she came home to Pont-L'Évêque.

So the poor little chap was going to be tossed for months and months at sea! His previous voyages had not alarmed her. You were sure to come back safely from England or Brittany, but America, the Colonies, the Islands were lost in a faint cloudy region on the other side of the world.

From that day Félicité thought only of her nephew. On sunny days she was troubled by thinking of his thirst; when it was stormy, she was afraid of the lightning lest it should strike him. As she listened to the wind moaning in the chimney or stripping off the slates, she saw him bruised by that same tempest at the top of a shattered mast, with his body thrown back under a sheet of foam; or (remembering the illustrated geography) he was being devoured by savages, captured by monkeys in the forest, or dying on some desert shore. She never spoke of her anxiety.

Madame Aubin had anxieties of her own about her daughter. The good nuns considered her an affectionate but delicate child. The least emotion unnerved her. She had to give up the piano.

Her mother insisted on hearing regularly from the Convent. One morning, when the letter-carrier did not come, she lost patience, and walked up and down the parlour from her chair to the window. It was astonishing. No news for four days!

To console Madame Aubin by her own example, Félicité said: "It is six months since I had a letter!"

"From whom?"

"Why, from my nephew," answered the servant gently.

"Oh! your nephew!" And Madame Aubin resumed her walk and shrugged her shoulders, as much as to say: "I wasn't thinking about him, and besides what does a mere scamp of a cabin boy matter? Now my daughter . . . why, think of it!"

Félicité, though she had been brought up roughly enough, was indignant with Madame, and then forgot all about it. It seemed natural enough to her to lose your head over the little girl. For her, the two children were equally important. They were united in her heart by the same bond, and their destinies must be the same.

The chemist informed her that Victor's ship had reached Havana. He had read the news in a paper.

Cigars made her picture Havana as a place where no one did anything but smoke, and she could see Victor moving about among negroes in a cloud of tobacco. Could a man, she wondered, "in case he had to," come home by land? How far was it from Pont-L'Évêque? She asked Monsieur Bourais questions to find out.

He took down his atlas and began to explain the longitudes. Félicité's confusion aroused a broad pedantic smile. At last he marked with his pencil a tiny black spot in an oval place on the map, and said, "Here it is." She stooped over the map. The network of coloured lines tired her eyes without conveying anything to her. When Baurais asked her to tell him what was the matter, she begged him to show her the house in which Victor lived. Bourais threw up his hands, sneezed, and went into peals of laughter. Her simplicity delighted him. And Félicité could not understand why! How could she, when she expected, no doubt, actually to see a picture of her nephew, her mind was so simple!

A fortnight later Lièbard came into the kitchen at market time as usual, and gave her a letter from her brother-in-law. As neither could read she carried it to her mistress.

Madame Aubin, who was counting the stitches in her knitting, set down her work and broke the seal of the letter. She started and murmured with a meaning look: "It's bad news . . . that they have to tell you. . . . Your nephew . . ."

He was dead. The letter said no more.

Félicité fell on a chair with her head leaning against the wall. She closed her eyelids, which suddenly went pink. Then, with bent forehead, hands hanging down, and rigid eyes, she kept saying at intervals: "Poor little fellow! Poor little fellow!"

Lièbard watched her and sighed. Madame Aubin trembled a little. She suggested that Félicité ought to go and see her sister at Trouville. Félicité replied with a gesture that it was no use.

There was a silence. The worthy Lièbard thought it was time to withdraw.

Then Félicité said:

"They don't care, they don't!"

Her head drooped again, and now and then she picked up mechanically the long needles on her work table.

Some women went through the yard with a barrow of dripping linen.

As she saw them through the window, she remembered her washing. She had put it to soak yesterday. To-day she must wring it out. She left the room.

Her plank and tub were at the edge of the Toucques. She threw a heap of linen on the bank, rolled up her sleeves, and, taking her wooden beater, she dealt such blows that they could be heard in the neighbouring gardens. The fields were empty. The river stirred faintly in the wind. Below, long grasses waved like the hair of corpses floating on the water. She mastered her grief and was very brave until the evening, but once in her room she gave way to it entirely, lying stretched out on the mattress with her face buried in the pillow and her hands clenched against her temples.

Much later she heard the circumstances of Victor's end from the captain himself. They had bled him too much for yellow fever at the hospital. Four doctors were holding him at once. He had died instantly and the chief had said: "Bah! that's another one gone!"

His parents had always been cruel to him. She preferred not to see them again, and they made no advances, either because they had forgotten all about her, or because they were hardened in their desperate poverty.

Virginie began to grow weaker.

Constriction in the chest, coughing, chronic fever, and the marble veins on her cheek bones betrayed some deep-seated ailment. Monsieur Poupart advised a stay in Provence. Madame Aubin decided on it and would have brought home her daughter at once had it not been for the climate of Pont-L'Évêque.

She contracted with a job-master who drove her to the Convent every Tuesday. There is a terrace in the garden which overlooks the Seine. Virginie walked there over the fallen vine leaves on her mother's arm. A beam of sunlight through the clouds sometimes made her blink, as she gazed at the sails in the distance and the wide horizon from the Château de Tancarville to the lighthouses of Havre. Afterwards they would rest in the harbour. Her mother had procured a small cask of excellent Malaga; and Virginie, laughing at the idea of getting tipsy, used to drink a thimbleful of it, but no more.

You could see her strength coming back. The autumn glided by softly. Félicité reassured Madame Aubin, but one evening, when she had been out on an errand in the neighbourhood, she found Monsieur Poupart's gig at the door. He was in the hall and Madame Aubin was tying her bonnet.

"Give me my foot-warmer, and my purse and gloves! Hurry, be quick about it!"

Virginie had inflammation of the lungs. It might be hopeless.

"Not yet!" said the doctor, and they both got into the carriage in a whirl of snowflakes. Night was coming on, and it was very cold.

Félicité rushed into the church to light a candle. Then she ran after the gig, caught up with it in an hour, jumped in lightly behind, and hung on to the fringes. Suddenly she thought: "The courtyard has not been shut up! Suppose thieves break in!" And she jumped down.

At dawn next day she was at the doctor's door. He had come in and started off for the country again. Then she waited in the inn, thinking that a letter would come by somebody or other. Finally, when it was growing dark, she took the Lisieux coach.

The Convent was at the end of a steep lane. When she was half way up, she heard strange sounds, a passing-bell was tolling. "It's for someone else," thought Félicité, and she struck the knocker violently.

After some minutes, there was a sound of shuffling slippers, the door opened partly, and a nun appeared.

The good sister, with an air of compunction, said that "she had just passed away." At that moment the bell of St. Leonard's tolled harder than ever.

Félicité went up to the second floor. From the doorway she saw Virginie stretched out on her back with clasped hands, open mouth, and her head thrown back under a black crucifix which leaned towards her, between curtains hanging stiffly, less pale than her face.

Madame Aubin, at the foot of the bed which she was clasping with her arms, was choking with agonised sobs. The Mother Superior was standing on the right. Three candlesticks on the chest of drawers made red spots, and a white fog came seeping in through the windows. Some nuns came and led Madame Aubin away.

For two nights Félicité never left the dead child. She kept repeating the same prayers, sprinkled holy water on the sheets, came and sat down again, and watched her. At the end of her first vigil, she noticed that the face had become yellow, the lips had turned blue, the nose was sharper, and the eyes had sunk in. She kissed them several times and would not have been very much surprised if Virginie had opened them again. To minds like hers the supernatural is perfectly simple. She made the girl's toilet, wrapped her in her shroud, lifted her into the coffin, laid a wreath on her head, and spread out her hair. It was fair and surprisingly long for her age. Félicité cut off a big lock of it, and slipped half of it into her bosom, determined never to part with it.

The body was brought back to Pont-L'Évêque, in accordance with the wish of Madame Aubin, who followed the hearse in a closed carriage.

It took another three-quarters of an hour after the Mass to reach the cemetery. Paul walked in front, sobbing. Monsieur Bourais followed, and then came the principal citizens of Pont-L'Évêque, the women in black mantles, and Félicité. She thought of her nephew, and since she had been unable to pay him these honours, her grief was doubled, as if the one were being buried with the other.

Madame Aubin's despair was unbounded. At first she rebelled against God, deeming it unjust for Him to have taken her daughter from her, who had never done any harm and whose conscience was clear! Ah! no! she ought to have taken Virginie to the South! Other doctors would have saved her. Now she accused herself, longed to join her child, and cried out in distress in the middle of her dreams. One dream especially haunted her. Her husband, dressed as a sailor, came back from a long voyage, and shed tears as he told her that he was ordered to carry Virginie away. Then they consulted how to hide her somewhere.

Once she came in from the garden quite upset. Just now—and she pointed out the spot—father and daughter had appeared to her, standing side by side. They did nothing, but looked at her.

For several months after this she stayed passively in her room. Félicité lectured her gently. She must live for her son, and for the other, in remembrance of "her."

"Her?" answered Madame Aubin, as though just rousing from slumber. "Ah, yes! . . . yes! . . . you do not forget her!" This was an allusion to the cemetery, to which she was strictly forbidden to go.

Félicité went there every day.

On the stroke of four she would skirt the houses, climb the hill, open the gate, and come to Virginie's grave. It was a little pillar of pink marble with a stone underneath and a garden plot enclosed by chains. The beds were hidden under a carpet of flowers. She watered their leaves, freshened up the gravel, and knelt down to soften the earth better. Whenever Madame Aubin was able to come there, she felt relieved and somehow consoled.

The years slipped by, one much like another, marked only by the great feast days as they recurred—Easter, the Assumption, All Saints' Day. Household happenings marked dates which were mentioned afterwards. In 1825, for example, two glaziers whitewashed the hall. In 1827, a piece of the roof fell into the courtyard and nearly killed a man. In the summer of 1828, it was Madame's turn to offer the blessed bread. About this time, Bourais went away mysteriously. One by one the old acquaintances died: Guyot, Lièbard, Madame Lechaptois, Robelin, and Uncle de Gremanville, who had been paralysed for a long time.

One night the driver of the mail coach announced in Pont-L'Évêque the Revolution of July. A new sub-Prefect was appointed a few days later. It was Baron de Larsonnière, who had been a Consul in America, and brought with him, besides his wife, his sister-in-law and three grown-up young ladies. They were to be seen on the lawn in loose drapery, and they had a negro and a parrot. They called on Madame Aubin, and she did not fail to return the call. As soon as they were seen in the distance, Félicité ran and told her mistress. But only one thing could really move her—letters from her son.

He lived in taverns and could follow no career. She used to pay his debts and he made new ones. Madame Aubin's sighs, as she sat knitting by the window, reached Félicité spinning in the kitchen.

They used to walk together along the espaliered wall, always talking of Virginie and wondering if this or that would have pleased her, or what she would have said on this or that occasion.

All her little belongings filled a cupboard in the two-bedded room. Madame Aubin looked at them as seldom as possible. One summer day she made up her mind to do so, and some moths flew out of the cupboard.

Virginie's dresses were all in a row underneath a shelf on which there were three dolls, some hoops, some little pots and pans, and the basin which she had used. They took out her petticoats as well, and her stockings and handkerchiefs, and spread them out on the two beds before folding them up again. The sunlight shone on these poor things, bringing out their stains and the creases made by the little girl's movements. The sky was warm and blue, a blackbird warbled, and life seemed bathed in a deep sweet peace. They came across a little plush hat with thick, chestnut-coloured fur, but the moths had eaten it. Félicité begged for it. They gazed at each other and their eyes filled with tears. At last the mistress opened her arms, the servant threw herself into them, and they clasped each other in a hearty embrace, staunching their grief with a kiss which made them equal.

It was the first time in their lives, for Madame Aubin was not expansive by nature.

Félicité was as grateful as though she had received a great favour, and from that day cherished her mistress with an animal's devotion and religious worship.

The kindness of her heart opened out.

When she heard the drums of a regiment marching in the street, she would stand at the door with a pitcher of cider and offer it to the soldiers to drink. She took care of cholera patients. She protected the Polish refugees, and one of these proposed to marry her. They quarrelled, nevertheless; for as she returned from the Angelus one morning, she found he had got into her kitchen and made with vinegar a salad for himself which he was eating quietly.

After the Poles came Père Colmiche, an ancient man who was reputed to have committed atrocities in '93. He lived beside the river in a ruined pig-sty. The little boys used to stare at him through the cracks in his wall, and to throw pebbles at him which fell on the mattress upon which he lay constantly shaken with catarrh. His hair was very long, his eyes inflamed, and he had a tumor on his arm which was bigger than his head. Félicité found him some linen and tried to clean up his miserable den. She longed to establish him in the bakehouse without letting him annoy Madame. When the tumor burst, she used to dress it every day. Sometimes she would bring him cake and put him out in the sunlight on a truss of straw. The poor old man, slobbering and trembling, would thank her in a faint voice, fearful of losing her, and would stretch out his hand as he saw her going away. He died; and she had a Mass said for the repose of his soul.

That very day a great happiness befell her. Just at dinner time Madame de Larsonnière's negro appeared, carrying the parrot in its cage, with perch, chain, and padlock. There was a note from the Baroness informing Madame Aubin that her husband had been promoted to a Prefecture, and they were going away that evening. She begged her to accept the bird as a memento and a token of her esteem.

For a long time the parrot had absorbed Félicité's attention, because he came from America. The name reminded her of Victor, so much so that she had asked the negro about it. Once she had gone so far as to say: "How happy Madame would be to have him!"

The negro had repeated this remark to his mistress. Since she could not take the bird away with her, this was how she got rid of him.

IV

His name was Loulou. His body was green, the tips of his wings were rosy pink, his brow was blue, and his throat was golden.

But he had a tiresome habit of biting his perch, tearing out his feathers, flinging his dirt about, and spattering the water from his bath. He annoyed Madame Aubin, and she presented him to Félicité.

She undertook to train him. Soon he could repeat: "Good boy! Your servant, sir! How dy'ye do, Marie?" He was placed beside the door, and several people were surprised to find that he did not answer to the name of Jacquot, for all parrots are called Jacquot. He was compared to a turkey and a log, and this always stabbed Félicité to the heart. And Loulou was strangely obstinate. If you looked at him, he wouldn't speak!

All the same he was fond of society. On Sunday, when the Rochefeuille girls, Monsieur de Houppeville, and some new acquaintances —Onfroy the chemist, Monsieur Varin, and Captain Mathieu—were playing cards, he used to beat the windows with his wings and fling himself about so furiously that you couldn't hear yourself talk.

It would seem as if Bourais' face struck him as extremely funny. The moment he saw it he began to laugh, and laughed with all his might. His shrieks rang through the courtyard and the echo repeated them. The neighbours would come to their windows and laugh too, while Monsieur Bourais, to escape the parrot's eye, would slip along under the wall, hiding his face in his hat, reach the river, and enter by the garden gate. There was no tenderness in the scowls which he darted at that bird.

Loulou had been buffeted by the butcher's boy for daring to stick his head into his basket. Ever since he had been trying to nip him through his shirt. Fabu threatened to wring his neck, although he was by no means cruel in spite of his tattooed arm and great whiskers. On the contrary, he secretly liked the parrot, and in his merry humour even wanted to teach him to swear. Félicité, alarmed by such doings, put the bird in the kitchen. His little chain was removed and he wandered round the house.

When he wanted to come downstairs, he used to lean on each step with his beak, raise his right foot, and then his left. Félicité was afraid such gymnastics made him giddy. He fell ill and could neither talk nor eat any longer. He had a growth under his tongue as birds often have. She cured him by tearing the skin off with her finger nails. One day Monsieur Paul thoughtlessly blew some cigar smoke into his face, and another day when Madame Lormeau was teasing him with the tip of her umbrella, he snapped at the ferrule. At last he got lost.

Félicité had set him down on the grass to get some fresh air and went away for a moment. When she came back, there was no parrot to be seen. First she hunted for him in the shrubbery, on the river bank, and over the roofs, paying no attention to her mistress's cries of "Take care! You've lost your wits!" Then she explored all the gardens in Pont-L'Évêque, and stopped everyone who passed by.

"You don't happen to have seen my parrot by any chance, have you?" She described the parrot to those who did not know him. All at once, she seemed to see something green fluttering behind the mills at the foot of the hill. But there was nothing on the hilltop. A pedlar assured her that he had just come across the parrot in Mère Simon's shop at Saint-Melaine. She hurried there. They had no idea what she meant. At last she same home exhausted, with her slippers in tatters and despair in her soul. As she was sitting beside Madame on the garden seat, telling her the whole story of her adventures, something light dropped on to her shoulder. It was Loulou! What on earth had he been doing? Taking a walk in the neighbourhood, perhaps!

She had some trouble in getting over this, or rather she never did get over it. After a chill she had quinsy, and soon afterwards an ear-ache. Three years later she was deaf, and she spoke very loud, even in church. Although Félicité's sins might have been shouted in every corner of the diocese without dishonouring her or scandalising anybody, the priest thought it advisable to hear her confession in the sacristy.

Imaginary noises in her head completed her misfortune. Her mistress would often say to her: "Good heavens! how stupid you are!" And she would reply: "Yes, Madame," and look round for something.

Her little circle of ideas grew narrower and narrower. The peal of church bells and the lowing of cattle no longer existed for her. Human beings moved in ghostly silence. Only one sound reached her ears now—the parrot's voice.

Loulou, as if to amuse her, copied the clatter of the turnspit, the shrill cry of a man hawking fish, and the noise of the joiner's saw in the opposite house. Whenever the doorbell rang, he used to mimic Madame Aubin's "Félicité! the door! the door!"

They used to carry on conversations. He would repeat endlessly the three phrases in his repertory, and she would answer in words which were just as disconnected, but which expressed what lay in her heart. In her isolation, Loulou was almost a son and a lover to her. He would climb up her fingers, nibble at her lips, and cling to her shawl. When she bent her forehead and shook her head gently, as nurses do, the great wings of her bonnet and the wings of the bird fluttered together.

When the clouds gathered and the thunder rumbled, Loulou would shriek, possibly remembering the downpours in his native forests. The streaming rain would drive him absolutely mad. He would flap about wildly, dash up to the ceiling, upset everything, and go out through the window to splash about in the garden. But he would soon come back to perch on one of the andirons, and would hop about drying his feathers, showing his tail and his beak in turn.

One morning in the terrible winter of 1837, she had put him in front of the fire because of the cold. She found him dead, in the middle of his cage, head down, with his claws in the bars. No doubt he had died of congestion. But Félicité decided that he had been poisoned with parsley, and though she had no proof of it, she was inclined to suspect Fabu.

She wept so bitterly that her mistress said to her: "Well, then, have the bird stuffed!"

She asked the chemist's advice, for he had always been kind to the parrot. He wrote to Havre, and a man called Fellacher undertook the job. But as parcels sometimes got lost in the mail coach, she decided to take the parrot as far as Honfleur herself.

Along the roadside were leafless apple trees stretching endlessly. The ditches were covered with ice. Dogs barked on the farms, and Félicité, with her hands under her cloak, and her little black wooden shoes and her basket, walked quickly in the middle of the road.

She crossed the forest, passed Le Haut-Chêne, and came to St. Gatien.

The mail coach rushed at full gallop like a hurricane behind her in a cloud of dust with gathering momentum down the steep hill. Seeing this woman, who did not get out of the way, the driver stood up in front and the postilion shouted, while the four horses which he could not control increased their speed, and the two leaders grazed her just as he threw them to one side with a jerk of the reins. He was wild with fury and, raising his arm as he raced by, he gave her such a lash from her waist to her neck with his long whip that she fell on her back.

The first thing she did, when she recovered consciousness, was to open her basket. Fortunately, Loulou was none the worse. She felt her right cheek bleeding, and when she put her hand on it, it was red. The blood was flowing.

She sat down on a pile of stones and bandaged her face with her handkerchief. Then she ate a crust which she had put in her basket as a precaution, and consoled herself for her wound by gazing at the bird.

When she reached the hilltop of Ecquemauville, she saw the lights of Honfleur twinkling in the night like a host of stars. Far off, the sea stretched dimly. Then she was seized with faintness and paused. Her miserable childhood, the wreck of her first love, her nephew's departure, Virginie's death, all flooded in on her at once, like the waves of a making tide, rose in her throat, and choked her.

Later she made a point of speaking to the captain of the boat, and besought him to take care of the package, but did not tell him what it contained.

Fellacher kept the parrot a long time. He kept promising to send it back the following week. After six months he announced that a case was on its way, and then she heard no more of it. It seemed as if Loulou would never come back. "They have stolen him," was her thought.

At last he arrived, and he looked magnificently. There he stood erect on a branch screwed into a mahogany base, with one claw in the air and his head cocked on one side, biting at a nut, which the ornithologist, with a sense of drama, had gilded.

Félicité shut him up in her room. Very few people were admitted to this place, which held so many religious objects and varied odds and ends that it looked like a chapel turned into a bazaar.

A huge wardrobe interfered with the door as you came in. Opposite the window which overlooked the garden, a little round window offered a glimpse of the courtyard. There was a table beside the folding bed with a jug, two combs, and a cube of blue soap on a chipped plate. The walls were covered with rosaries, medals, several gracious Virgins, and a holy water stoup made out of a cocoanut. On the chest of drawers, which was covered with a cloth like an altar, were the shell box which Victor had given her, a watering-pot, a toy balloon, copybooks, the illustrated Geography, and a pair of girl's boots. And, tied by its ribbons to the nail of the looking glass, hung the little felt hat. Félicité carried her ritual so far as to keep one of Monsieur's frock coats. All the old rubbish which Madame Aubin had cast aside she carried off to her room. And so there were artificial flowers along the edge of the chest of drawers and a portrait of the Comte d'Artois in the tiny window recess.

Loulou was set on a bracket over the chimney piece which jutted out into the room. Every morning when she woke she saw him there in the dawn, and remembered old times and the least details of insignificant acts in a painless and peaceful quietude.

She had intercourse with no one, and lived like one who walks in her sleep. Only the Corpus Christi processions were able to rouse her. Then she would go about begging mats and candlesticks from the neighbours to ornament the altar which was put up in the street.

In church she was always gazing at the Holy Ghost in the window, and noticed that he looked rather like the parrot. The likeness was more remarkable, she thought, on a crude chromo representing the baptism of Our Lord. With his purple wings and emerald body, the dove was the image of Loulou.

She bought the picture and hung it up in place of the Comte d'Artois, so that she could see them both together at a single glance. They were united in her thoughts, and the parrot was consecrated by his connection with the Holy Ghost, which grew more and more vivid and intelligible to her. The Father could not have chosen to express Himself through a dove, for these birds cannot speak. He must have chosen one of Loulou's ancestors. Though Félicité used to look at the picture while she was saying her prayers, now and then her glance turned toward the parrot.

She was anxious to join the Ladies of the Blessed Virgin, but Madame Aubin dissuaded her.

Then a great event loomed up before their eyes—Paul's marriage.

He had been successively a solicitor's clerk, in business, in the Customs, in the Internal Revenue, and had even made an effort to get into the Bureau of Forestry, when, at the age of thirty-six, he was inspired to discover his real vocation—the Registrar's Office. There he had shown such marked talent that an inspector had offered him his daughter's hand and promised him his patronage. Paul, now grown serious, brought the girl to see his mother.

She criticised the ways of Pont-L'Évêque sharply enough, gave herself high and mighty airs, and hurt Félicité's feelings. Madame Aubin was glad when she went away.

A week later news came of Monsieur Bourais' death at an inn in Lower Brittany. The rumour of his suicide was confirmed, and doubts arose about his honesty. Madame Aubin scrutinised his accounts, and soon learned the whole story of his misdeeds—embezzled arrears, secret sales of lumber, forged receipts, and so on. Besides all that, he had an illegitimate child, and "relations with a person at Dozulé."

These disgraceful facts greatly upset her. In March, 1853, she was seized with a pain in the chest. Her throat seemed to be coated with film, and leeches did not help the difficulty she found in breathing. She died on the ninth evening of her illness.

She was just seventy-two.

She passed as being younger, thanks to the bands of brown hair which framed her pale, pock-marked face. She left few friends to regret her passing, for she had a haughtiness of manner which kept folk off.

But Félicité mourned for her as servants seldom mourn for their mistresses. It upset her notions, and seemed to reverse the whole order of things, that Madame should die before her. It was inconceivable and monstrous.

Ten days later the heirs hastily arrived from Besançon. The daughter-in-law ransacked the drawers, chose some pieces of furniture, and sold the remainder. Then they went back to their Registrar's business.

Madame's armchair, her little round table, her foot-warmer, her eight chairs, were all gone. Yellow patches in the middle of the panels showed where the engravings had hung. They had carried off the two little beds and mattresses, and all the relics of Virginie had disappeared from the cupboard. Félicité wandered from floor to floor in a sorrowful daze.

Next day there was a notice on the door, and the chemist shouted in her ear that the house was for sale.

She tottered, and had to sit down. What distressed her most of all was giving up her room, which was so suitable for poor Loulou. She wrapped him in a gaze of anguish as she implored the Holy Ghost, and formed the idolatrous habit of kneeling in front of the parrot whenever she said her prayers. Occasionally the sun shone through the little window of her attic and caught his glass eye, and a great luminous ray would shoot out from it and put her in an ecstasy.

Her mistress left her three hundred and eighty francs a year. The garden kept her in vegetables, and as for clothes, she had enough to last her until the end of her days. She saved candles by going to bed at twilight.

She seldom went out, as she did not like to pass the dealer's shop in which some of the old furniture was exposed for sale. Since her fit of giddiness she dragged one leg and, as her strength was fading, Mère Simon, whose grocery business had come to grief, came every morning to split wood and pump water for her.

Her sight grew feeble. She no longer opened the shutters. Years went by, and the house was neither let nor sold.

Félicité never asked for repairs because she was afraid of eviction. The boards on the roof rotted. Her bolster was damp all one winter. After Easter she spat blood. Then Mère Simon called in a doctor. Félicité wanted to know what was the matter with her. But she was too deaf to hear. The only word which reached her ears was "pneumonia." It was a familiar word to her, and she answered softly: "Ah! like Madame!" thinking it only natural that she should follow her mistress.

The time for the Corpus Christi shrines drew nigh. The first shrine was always at the bottom of the hill, the second in front of the Post Office, and the third half-way up the street. There was some rivalry about the last shrine, and finally the women of the parish chose Madame Aubin's courtyard.

The difficult breathing and fever increased. Félicité was vexed that she could do nothing for the shrine. If only she could put something on it! Then she thought of the parrot. The neighbours protested that it would not be decent, but the curé gave her permission, which delighted her so much that she begged him to accept Loulou, her only treasure, when she died.

From Tuesday till Saturday, the eve of the feast-day, she coughed more often. By evening her face shrivelled up, her lips stuck to her gums, and she had attacks of vomiting. At dawn next morning, feeling very low, she sent for the priest.

Three kind women were beside her during the Extreme Unction. Then she said that she must speak to Fabu. He came in his Sunday best, quite ill at ease in the funereal atmosphere.

"Forgive me," she said, making an effort to stretch out her arms, "I thought it was you who had killed him."

What did she mean by such nonsense? She had suspected him of murder—a man like him. He was furious and started to make a row.

"Don't you see," said the women, "that she has lost her senses?"

From time to time Félicité talked with shadows around her bed. The women went away, and Mère Simon had her breakfast. A little later she took Loulou and laid him close to Félicité, saying:

"Come, now, say good-bye to him!"

Loulou was not a corpse, but the worms had devoured him. One of his wings was broken, and the stuffing was coming out of his stomach. But Félicité was blind now. She kissed him on the forehead and held him close against her cheek. Mère Simon took him back from her and placed him on the shrine.

V

The fragrance of summer rose from the meadows, flies were buzzing, the sun made the river shine and heated the slates on the roof. Mère Simon came back into the room and fell asleep softly. She was roused by the sound of church bells. The people were coming out from Vespers. Félicité's delirium subsided. She thought of the procession, and saw it as if she were taking part in it herself.

All the school children, the choir, and the firemen walked on the pavement, while in the middle of the road the verger led the way with his halberd, and the beadle with a large cross. Then came the schoolmaster watching the little boys, and the Sister Superior anxious about the little girls. Three of the most adorable little girls, with curls like angels, were scattering rose petals in the air, the deacon conducted the band with outstretched arms, and two thurifers turned back at every step towards the Blessed Sacrament, which was carried by Monsieur the Curé, wearing his beautiful chasuble, under a canopy of rich red velvet held up by the four churchwardens. A crowd of people surged behind between the white draperies covering the walls of the houses, and they reached the bottom of the hill.

A cold sweat moistened Félicité's temples. Mère Simon sponged them with a piece of linen, saying to herself that one day she would have to go the same road.

The roar of the crowd increased, was very loud for a moment, and then died away.

A fusillade shook the window. It was the postilions saluting the monstrance. Félicité turned her eyes round and said as loud as she could: "Does he look well?" The parrot was on her mind.

Her agony began.

The death rattle became faster and faster and made her sides heave. Bubbles of foam came at the corners of her mouth, and her whole body trembled.

Soon the booming of the ophicleides, the high voices of the children, and the deep voices of the men could be distinguished. Now and then all was silent, and the tread of feet, deadened by the flowers on which they trampled, sounded like a flock drifting across grass.

The clergy appeared in the courtyard. Mère Simon climbed up on a chair to reach the attic window, and so looked down on the shrine. Green garlands hung over it, and it was adorned with a flounce of English lace. In the middle of it was a small frame with relics in it. There were two orange trees at the corners, and all along stood silver candlesticks and china vases full of sunflowers, lilies, peonies, foxgloves and tufts of hortensia. This blazing mass of colour from the altar to the carpet spread over the pavement. Some rare objects caught the eye. There was a silver-gilt sugar bowl with a crown of violets, pendants of Alençon stone sparkled on moss, and two Chinese screens unfolded their landscapes. Loulou was smothered in roses, and showed nothing but his blue forehead, like a bar of lapis lazuli.

The churchwardens, the choir, and the children took their places round the three sides of the courtyard. The priest went slowly up the steps, and placed his great, radiant golden sun upon the lace of the shrine. They all knelt down. There was a great silence. The censers swung slowly to and fro on the full length of their chains.

An azure vapour rose and entered Félicité's room. It came to her nostrils. She inhaled it sensuously, mystically. She closed her eyes. Her lips smiled. Her heart-beat dwindled one by one, more fleeting and soft each moment, as a fountain sinks, an echo vanishes. When she sighed her last breath, she thought she saw an opening in Heaven, and a gigantic parrot fluttering over her head.

Benzoin for the Turbinates

BY ST. CLAIR McKELWAY

WHEN, AFTER THE customary period of discomfort, I got over my last cold of the winter of 1939–40, I made up my mind to start the winter of 1940–41 by taking my first cold of the new season to an up-to-date hospital and asking the medical profession to handle it. I wanted to find out just what science could do for a cold. I talked my plan over with a friend of mine, a nose-and-ear specialist, and he said that, medically, the experience probably would not be worth the money it would cost me, but I told him I would make provisions for the extravagance during the summer. In that case, he said, all I would have to do would be to telephone him when the first cold of the winter came along and he would have me admitted to his favorite hospital, a luxurious establishment on the East River. Then, he said, he would call in a general practitioner he knew of who made a hobby of keeping up with the latest news in the field of medicine known as "respiratory infections."

"But I thought a cold would be right up the alley of a nose man," I said.

"Oh no," said my friend. "I fool with the mucous membrane inside the head—the back of the nose, the sinuses, and the little canals that run into the ears. I confine myself to about a foot and a half of mucous membrane, all told, and as it is, I am frequently baffled. I don't even like much to go down as far as the throat if I can help it. When something like a common cold, an acute infection or inflammation of that kind, breaks out in my territory, I prefer to lay off until things begin to clear up again and I can see what I'm doing. If you came in my office with a bang-up common cold, I might give you some stuff to take, swab you out, and tell you to stay in bed until you got over it, but I wouldn't really work on your nose until the cold had gone. A cold affects the whole body. When you begin to get over this cold you expect to catch next winter, I'll have a look at you after I admit you to the hospital, and later on, if you want to do it up brown, I'll see to the nasal mucous membrane and the sinuses. But the general man will really do most of the work on you."

On the evening of February 25th, I sneezed a few times, and woke up the next morning with a cold. I took my temperature, found that it was almost two degrees above normal, and called my friend the nose-and-ear man. An hour later I was in the hospital, and in bed. The general practitioner turned up almost immediately. My friend had told him of my peculiar case and he seemed interested. He said he would not have to go to any great trouble to take care of me because he had a number of other patients in the same hospital and made a point of calling there at least once a day. He was middle-aged, with an intelligent face, apparently the kind of doctor who doesn't go in much for hocus-pocus. I asked him to give me the works, and told him I would probably put a good many questions to him and perhaps ask him to bring me one of the latest medical reports on the progress of the profession's fight against the common cold. "It's a fascinating subject," he said. "I'll bring you some stuff to read later on if you like." Then, pulling up my pajama shirt, he began to thump my chest.

"I've always wondered just what that thumping is for," I said.

He laughed. "As a matter of fact," he said, "it's sort of a reflex action with a doctor. Of course, if you had pneumonia, I could probably tell by this thumping that the lungs were badly congested, but, between us, it doesn't really mean a great deal." He looked at my throat, made me say ah, and felt my pulse. A floor nurse came in, punctured my middle finger, and went off with some of my blood.

I looked at the doctor inquiringly.

"Doing all this and explaining as I go along makes the whole thing seem pretty silly," he said. "It has some sense to it, but I hate to admit how much. I look in your throat just to see if you have anything remarkable in there, like diphtheria spots or something that looks like a streptococcus infection. We'll take a blood count from that blood, and if you have pneumonia, your blood count will be high. It is caused by a specific germ that has been identified. With a common cold, the blood count will be normal.

"You know, a common cold would be extremely difficult to diagnose in a strictly scientific manner," he went on reflectively. "The symptoms of the common cold are the same, at the outset, as measles and a number of other diseases. The doctor usually takes the patient's diagnosis and, providing he finds no obvious complications, proceeds on the theory that what he is treating is a cold. You say you have a cold. Well, you've had them before, and you ought to know what a cold feels like. I take your word for it. But if you were deaf and dumb and couldn't communicate with me in any way at all and came to see me with these same symptoms, I don't mind saying I might have one hell of a time figuring out what was the matter with you. Running nose and a little fever, I would say to myself, but I wouldn't be able to find out how you *felt* and I wouldn't know for sure whether it was just a cold or God knows what. I'd have to wait and see."

I was feeling fairly good, although I could tell by the way my nose was and by the chills running up and down my back that, unless this was measles or something else, it was what a layman would refer to as "a cold that feels grippy" or "a hell of a bad cold" when he calls his office to say he won't be in. It seemed to be the sort of cold I would ordinarily have stayed home with two days, going out still coughing and recovering entirely about a week after that. I asked the doctor to tell me what the treatment was to be, so that I could understand it as we went along.

"You'll be given lots of liquids, in the first place," he said. "Orange juice, lemon juice, water, and so on. Then you'll have some special capsules, some nose drops, an occasional gargle, and the room will be kept warm. You won't feel much like smoking and it would probably be better if you didn't, but we're not absolutely sure it makes any difference, so you can smoke if vou want to. We'll have you out of here in three or four days."

The nurse came in with a tall, three-legged table and a large glass vessel with a long glass neck, like a chemist's retort. She set it up in a corner and went out again, an intent expression on her face. It looked to me as if this meant business, and I asked the doctor what it was. "It's just an inhalator," he said. "It has plain water inside, with a little benzoin. She'll put an electric burner under it now and it will boil and the steam will add humidity to the room."

"What will the benzoin do?"

"As a matter of fact," he said, grinning, "the effect of the benzoin is largely psychological. It smells medical. But there is a chance that the fumes will help soothe your nose and throat."

"What's in the capsules, then?"

"They'll make you drowsy and help you to relax and give your system a better chance to fight off the cold. There's codeine in them, which is a narcotic that seems to have some specific quality in breaking up colds. Not always, mind you, but often enough to be fairly impressive. Then there's phenacetin, a coal-tar preparation which helps diminish whatever pain you may be having—aching, general discomfort, and so forth. It also helps to keep the temperature down. And a little caffeine to counteract the heart-depressant effects of the codeine and the phenacetin."

I asked him to write down these terms for me, and he did.

"Won't there be any other treatment besides what you've described?" I asked.

"Nope," he said. "That's about the works. Of course, I could give you a few other fancy things of extremely doubtful value, but for combatting this cold—the ordinary, acute, grippy infection of the upper respiratory tract—what you're going to get is the works."

My friend the nose-and-ear man came in, took one look at my nose, and said he wouldn't touch it now with a ten-foot pole. "I'll leave you some nose drops," he said. "The doctor here and myself both use the same kind. About the day after tomorrow, I may be able to get in there and see if there's anything for me to do."

I asked what the nose drops did.

"They shrink the mucous membrane so as to keep your nose as far open as possible," he said.

The nurse, having started the inhalator, brought me two of the capsules and a large glass of orange juice. I took the capsules and drank the orange juice. My two doctors and I chatted for a while, and I asked them if many people went into hospitals with common colds like mine.

"More than you might think," the general man said. "A good many old people, naturally, who are rightly afraid of developing pneumonia. Quite a few mild hypochondriacs who aren't so much afraid of disease, really, as they are crazy about hospitals. They come in here, get very elated, call up all their friends, and make big plans for the future. They find it a stimulating escape. There's a banker who comes here every time he catches cold and has himself a hell of a fine time. Then a good many ordinary men and women with money to spare have reached the conclusion that it's a good idea to give in to a cold and let us handle it, at the same time getting themselves a nice rest."

I hinted that I had expected the handling of a cold by two doctors in a first-class hospital to be a good deal more aggressive than it appeared to be so far.

"Don't excite yourself now," the nose man said. "I told you it wouldn't be worth the money."

The nurse brought another half-pint of orange juice and left it on the bedside table.

"As I see it," I said to my doctors, "no sledge-hammer blows are being struck by science in the battle against the common cold. I could do all this at home, except for the benzoin."

"Sure," said the general man. "This is the luxurious way, that's all. But, as a matter of fact, I'll bet you'll be more cured when you leave here than you are ordinarily when you treat yourself at home. At home, even with a wife or a maid to look after you, you probably keep getting up and putting on a bathrobe and going out to the living room to get a book or something, you worry about when you're going to get back to work, and you forget to take all the capsules and liquids and nose drops at the right time, or you say nuts to them if you do remember, and consequently you don't get over your cold as quickly or as completely as you'll get over it here."

"Whereas here," said the nose man, "there's no use in worrying about when you'll get out, because you can't get out until I release you."

"If you tried to get out before you were released, they'd just put you in a straitjacket," said the general man.

"Go away, fellows," I said.

"I'll bring you that stuff to read," the general man said. "You'll see how the common cold has got science up a tree."

We said goodbye. Snuffling and somewhat disappointed, I drank the second half-pint of orange juice and the nurse came in and administered the nose drops. The inhalator was snuffling now, too, in a soothing way, giving off businesslike puffs of steamy benzoin. In a few minutes I went to sleep.

That day and the next I felt much worse than I usually feel with a bad cold. I slept a great part of the time and didn't feel like reading or even talking. I drank all the liquids the nurse brought me, snuffed in the nose drops three times a day, took the special capsules, and breathed the benzoin fumes. On the third day, the capsules having been discontinued, I felt better. My nose was no longer stuffed up, and I could sense that the cold was in the interregnum stage that often occurs after it has begun to get out of the nose and hasn't yet quite got into the chest.

The nose man came in, looked at my sinuses by means of lights and mirrors, and said there was nothing wrong with them. "Keep taking the nose drops for a couple more days," he said. "I probably won't come in again. I've got a wonderful case down at the clinic, a guy with a sinus coming right out of his forehead. That's the sort of thing I live for. So long."

When the general man came in that morning, I asked him if there was any chance of keeping this cold from getting into my chest.

"Only the gargle," he said. "You'll be given a gargle four or five times today. The gargle isn't very interesting," he added hastily. "Just hot salt water, with a little aspirin and sodium bicarbonate in it."

"What do the hot water, salt, soda, and aspirin do?"

"The hot water increases the amount of blood in the blood vessels of the throat and thus builds up the resistance of the mucous membrane. The salt is a germicide, or disinfectant, the aspirin relieves the irritation and tends to keep you from coughing, and the soda just helps the aspirin to dissolve more homogeneously. Now if you ask me what a germicide does in the case of the common cold you'll have me, because what a germicide does is kill germs and we aren't at all sure that there *are* any germs connected with the common cold."

I asked him to crank up the bed a bit, so I could sit up straight.

"I knew in a vague way that the exact germ for the common cold hadn't been found," I said, "but there's no doubt about the cold being caused by a germ, is there?"

"All kinds of doubt," he said. "I've brought you a pretty exhaustive paper written recently by two medical men who are scientifically from Missouri, and you can read it if you like and we can talk about it tomorrow. The gist of it is that it is beginning to look as if the common cold is more probably caused by sudden changes of temperature than by a germ."

He took the medical paper out of his bag.

"This just about has everything in it anybody knows about the common cold," he said. "It goes back to Hippocrates. You know, for hundreds of years—at the apex of the age of reason, as a matter of fact—the accepted theory was that colds and all kinds of catarrh, which is Greek for 'flow down,' were caused by stuff flowing down from the brain. They thought that was where all the mucus came from and that when there was an oversupply of mucus in the brain, it flowed down and gave you a cold. We've demolished that theory, but we still don't know what causes a cold. This paper will tell you what goes on inside the nose and how it is constructed, and if it doesn't frighten you to death, you'll see why a cold may very well have nothing to do with germs at all."

"How do you know it doesn't flow down from the brain?" I asked. "It sounds to me as if they had something there. I think I can feel it flowing down right now."

"There's no way for it to flow down," he said. "Honest to God, we *know* that. We don't know much, but we know that."

The paper, which I read that afternoon and evening, shows, among other things, that the nose is badly constructed, or at least is built along visionary rather than practical lines. The idea behind the nose was that it should, in addition to its function as the organ of smell, act as a sort of air-conditioning apparatus for the lungs. For this purpose, each nostril is lined with three little organs, known as the superior, middle, and inferior turbinates. These turbinates are supposed to stand erect when the air coming in is cold, warm it up, and at the same time develop a lot of moisture as it passes through, so as to add humidity to it. This is what the turbinates are supposed to do, but even the superior turbinate, it seems, is notoriously slipshod. A number of tests show, in fact, that generally speaking the turbinates have never been able to handle their responsibilities in a workmanlike manner.

A common performance of the turbinates goes something like this: You sit in your office, or your home, all morning on a cold day and the turbinates have little or nothing to do. If the air is a bit dry, they may work up some humidity by secreting moisture, which causes you to blow your nose now and then, but otherwise they remain dormant, living in a fool's paradise. Then you put on your hat and coat and go outdoors. You would think that the turbinates would take this calmly, but not at all. They stand erect immediately and far too fast and begin to secrete moisture on a scale much too extensive. Your nose becomes clogged by the swelling of the turbinates and runs freely because of the overexuberant moisture-secreting that is going on at the same time. This causes you to fight for survival by breathing directly through the mouth. The mouth has no proper equipment for warming the air or for adding humidity to it, except incidentally, in a haphazard way. The lungs are not prepared for cold, dry air, and presumably are harmed by it; if they are not harmed by it, then the whole conception of the turbinates is as foolish as their execution. At any rate, the turbinates go all to pieces for several minutes when you go suddenly out into the cold, and the medical profession is beginning to think that the mucous membrane inside the throat and at the back of the nose is irritated by the unwarmed, dry air and that this irritation, and not a germ, is what causes the common cold.

The turbinates are extremely sensitive, and thus untrustworthy and likely to go off half-cocked. They appear to have a hookup with the brain and with the sensory nerves, which adds to their inefficiency. For example, you may be sitting in a warm room with a window open somewhere in the house, which causes a cool draft to pass over your ankles. Your ankles don't mind this particularly and are definitely not cold, but your turbinates, which have a busybody quality about them, interpret this sensation to mean that you have gone out in the cold air and they begin to swell up and dribble. The medical profession doesn't know what the exact effect of a mixup like that is, but it supposes, reasonably enough, that all that warming and watering at a time when the air is already warm and humid throws the mucous membrane out of gear, just as it does when the turbinates work so hard as to make breathing through the nose almost impossible, and that the inflammation known as the common cold may be the result.

The turbinates are defective in still another way. Leading into them are small blood vessels, which pass through bony structure on the way. They are thus unable to expand and can carry only a certain amount of blood. But the blood vessels leading up to these bony, constricted areas are larger than the blood vessels that go into the turbinates. So when the turbinates, in order to swell up, call for more blood, the blood accommodatingly tries to rush to them and is hopelessly dammed up by the inadequate blood vessels that pass through the bony area. This causes some kind of irritation, obviously. But worse than that, once the blood has managed to get to the turbinates, making them swell, it has to pass through similarly narrow and constricted veins in order to get out again when the turbinates decide that everything is all clear and it is time to go limp again. Thus, for some little time after the turbinates have called everything off, they remain erect because the blood has to stand around in front of these narrow exits. The medical profession is inclined to think this sort of thing also probably irritates the mucous membrane. Knowing this much about how the turbinates carry on their work, it is easy enough to imagine what they do if your feet are cold and wet; or if you get overheated, so that the turbinates think everything is wonderful, and then sit down on a bench and cool off quickly; or if you do any of the various things which traditionally are supposed to give you a cold.

"The turbinates seem to be nuts," I remarked when the general doctor came in the next morning. "And, incidentally, this cold seems to be going down into my chest."

"Well," he said, "if it is, it is probably because the turbinates *are* nuts."

"My God," I said, "I hadn't got around to wondering what the turbinates do when you actually have a cold. What do they do?"

"They lose all sense of reality, to put it mildly," he said. "The irritation to the mucous membrane, whatever causes *it,* excites the turbinates practically to the point of insanity. They swell up and stay swelled up, so you can hardly breathe at all through the nose, and the usually thin and watery nasal discharge which they secrete in order to humidify the air becomes thick and dry. In other words, your nose gets stuffed up. This causes you to breathe almost entirely through your mouth, and whether the air is humid and warm or cold and dry, the lungs apparently don't care for air that comes to them directly through the mouth. It seems, at least, to set up an irritation, or infection, in the bronchial tubes, and that is why the cold is now going into your chest, if it *is* going into your chest as you say. The nose drops are supposed to quiet down the turbinates and keep the nostrils open, but, of course, no nose drops work perfectly all the time."

"How do the turbinates seem to feel about benzoin?"

"Benzoin seems to soothe them somewhat, but not much more than stroking soothes a scared rabbit."

"Well, I feel better than I ordinarily do on the fourth day," I said, "and this cold doesn't seem to be going into the chest as much as most of them do."

"Thanks," he said.

"What about these injections that are supposed to prevent colds?" I asked. "I see by this medical paper that some chimpanzees that have been given the injections have colds just the same and some don't."

"They have not been entirely successful," the doctor said. "They are designed to attack the causes of secondary and tertiary infections which follow the initial infection or irritation known as the common cold. In many cases they seem to make the cold milder for this reason. The idea is that, whatever causes the initial inflammation, it weakens the general resistance of the mucous membrane, and the pneumococcus, various kinds of streptococcus, and other known germs or viruses rush right in. The injections work up a partial immunity to these secondary and tertiary invaders. But they don't always work. One theory is that these injections cause a purely chemical reaction which for some reason tends to counteract the general irritation, or infection. Like codeine. Codeine really seems to have some specific effect on a cold, but it doesn't always have it, and when it does have it, we don't know why it does. There's another preparation made from a cold vaccine which is taken internally, like a pill. I think it was forty per cent of a group of people who reported great improvement after taking this, but forty per cent of another group who were given pills containing nothing at all also reported great improvement. One reason we are beginning to think a cold isn't caused by a germ is that a cold, unlike most infectious diseases, seems to develop no immunity. You can have one cold right on top of another, as you know. We're up a tree, as I said before."

"This business of the common cold not being caused by a germ at all sort of strikes at the foundation of American civilization, doesn't it?"

"Don't get me wrong," the doctor said. "The no-germ theory hasn't been proved, any more than the germ theory. The thing is we just don't know. There's a great deal to be said for the germ theory, although it seems right now that there is more to be said for the no-germ theory. And anyway, influenza is a contagious disease definitely caused by a germ, so the precautions people usually take to keep from giving other people their colds are just as well. The funny thing about influenza is that the turbinates don't seem to be particularly affected by it. You don't get the same acute snuffling or stuffed-up feeling with influenza that you do with the common, grippy cold, yet with influenza you are a whole lot sicker than you are with a common cold."

"I guess I ought to get out of here tomorrow," I said.

"No reason why you shouldn't," he said. "You've had no fever for two days and there doesn't seem to be any serious bronchial infection. You'll cough a little for a day or two, and then you ought to be O.K."

The doctor sneezed suddenly.

"I hope I haven't given you my cold," I said.

"You may have," he said. "If there *are* any common cold germs, I have doubtless picked some of them up from you. On the other hand, it is probably just the turbinates seeing ghosts. Of course, a piece of dust or something may have got up my nose just then and made me sneeze, the sneeze being a reflex action designed by nature to clear the nose of any irritating substance. But this reflex action isn't absolutely dependable either, any more than the turbinates are. I suspect that what happened just now was that the turbinates, for some reason known only to themselves, got excited and worked up an over-abundant amount of moisture; this moisture, trickling through my nose, fooled my sensory nervous system into thinking that there was some irritating substance in there and caused me to sneeze. Sneezing, incidentally, isn't such a good method of ridding the nose of an irritating substance because sneezing itself irritates the nose."

"And perhaps causes or contributes to an inflammation of the mucous membrane of the upper respiratory tract?"

"Exactly," he said.

September 1, 1939

BY W. H. AUDEN

I sit in one of the dives
On Fifty-Second Street
Uncertain and afraid
As the clever hopes expire
Of a low dishonest decade:
Waves of anger and fear
Circulate over the bright
And darkened lands of the earth,
Obsessing our private lives;
The unmentionable odour of death
Offends the September night.

Accurate scholarship can
Unearth the whole offence
From Luther until now
That has driven a culture mad,
Find what occurred at Linz,
What huge imago made
A psychopathic god:
I and the public know
What all schoolchildren learn,
Those to whom evil is done
Do evil in return.

Exiled Thucydides knew
All that a speech can say
About Democracy,
And what dictators do,
The elderly rubbish they talk
To an apathetic grave;
Analysed all in his book,

The enlightenment driven away,
The habit-forming pain,
Mismanagement and grief:
We must suffer them all again.

Into this neutral air
Where blind skyscrapers use
Their full height to proclaim
The strength of Collective Man,
Each language pours its vain
Competitive excuse:
But who can live for long
In an euphoric dream;
Out of the mirror they stare,
Imperialism's face
And the international wrong.

Faces along the bar
Cling to their average day:
The lights must never go out,
The music must always play,
All the conventions conspire
To make this fort assume
The furniture of home;
Lest we should see where we are,
Lost in a haunted wood,
Children afraid of the night
Who have never been happy or good.

The windiest militant trash
Important Persons shout
Is not so crude as our wish:
What mad Nijinsky wrote
About Diaghilev
Is true of the normal heart;
For the error bred in the bone
Of each woman and each man
Craves what it cannot have,
Not universal love
But to be loved alone.

From the conservative dark
Into the ethical life
The dense commuters come,
Repeating their morning vow;
"I will be true to the wife,
I'll concentrate more on my work,"
And helpless governors wake
To resume their compulsory game:
Who can release them now,
Who can reach the deaf.
Who can speak for the dumb?

All I have is a voice
To undo the folded lie,
The romantic lie in the brain
Of the sensual man-in-the-street
And the lie of Authority
Whose buildings grope the sky:
There is no such thing as the State
And no one exists alone;
Hunger allows no choice
To the citizen or the police;
We must love one another or die.

Defenceless under the night
Our world in stupour lies;
Yet, dotted everywhere,
Ironic points of light
Flash out wherever the Just
Exchange their messages:
May I, composed like them
Of Eros and of dust,
Beleaguered by the same
Negation and despair,
Show an affirming flame.

Of this Time, of that Place

BY LIONEL TRILLING

IT WAS A FINE September day. By noon it would be summer again but now it was true autumn with a touch of chill in the air. As Joseph Howe stood on the porch of the house in which he lodged, ready to leave for his first class of the year, he thought with pleasure of the long indoor days that were coming. It was a moment when he could feel glad of his profession.

On the lawn the peach tree was still in fruit and young Hilda Aiken was taking a picture of it. She held the camera tight against her chest. She wanted the sun behind her but she did not want her own long morning shadow in the foreground. She raised the camera but that did not help, and she lowered it but that made things worse. She twisted her body to the left, then to the right. In the end she had to step out of the direct line of the sun. At last she snapped the shutter and wound the film with intense care.

Howe, watching her from the porch, waited for her to finish and called good morning. She turned, startled, and almost sullenly lowered her glance. In the year Howe had lived at the Aikens', Hilda had accepted him as one of her family, but since his absence of the summer she had grown shy. Then suddenly she lifted her head and smiled at him, and the humorous smile confirmed his pleasure in the day. She picked up her bookbag and set off for school.

The handsome houses on the streets to the college were not yet fully awake but they looked very friendly. Howe went by the Bradby house where he would be a guest this evening at the first dinner-party of the year. When he had gone the length of the picket fence, the whitest in town, he turned back. Along the path there was a fine row of asters and he went through the gate and picked one for his buttonhole. The Bradbys would be pleased if they happened to see him invading their lawn and the knowledge of this made him even more comfortable.

He reached the campus as the hour was striking. The students were hurrying to their classes. He himself was in no hurry. He stopped at his dim cubicle of an office and lit a cigarette. The prospect of facing his class had suddenly presented itself to him and his hands were cold, the lawful seizure of power he was about to make seemed momentous. Waiting did not help. He put out his cigarette picked up a pad and theme paper and went to his classroom.

As he entered, the rattle of voices ceased and the twenty-odd freshmen settled themselves and looked at him appraisingly. Their faces seemed gross, his heart sank at their massed impassivity, but he spoke briskly.

"My name is Howe," he said and turned and wrote it on the blackboard. The carelessness of the scrawl confirmed his authority. He went on, "My office is 412 Slemp Hall and my office-hours are Monday, Wednesday and Friday from eleven-thirty to twelve-thirty."

He wrote, "M., W., F., 11:30-12:30." He said, "I'll be very glad to see any of you at that time. Or if you can't come then, you can arrange with me for some other time."

He turned again to the blackboard and spoke over his shoulder. "The text for the course is Jarman's *Modern Plays,* revised edition. The Co-op has it in stock." He wrote the name, underlined "revised edition" and waited for it to be taken down in the new notebooks.

When the bent heads were raised again he began his speech of prospectus. "It is hard to explain—" he said, and paused as they composed themselves. "It is hard to explain what a course like this is intended to do. We are going to try to learn something about modern literature and something about prose composition."

As he spoke, his hands warmed and he was able to look directly at the class. Last year on the first day the faces had seemed just as cloddish, but as the term wore on they became gradually alive and quite likable. It did not seem possible that the same thing could happen again.

"I shall not lecture in this course," he continued. "Our work will be carried on by discussion and we will try to learn by an exchange of opinion. But you will soon recognize that my opinion is worth more than anyone else's here."

He remained grave as he said it, but two boys understood and laughed. The rest took permission from them and laughed too. All Howe's private ironies protested the vulgarity of the joke but the laughter made him feel benign and powerful.

When the little speech was finished, Howe picked up the pad of paper he had brought. He announced that they would write an extemporaneous theme. Its subject was traditional, "Who I am and why I came to Dwight College." By now the class was more at ease and it gave a ritualistic groan of protest. Then there was a stir as fountain pens were brought out and the writing arms of the chairs were cleared and the paper was passed about. At last all the heads bent to work and the room became still.

Howe sat idly at his desk. The sun shone through the tall clumsy windows. The cool of the morning was already passing. There was a scent of autumn and of varnish, and the stillness of the room was deep and oddly touching. Now and then a student's head was raised and scratched in the old elaborate students' pantomime that calls the teacher to witness honest intellectual effort.

Suddenly a tall boy stood within the frame of the open door. "Is this," he said, and thrust a large nose into a college catalogue, "is this the meeting place of English 1A? The section instructed by Dr. Joseph Howe?"

He stood on the very sill of the door, as if refusing to enter until he was perfectly sure of all his rights. The class looked up from work, found him absurd and gave a low mocking cheer.

The teacher and the new student, with equal pointedness, ignored the disturbance. Howe nodded to the boy, who pushed his head forward and then jerked it back in a wide elaborate arc to clear his brow of a heavy lock of hair. He advanced into the room and halted before Howe, almost at attention. In a loud clear voice he announced, "I am Tertan, Ferdinand R., reporting at the direction of Head of Department Vincent."

The heraldic formality of this statement brought forth another cheer. Howe looked at the class with a sternness he could not really feel, for there was indeed something ridiculous about this boy. Under his displeased regard the rows of heads dropped to work again. Then he touched Tertan's elbow, led him up to the desk and stood so as to shield their conversation from the class.

"We are writing an extemporaneous theme," he said. "The subject is, 'Who I am and why I came to Dwight College'."

He stripped a few sheets from the pad and offered them to the boy. Tertan hesitated and then took the paper but he held it only tentatively. As if with the effort of making something clear, he gulped, and a slow smile fixed itself on his face. It was at once knowing and shy.

"Professor," he said, "to be perfectly fair to my classmates"—he made a large gesture over the room—"and to you"—he inclined his head to Howe—"this would not be for me an extemporaneous subject."

Howe tried to understand. "You mean you've already thought about it—you've heard we always give the same subject? That doesn't matter."

Again the boy ducked his head and gulped. It was the gesture of one who wishes to make a difficult explanation with perfect candor. "Sir," he said, and made the distinction with great care, "the topic I did not expect but I have given much ratiocination to the subject."

Howe smiled and said, "I don't think that's an unfair advantage. Just go ahead and write."

Tertan narrowed his eyes and glanced sidewise at Howe. His strange mouth smiled. Then in quizzical acceptance, he ducked his head, threw back the heavy dank lock, dropped into a seat with a great loose noise and began to write rapidly.

The room fell silent again and Howe resumed his idleness. When the bell rang, the students who had groaned when the task had been set now groaned again because they had not finished. Howe took up the papers and held the class while he made the first assignment. When he dismissed it, Tertan bore down on him, his slack mouth held ready for speech.

"Some professors," he said, "are pedants. They are Dryasdusts. However, some professors are free souls and creative spirits. Kant, Hegel and Nietzsche were all professors." With this pronouncement he paused. "It is my opinion," he continued, "that you occupy the second category."

Howe looked at the boy in surprise and said with good-natured irony, "With Kant, Hegel and Nietzsche?"

Not only Tertan's hand and head but his whole awkward body waved away the stupidity. "It is the kind and not the quantity of the kind," he said sternly.

Rebuked, Howe said as simply and seriously as he could, "It would be nice to think so." He added, "Of course I am not a professor."

This was clearly a disappointment but Tertan met it. "In the French sense," he said with composure. "Generically, a teacher."

Suddenly he bowed. It was such a bow, Howe fancied, as a stage-director might teach an actor playing a medieval student who takes leave of Abelard—stiff, solemn, with elbows close to the body and feet together. Then, quite as suddenly, he turned and left.

A queer fish, and as soon as Howe reached his office he sifted through the batch of themes and drew out Tertan's. The boy had filled many sheets with his unformed headlong scrawl. "Who am I?" he had begun. "Here, in a mundane, not to say commercialized academe, is asked the question which from time long immemorably out of mind has accreted doubts and thoughts in the psyche of man to pester him as a nuisance. Whether in St. Augustine (or Austin as sometimes called) or Miss Bashkirtsieff or Frederic Amiel or Empedocles, or in less lights of the intellect than these, this posed question has been ineluctable."

Howe took out his pencil. He circled "academe" and wrote "vocab." in the margin. He underlined "time long immemorably out of mind" and wrote "Diction!" But this seemed inadequate for what was wrong. He put down his pencil and read ahead to discover the principle of error in the theme. "Today as ever, in spite of gloomy prophets of the dismal science (economics) the question is uninvalidated. Out of the starry depths of heaven hurtles this spear of query demanding to be caught on the shield of the mind ere it pierces the skull and the limbs be unstrung."

Baffled but quite caught, Howe read on. "Materialism, by which is meant the philosophic concept and not the moral idea, provides no aegis against the question which lies beyond the tangible (metaphysics). Existence without alloy is the question presented. Environment and heredity relegated aside, the rags and old clothes of practical life discarded, the name and the instrumentality of livelihood do not, as the prophets of the dismal science insist on in this connection, give solution to the interrogation which not from the professor merely but veritably from the cosmos is given. I think, therefore I am (cogito etc.) but who am I? Tertan I am, but what is Tertan? Of this time, of that place, of some parentage, what does it matter?"

Existence without alloy: the phrase established itself. Howe put aside Tertan's paper and at random picked up another. "I am Arthur J. Casebeer, Jr.," he read. "My father is Arthur J. Casebeer and my grandfather was Arthur J. Casebeer before him. My mother is Nina Wimble Casebeer. Both of them are college graduates and my father is in insurance. I was born in St. Louis eighteen years ago and we still make our residence there."

Arthur J. Casebeer, who knew who he was, was less interesting than Tertan, but more coherent. Howe picked up Tertan's paper again. It was clear that none of the routine marginal comments, no "sent. str." or "punct." or "vocab." could cope with this torrential rhetoric. He read ahead, contenting himself with underscoring the errors against the time when he should have the necessary "conference" with Tertan.

It was a busy and official day of cards and sheets, arrangements and small decisions and it gave Howe pleasure. Even when it was time to attend the first of the weekly Convocations he felt the charm of the beginning of things when intention is still innocent and uncorrupted by effort. He sat among the young instructors on the platform and joined in their humorous complaints at having to assist at the ceremony but actually he got a clear satisfaction from the ritual of prayer and prosy speech and even from wearing his academic gown. And when the Convocation was over the pleasure continued as he crossed the campus, exchanging greetings with men he had not seen since the spring. They were people who did not yet, and perhaps never would, mean much to him, but in a year they had grown amiably to be part of his life. They were his fellow-townsmen.

The day had cooled again at sunset and there was a bright chill in the September twilight. Howe carried his voluminous gown over his arm, he swung his doctoral hood by its purple neckpiece and on his head he wore his mortarboard with its heavy gold tassel bobbing just over his eye. These were the weighty and absurd symbols of his new profession and they pleased him. At twenty-six Joseph Howe had discovered that he was neither so well off nor so bohemian as he had once thought. A small income, adequate when supplemented by a sizable cash legacy, was genteel poverty when the cash was all spent. And the literary life—the room at the Lafayette or the small apartment without a lease, the long summers on the Cape, the long afternoons and the social evenings—began to weary him. His writing filled his mornings and should perhaps have filled his life, yet it did not. To the amusement of his friends and with a certain sense that he was betraying his own freedom, he had used the last of his legacy for a year at Harvard. The small but respectable reputation of his two volumes of verse had proved useful—he continued at Harvard on a fellowship and when he emerged as Dr. Howe he received an excellent appointment, with prospects, at Dwight.

He had his moments of fear when all that had ever been said of the dangers of the academic life had occurred to him. But after a year in which he had tested every possibility of corruption and seduction he was ready to rest easy. His third volume of verse, most of it written in his first year of teaching, was not only ampler but, he thought, better than its predecessors.

There was a clear hour before the Bradby dinner-party and Howe looked forward to it. But he was not to enjoy it, for lying with his mail on the hall table was a copy of this quarter's issue of *Life and Letters,* to which his landlord subscribed. Its severe cover announced that its editor, Frederic Woolley, had this month contributed an essay called "Two Poets," and Howe, picking it up, curious to see who the two poets might be, felt his own name start out at him with cabalistic power—Joseph Howe. As he continued to turn the pages his hand trembled.

Standing in the dark hall, holding the neat little magazine, Howe knew that his literary contempt for Frederic Woolley meant nothing, for he suddenly understood how he respected Woolley in the way of the world. He knew this by the trembling of his hand. And of the little world as well as the great, for although the literary groups of New York might dismiss Woolley, his name carried high authority in the academic world. At Dwight it was even a revered name, for it had been here at the college that Frederic Woolley had made the distinguished scholarly career from which he had gone on to literary journalism. In middle life he had been induced to take the editorship of *Life and Letters,* a literary monthly not widely read but heavily endowed and in its pages he had carried on the defense of what he sometimes called the older values. He was not without wit, he had great knowledge and considerable taste and even in the full movement of the "new" literature he had won a certain respect for his refusal to accept it. In France, even in England, he would have been connected with a more robust tradition of conservatism, but America gave him an audience not much better than genteel. It was known in the college that to the subsidy of *Life and Letters* the Bradbys contributed a great part.

As Howe read, he saw that he was involved in nothing less than an event. When the Fifth Series of *Studies in Order and Value* came to be collected, this latest of Frederic Woolley's essays would not be merely another step in the old direction. Clearly and unmistakably, it was a turning point. All his literary life Woolley had been concerned with the relation of literature to mortality, religion and the private and delicate pieties and he had been unalterably opposed to all that he had called "inhuman humanitarianism." But here, suddenly, dramatically late, he had made an about-face, turning to the public life and to the humanitarian politics he had so long despised. This was the kind of incident the histories of literature make much of. Frederic Woolley was opening for himself a new career and winning a kind of new youth. He contrasted the two poets, Thomas Wormser who was admirable, Joseph Howe who was almost dangerous. He spoke of the "precious subjectivism" of Howe's verse. "In times like ours," he wrote, "with millions facing penury and want, one feels that the qualities of the *tour d'ivoire* are well-nigh inhuman, nearly insulting. The *tour d'ivoire* becomes the *tour d'ivresse* and it is not self-intoxicated poets that our people need." The essay said more: "The problem is one of meaning. I am not ignorant that the creed of the esoteric poets declares that a poem does not and should not *mean* anything, that it *is* something. But poetry is what the poet makes it, and if he is a true poet he makes what his society needs. And what is needed now is the tradition in which Mr. Wormser writes, the true tradition of poetry. The Howes do no harm, but they do no good when positive good is demanded of all responsible men. Or do the Howes indeed do no harm? Perhaps Plato would have said they do, that in some ways theirs is the Phrygian music that turns men's minds from the struggle. Certainly it is true that Thomas Wormser writes in the lucid Dorian mode which sends men into battle with evil."

It was easy to understand why Woolley had chosen to praise Thomas Wormser. The long, lilting lines of *Corn Under Willows* hymned, as Woolley put it, the struggle for wheat in the Iowa fields and expressed the real lives of real people. But why out of the dozen more notable examples he had chosen Howe's little volume as the example of "precious subjectivism" was hard to guess. In a way it was funny, this multiplication of himself into "the Howes." And yet this becoming the multiform political symbol by whose creation Frederic Woolley gave the sign of a sudden new life, this use of him as a sacrifice whose blood was necessary for the rites of rejuvenation, made him feel oddly unclean.

Nor could Howe get rid of a certain practical resentment. As a poet he had a special and respectable place in the college life. But it might be another thing to be marked as the poet of a wilful and selfish obscurity.

As he walked to the Bradbys' Howe was a little tense and defensive. It seemed to him that all the world knew of the "attack" and agreed with it. And indeed the Bradbys had read the essay but Professor Bradby, a kind and pretentious man, said, "I see my old friend knocked you about a bit, my boy," and his wife Eugenia looked at Howe with her childlike blue eyes and said, "I shall *scold* Frederic for the untrue things he wrote about you. You aren't the least obscure." They beamed at him. In their genial snobbery they seemed to feel that he had distinguished himself. He was the leader of Howeism. He enjoyed the dinner-party as much as he had thought he would.

And in the following days, as he was more preoccupied with his duties, the incident was forgotten. His classes had ceased to be mere groups. Student after student detached himself from the mass and required or claimed a place in Howe's awareness. Of them all it was Tertan who first and most violently signalled his separate existence. A week after classes had begun Howe saw his silhouette on the frosted glass of his office door. It was motionless for a long time, perhaps stopped by the problem of whether or not to knock before entering. Howe called, "Come in!" and Tertan entered with his shambling stride.

He stood beside the desk, silent and at attention. When Howe asked him to sit down, he responded with a gesture of head and hand as if to say that such amenities were beside the point. Nevertheless he did take the chair. He put his ragged crammed briefcase between his legs. His face, which Howe now observed fully for the first time, was confusing, for it was made up of florid curves, the nose arched in the bone and voluted in the nostril, the mouth loose and soft and rather moist. Yet the face was so thin and narrow as to seem the very type of asceticism. Lashes of unusual length veiled the eyes and, indeed, it seemed as if there were a veil over the whole countenance. Before the words actually came, the face screwed itself into an attitude of preparation for them.

"You can confer with me now?" Tertan said.

"Yes, I'd be glad to. There are several things in your two themes I want to talk to you about." Howe reached for the packet of themes on his desk and sought for Tertan's. But the boy was waving them away.

"These are done perforce," he said. "Under the pressure of your requirement. They are not significant, mere duties." Again his great hand flapped vaguely to dismiss his themes. He leaned forward and gazed at his teacher.

"You are," he said, "a man of letters? You are a poet?" It was more declaration than question.

"I should like to think so," Howe said.

At first Tertan accepted the answer with a show of appreciation, as though the understatement made a secret between himself and Howe. Then he chose to misunderstand. With his shrewd and disconcerting control of expression, he presented to Howe a puzzled grimace. "What does that mean?" he said.

Howe retracted the irony. "Yes. I am a poet." It sounded strange to say.

"That," Tertan said, "is a wonder." He corrected himself with his ducking head. "I mean that is wonderful."

Suddenly he dived at the miserable briefcase between his legs, put it on his knees and began to fumble with the catch, all intent on the difficulty it presented. Howe noted that his suit was worn thin, his shirt almost unclean. He became aware, even, of a vague and musty odor of garments worn too long in unaired rooms. Tertan conquered the lock and began to concentrate upon a search into the interior. At last he held in his hand what he was after, a torn and crumpled copy of *Life and Letters*.

"I learned it from here," he said, holding it out.

Howe looked at him sharply, his hackles a little up. But the boy's face was not only perfectly innocent, it even shone with a conscious admiration. Apparently nothing of the import of the essay had touched him except the wonderful fact that his teacher was a "man of letters." Yet this seemed too stupid and Howe, to test it, said, "The man who wrote that doesn't think it's wonderful."

Tertan made a moist hissing sound as he cleared his mouth of saliva. His head, oddly loose on his neck, wove a pattern of contempt in the air. "A critic," he said, "who admits *prima facie* that he does not understand." Then he said grandly, "It is the inevitable fate."

It was absurd, yet Howe was not only aware of the absurdity but of a tension suddenly and wonderfully relaxed. Now that the "attack" was on the table between himself and this strange boy and subject to the boy's funny and absolutely certain contempt, the hidden force of his feeling was revealed to him in the very moment that it vanished. All unsuspected, there had been a film over the world, a transparent but discoloring haze of danger. But he had no time to stop over the brightened aspect of things. Tertan was going on. "I also am a man of letters. Putative."

"You have written a good deal?" Howe meant to be no more than polite and he was surprised at the tenderness he heard in his words.

Solemnly the boy nodded, threw back the dank lock and sucked in a deep anticipatory breath. "First, a work of homiletics, which is a defense of the principles of religious optimism against the pessimism of Schopenhauer and the humanism of Nietzsche."

"Humanism? Why do you call it humanism?"

"It is my nomenclature for making a deity of man," Tertan replied negligently. "Then three fictional works, novels. And numerous essays in science, combating materialism. Is it your duty to read these if I bring them to you?"

Howe answered simply, "No, it isn't exactly my duty but I shall be happy to read them."

Tertan stood up and remained silent. He rested his bag on the chair. With a certain compunction—for it did not seem entirely proper that, of two men of letters, one should have the right to blue-pencil the other, to grade him or to question the quality of his "sentence structure"—Howe reached for Tertan's papers. But before he could take them up, the boy suddenly made his bow-to-Abelard, the stiff inclination of the body with the hands seeming to emerge from the scholar's gown. Then he was gone.

But after his departure something was still left of him. The timbre of his curious sentences, the downright finality of so quaint a phrase as "It is the inevitable fate" still rang in the air. Howe gave the warmth of his feeling to the new visitor who stood at the door announcing himself with a genteel clearing of the throat.

"Dr. Howe, I believe?" the student said. A large hand advanced into the room and grasped Howe's hand. "Blackburn, sir, Theodore Blackburn, vice-president of the Student Council. A great pleasure, sir."

Out of a pair of ruddy cheeks a pair of small eyes twinkled good-naturedly. The large face, the large body were not so much fat as beefy and suggested something "typical," monk, politician, or innkeeper.

Blackburn took the seat beside Howe's desk. "I may have seemed to introduce myself in my public capacity, sir," he said. "But it is really as an individual that I came to see you. That is to say, as one of your students to be."

He spoke with an "English" intonation and he went on, "I was once an English major, sir."

For a moment Howe was startled, for the roast-beef look of the boy and the manner of his speech gave a second's credibility to one sense of his statement. Then the collegiate meaning of the phrase asserted itself, but some perversity made Howe say what was not really in good taste even with so forward a student, "Indeed? What regiment?"

Blackburn stared and then gave a little pouf-pouf of laughter. He waved the misapprehension away. "*Very* good, sir. It certainly is an ambiguous term." He chuckled in appreciation of Howe's joke, then cleared his throat to put it aside. "I look forward to taking your course in the romantic poets, sir," he said earnestly. "To me the romantic poets are the very crown of English literature."

Howe made a dry sound, and the boy, catching some meaning in it, said, "Little as I know them, of course. But even Shakespeare who is so dear to us of the Anglo-Saxon tradition is in a sense but the preparation for Shelley, Keats and Byron. And Wadsworth."

Almost sorry for him, Howe dropped his eyes. With some embarrassment, for the boy was not actually his student, he said softly, "Wordsworth."

"Sir?"

"Wordsworth, not Wadsworth. You said Wadsworth."

"Did I, sir?" Gravely he shook his head to rebuke himself for the error. "Wordsworth, of course—slip of the tongue." Then, quite in command again, he went on. "I have a favor to ask of you, Dr. Howe. You see, I began my college course as an English major,"—he smiled —"as I said."

"Yes?"

"But after my first year I shifted. I shifted to the social sciences. Sociology and government—I find them stimulating and very *real.*" He paused, out of respect for reality. "But now I find that perhaps I have neglected the other side."

"The other side?" Howe said.

"Imagination, fancy, culture. A well rounded man." He trailed off as if there were perfect understanding between them. "And so, sir, I have decided to end my senior year with your course in the romantic poets."

His voice was filled with an indulgence which Howe ignored as he said flatly and gravely, "But that course isn't given until the spring term."

"Yes, sir, and that is where the favor comes in. Would you let me take your romantic prose course? I can't take it for credit, sir, my program is full, but just for background it seems to me that I ought to take it. I do hope," he concluded in a manly way, "that you will consent."

"Well, it's no great favor, Mr. Blackburn. You can come if you wish, though there's not much point in it if you don't do the reading."

The bell rang for the hour and Howe got up.

"May I begin with this class, sir?" Blackburn's smile was candid and boyish.

Howe nodded carelessly and together, silently, they walked to the classroom down the hall. When they reached the door Howe stood back to let his student enter, but Blackburn moved adroitly behind him and grasped him by the arm to urge him over the threshold. They entered together with Blackburn's hand firmly on Howe's biceps, the student inducting the teacher into his own room. Howe felt a surge of temper rise in him and almost violently he disengaged his arm and walked to the desk, while Blackburn found a seat in the front row and smiled at him.

II

The question was, At whose door must the tragedy be laid?

All night the snow had fallen heavily and only now was abating in sparse little flurries. The windows were valanced high with white. It was very quiet, something of the quiet of the world had reached the class and Howe found that everyone was glad to talk or listen. In the room there was a comfortable sense of pleasure in being human.

Casebeer believed that the blame for the tragedy rested with heredity. Picking up the book he read, "The sins of the fathers are visited on their children." This opinion was received with general favor. Nevertheless Johnson ventured to say that the fault was all Pastor Manders' because the Pastor had made Mrs. Alving go back to her husband and was always hiding the truth. To this Hibbard objected with logic enough, "Well then, it was really all her husband's fault. He *did* all the bad things." De Witt, his face bright with an impatient idea, said that the fault was all society's. "By society I don't mean upper-crust society," he said. He looked around a little defiantly, taking in any members of the class who might be members of upper-crust society. "Not in that sense. I mean the social unit."

Howe nodded and said, "Yes, of course."

"If the society of the time had progressed far enough in science," De Witt went on, "then there would be no problem for Mr. Ibsen to write about. Captain Alving plays around a little, gives way to perfectly natural biological urges, and he gets a social disease, a venereal disease. If the disease is cured, no problem. Invent salvarsan and the disease is cured. The problem of heredity disappears and li'l Oswald just doesn't get paresis. No paresis, no problem—no problem, no play."

This was carrying the ark into battle and the class looked at De Witt with respectful curiosity. It was his usual way and on the whole they were sympathetic with his struggle to prove to Howe that science was better than literature. Still, there was something in his reckless manner that alienated them a little.

"Or take birth-control, for instance," De Witt went on. "If Mrs. Alving had some knowledge of contraception, she wouldn't have had to have li'l Oswald at all. No li'l Oswald, no play."

The class was suddenly quieter. In the back row Stettenhover swung his great football shoulders in a righteous sulking gesture, first to the right, then to the left. He puckered his mouth ostentatiously. Intellect was always ending up by talking dirty.

Tertan's hand went up and Howe said, "Mr. Tertan." The boy shambled to his feet and began his long characteristic gulp. Howe made a motion with his fingers, as small as possible, and Tertan ducked his head and smiled in apology. He sat down. The class laughed. With more than half the term gone, Tertan had not been able to remember that one did not rise to speak. He seemed unable to carry on the life of the intellect without this mark of respect for it. To Howe the boy's habit of rising seemed to accord with the formal shabbiness of his dress. He never wore the casual sweaters and jackets of his classmates. Into the free and comfortable air of the college classroom he brought the stuffy sordid strictness of some crowded metropolitan high school.

"Speaking from one sense," Tertan began slowly, "there is no blame ascribable. From the sense of determinism, who can say where the blame lies? The preordained is the preordained and it cannot be said without rebellion against the universe, a palpable absurdity."

In the back row Stettenhover slumped suddenly in his seat, his heels held out before him, making a loud dry disgusted sound. His body sank until his neck rested on the back of his chair. He folded his hands across his belly and looked significantly out of the window, exasperated not only with Tertan but with Howe, with the class, with the whole system designed to encourage this kind of thing. There was a certain insolence in the movement and Howe flushed. As Tertan continued to speak, Howe stalked casually toward the window and placed himself in the line of Stettenhover's vision. He stared at the great fellow, who pretended not to see him. There was so much power in the big body, so much contempt in the Greek-athlete face under the crisp Greek-athlete curls, that Howe felt almost physical fear. But at last Stettenhover admitted him to focus and under his disapproving gaze sat up with slow indifference. His eyebrows raised high in resignation, he began to examine his hands. Howe relaxed and turned his attention back to Tertan.

"Flux of existence," Tertan was saying, "produces all things, so that judgment wavers. Beyond the phenomena, what? But phenomena are adumbrated and to them we are limited."

Howe saw it for a moment as perhaps it existed in the boy's mind—the world of shadows which are cast by a great light upon a hidden reality as in the old myth of the Cave. But the little brush with Stettenhover had tired him and he said irritably, "But come to the point, Mr. Tertan."

He said it so sharply that some of the class looked at him curiously. For three months he had gently carried Tertan through his verbosities, to the vaguely respectful surprise of the other students, who seemed to conceive that there existed between this strange classmate and their teacher some special understanding from which they were content to be excluded. Tertan looked at him mildly and at once came brilliantly to the point. "This is the summation of the play," he said and took up his book and read, " 'Your poor father never found any outlet for the overmastering joy of life that was in him. And I brought no holiday into his home, either. Everything seemed to turn upon duty and I am afraid I made your poor father's home unbearable to him, Oswald.' Spoken by Mrs. Alving."

Yes, that was surely the "summation" of the play and Tertan had hit it, as he hit, deviously and eventually, the literary point of almost everything. But now, as always, he was wrapping it away from sight. "For most mortals," he said, "there are only joys of biological urgings, gross and crass, such as the sensuous Captain Alving. For certain few there are the transmutations beyond these to a contemplation of the utter whole."

Oh, the boy was mad. And suddenly the word, used in hyperbole, intended almost for the expression of exasperated admiration, became literal. Now that the word was used, it became simply apparent to Howe that Tertan was mad.

It was a monstrous word and stood like a bestial thing in the room. Yet it so completely comprehended everything that had puzzled Howe, it so arranged and explained what for three months had been perplexing him that almost at once its horror became domesticated. With this word Howe was able to understand why he had never been able to communicate to Tertan the value of a single criticism or correction of his wild, verbose themes. Their conferences had been frequent and long but had done nothing to reduce to order the splendid confusion of the boy's ideas. Yet, impossible though its expression was, Tertan's incandescent mind could always strike for a moment into some dark corner of thought.

And now it was suddenly apparent that it was not a faulty rhetoric that Howe had to contend with. With his new knowledge he looked at Tertan's face and wondered how he could have so long deceived himself. Tertan was still talking and the class had lapsed into a kind of patient unconsciousness, a coma of respect for words which, for all that most of them knew, might be profound. Almost with a suffusion of shame, Howe believed that in some dim way the class had long ago had some intimation of Tertan's madness. He reached out as decisively as he could to seize the thread of Tertan's discourse before it should be entangled further.

"Mr. Tertan says that the blame must be put upon whoever kills the joy of living in another. We have been assuming that Captain Alving was a wholly bad man, but what if we assume that he became bad only because Mrs. Alving, when they were first married, acted toward him in the prudish way she says she did?"

It was a ticklish idea to advance to freshmen and perhaps not profitable. Not all of them were following.

"That would put the blame on Mrs. Alving herself, whom most of you admire. And she herself seems to think so." He glanced at his watch. The hour was nearly over. "What do you think, Mr. De Witt?"

De Witt rose to the idea, he wanted to know if society couldn't be blamed for educating Mrs. Alving's temperament in the wrong way. Casebeer was puzzled, Stettenhover continued to look at his hands until the bell rang.

Tertan, his brows louring in thought, was making as always for a private word. Howe gathered his books and papers to leave quickly. At this moment of his discovery and with the knowledge still raw, he could not engage himself with Tertan. Tertan sucked in his breath to prepare for speech and Howe made ready for the pain and confusion. But at that moment Casebeer detached himself from the group with which he had been conferring and which he seemed to represent. His constituency remained at a tactful distance. The mission involved the time of an assigned essay. Casebeer's presentation of the plea—it was based on the freshmen's heavy duties at the fraternities during Carnival Week—cut across Tertan's preparations for speech. "And so some of us fellows thought," Casebeer concluded with heavy solemnity, "that we could do a better job, give our minds to it more, if we had more time."

Tertan regarded Casebeer with mingled curiosity and revulsion. Howe not only said that he would postpone the assignment but went on to talk about the Carnival and even drew the waiting constituency into the conversation. He was conscious of Tertan's stern and astonished stare, then of his sudden departure.

Now that the fact was clear, Howe knew that he must act on it. His course was simple enough. He must lay the case before the Dean. Yet he hesitated. His feeling for Tertan must now, certainly, be in some way invalidated. Yet could he, because of a word, hurry to assign to official and reasonable solicitude what had been, until this moment, so various and warm? He could at least delay and, by moving slowly, lend a poor grace to the necessary, ugly act of making his report.

It was with some notion of keeping the matter in his own hands that he went to the Dean's office to look up Tertan's records. In the outer office the Dean's secretary greeted him brightly and at his request brought him the manila folder with the small identifying photograph pasted in the corner. She laughed. "He was looking for the birdie in the wrong place," she said.

Howe leaned over her shoulder to look at the picture. It was as bad as all the Dean's-office photographs were, but it differed from all that Howe had ever seen. Tertan, instead of looking into the camera, as no doubt he had been bidden, had, at the moment of exposure, turned his eyes upward. His mouth, as though conscious of the trick played on the photographer, had the sly superior look that Howe knew.

The secretary was fascinated by the picture. "What a funny boy," she said. "He looks like Tartuffe!"

And so he did, with the absurd piety of the eyes and the conscious slyness of the mouth and the whole face bloated by the bad lens.

"Is he *like* that?" the secretary said.

"Like Tartuffe? No."

From the photograph there was little enough comfort to be had. The records themselves gave no clue to madness, though they suggested sadness enough. Howe read of a father, Stanislaus Tertan, born in Budapest and trained in engineering in Berlin, once employed by the Hercules Chemical Corporation—this was one of the factories that dominated the sound end of the town—but now without employment. He read of a mother Erminie (Youngfellow) Tertan, born in Manchester, educated at a Normal School at Leeds, now housewife by profession. The family lived on Greenbriar Street which Howe knew as a row of once elegant homes near what was now the factory district. The old mansions had long ago been divided into small and primitive apartments. Of Ferdinand himself there was little to learn. He lived with his parents, had attended a Detroit high school and had transferred to the local school in his last year. His rating for intelligence, as expressed in numbers, was high, his scholastic record was remarkable, he held a college scholarship for his tuition.

Howe laid the folder on the secretary's desk. "Did you find what you wanted to know?" she asked.

The phrases from Tertan's momentous first theme came back to him. "Tertan I am, but what is Tertan? Of this time, of that place, of some parentage, what does it matter?"

"No, I didn't find it," he said.

Now that he had consulted the sad half-meaningless record he knew all the more firmly that he must not give the matter out of his own hands. He must not release Tertan to authority. Not that he anticipated from the Dean anything but the greatest kindness for Tertan. The Dean would have the experience and skill which he himself could not have. One way or another the Dean could answer the question, "What is Tertan?" Yet this was precisely what he feared. He alone could keep alive—not forever but for a somehow important time—the question, "What is Tertan?" He alone could keep it still a question. Some sure instinct told him that he must not surrender the question to a clean official desk in a clear official light to be dealt with, settled and closed.

He heard himself saying, "Is the Dean busy at the moment? I'd like to see him."

His request came thus unbidden, even forbidden, and it was one of the surprising and startling incidents of his life. Later, when he reviewed the events, so disconnected in themselves or so merely odd, of the story that unfolded for him that year, it was over this moment, on its face the least notable, that he paused longest. It was frequently to be with fear and never without a certainty of its meaning in his own knowledge of himself that he would recall this simple, routine request and the feeling of shame and freedom it gave him as he sent everything down the official chute. In the end, of course, no matter what he did to "protect" Tertan, he would have had to make the same request and lay the matter on the Dean's clean desk. But it would always be a landmark of his life that, at the very moment when he was rejecting the official way, he had been, without will or intention, so gladly drawn to it.

After the storm's last delicate flurry, the sun had come out. Reflected by the new snow, it filled the office with a golden light which was almost musical in the way it made all the commonplace objects of efficiency shine with a sudden sad and noble significance. And the light, now that he noticed it, made the utterance of his perverse and unwanted request even more momentous.

The secretary consulted the engagement pad. "He'll be free any minute. Don't you want to wait in the parlor?"

She threw open the door of the large and pleasant room in which the Dean held his Committee meetings and in which his visitors waited. It was designed with a homely elegance on the masculine side of the eighteenth century manner. There was a small coal-fire in the grate and the handsome mahogany table was strewn with books and magazines. The large windows gave on the snowy lawn and there was such a fine width of window that the white casements and walls seemed at this moment but a continuation of the snow, the snow but an extension of casement and walls. The outdoors seemed taken in and made safe, the indoors seemed luxuriously freshened and expanded.

Howe sat down by the fire and lighted a cigarette. The room had its intended effect upon him. He felt comfortable and relaxed, yet nicely organized, some young diplomatic agent of the eighteenth century, the newly fledged Swift carrying out Sir William Temple's business. The rawness of Tertan's case quite vanished. He crossed his legs and reached for a magazine.

It was that famous issue of *Life and Letters* that his idle hand had found and his blood raced as he sifted through it and the shape of his own name, Joseph Howe, sprang out at him, still cabalistic in its power. He tossed the magazine back on the table as the door of the Dean's office opened and the Dean ushered out Theodore Blackburn.

"Ah, Joseph!" the Dean said.

Blackburn said, "Good morning, Doctor." Howe winced at the title and caught the flicker of amusement over the Dean's face. The Dean stood with his hand high on the door-jamb and Blackburn, still in the doorway, remained standing almost under his long arm.

Howe nodded briefly to Blackburn, snubbing his eager deference. "Can you give me a few minutes?" he said to the Dean.

"All the time you want. Come in." Before the two men could enter the office, Blackburn claimed their attention with a long full "Er." As they turned to him, Blackburn said, "Can *you* give *me* a few minutes, Dr. Howe?" His eyes sparkled at the little audacity he had committed, the slightly impudent play with hierarchy. Of the three of them Blackburn kept himself the lowest, but he reminded Howe of his subaltern relation to the Dean.

"I mean, of course," Blackburn went on easily, "when you've finished with the Dean."

"I'll be in my office shortly," Howe said, turned his back on the ready "Thank you, sir," and followed the Dean into the inner room.

"Energetic boy," said the Dean. "A bit beyond himself but very energetic. Sit down."

The Dean lighted a cigarette, leaned back in his chair, sat easy and silent for a moment, giving Howe no signal to go ahead with business. He was a young Dean, not much beyond forty, a tall handsome man with sad, ambitious eyes. He had been a Rhodes scholar. His friends looked for great things from him and it was generally said that he had notions of education which he was not yet ready to try to put into practice.

His relaxed silence was meant as a compliment to Howe. He smiled and said, "What's the business, Joseph?"

"Do you know Tertan—Ferdinand Tertan, a freshman?"

The Dean's cigarette was in his mouth and his hands were clasped behind his head. He did not seem to search his memory for the name. He said, "What about him?"

Clearly the Dean knew something and he was waiting for Howe to tell him more. Howe moved only tentatively. Now that he was doing what he had resolved not to do, he felt more guilty at having been so long deceived by Tertan and more need to be loyal to his error.

"He's a strange fellow," he ventured. He said stubbornly, "In a strange way he's very brilliant." He concluded, "But very strange."

The springs of the Dean's swivel chair creaked as he came out of his sprawl and leaned forward to Howe. "Do you mean he's so strange that it's something you could give a name to?"

Howe looked at him stupidly. "What do you mean?" he said.

"What's his trouble?" the Dean said more neutrally.

"He's very brilliant, in a way. I looked him up and he has a top intelligence rating. But somehow, and it's hard to explain just how, what he says is always on the edge of sense and doesn't quite make it."

The Dean looked at him and Howe flushed up. The Dean had surely read Woolley on the subject of "the Howes" and the *tour d'ivresse*. Was that quick glance ironical?

The Dean picked up some papers from his desk and Howe could see that they were in Tertan's impatient scrawl. Perhaps the little gleam in the Dean's glance had come only from putting facts together.

"He sent me this yesterday," the Dean said. "After an interview I had with him. I haven't been able to do more than glance at it. When you said what you did, I realized there was something wrong."

Twisting his mouth, the Dean looked over the letter. "You seem to be involved," he said without looking up. "By the way, what did you give him at mid-term?"

Flushing, setting his shoulders, Howe said firmly, "I gave him A-minus."

The Dean chuckled. "Might be a good idea if some of our nicer boys went crazy—just a little." He said, "Well," to conclude the matter and handed the papers to Howe. "See if this is the same thing you've been finding. Then we can go into the matter again."

Before the fire in the parlor, in the chair that Howe had been occupying, sat Blackburn. He sprang to his feet as Howe entered.

"I said my office, Mr. Blackburn." Howe's voice was sharp. Then he was almost sorry for the rebuke, so clearly and naively did Blackburn seem to relish his stay in the parlor, close to authority.

"I'm in a bit of a hurry, sir," he said, "and I did want to be sure to speak to you, sir."

He was really absurd, yet fifteen years from now he would have grown up to himself, to the assurance and mature beefiness. In banks, in consular offices, in brokerage firms, on the bench, more seriously affable, a little sterner, he would make use of his ability to be administered by his job. It was almost reassuring. Now he was exercising his too-great skill on Howe. "I owe you an apology, sir," he said.

Howe knew that he did but he showed surprise.

"I mean, Doctor, after your having been so kind about letting me attend your class, I stopped coming." He smiled in deprecation. "Extra-curricular activities take up so much of my time. I'm afraid I undertook more than I could perform."

Howe had noticed the absence and had been a little irritated by it after Blackburn's elaborate plea. It was an absence that might be interpreted as a comment on the teacher. But there was only one way for him to answer. "You've no need to apologize," he said. "It's wholly your affair."

Blackburn beamed. "I'm so glad you feel that way about it, sir. I was worried you might think I had stayed away because I was influenced by——" He stopped and lowered his eyes.

Astonished, Howe said, "Influenced by what?"

"Well, by——" Blackburn hesitated and for answer pointed to the table on which lay the copy of *Life and Letters*. Without looking at it, he knew where to direct his hand. "By the unfavorable publicity, sir." He hurried on. "And that brings me to another point, sir. I am vice-president of Quill and Scroll, sir, the student literary society, and I wonder if you would address us. You could read your own poetry, sir, and defend your own point of view. It would be very interesting."

It was truly amazing. Howe looked long and cruelly into Blackburn's face, trying to catch the secret of the mind that could have conceived this way of manipulating him, this way so daring and inept —but not entirely inept—with its malice so without malignity. The face did not yield its secret. Howe smiled broadly and said, "Of course I don't think you were influenced by the unfavorable publicity."

"I'm still going to take—regularly, for credit—your romantic poets course next term," Blackburn said.

"Don't worry, my dear fellow, don't worry about it."

Howe started to leave and Blackburn stopped him with, "But about Quill, sir?"

"Suppose we wait until next term? I'll be less busy then."

And Blackburn said, "Very good, sir, and thank you."

In his office the little encounter seemed less funny to Howe, was even in some indeterminate way disturbing. He made an effort to put it from his mind by turning to what was sure to disturb him more, the Tertan letter read in the new interpretation. He found what he had always found, the same florid leaps beyond fact and meaning, the same headlong certainty. But as his eye passed over the familiar scrawl it caught his own name and for the second time that hour he felt the race of his blood.

"The Paraclete," Tertan had written to the Dean, "from a Greek word meaning to stand in place of, but going beyond the primitive idea to mean traditionally the helper, the one who comforts and assists, cannot without fundamental loss be jettisoned. Even if taken no longer in the supernatural sense, the concept remains deeply in the human consciousness inevitably. Humanitarianism is no reply, for not every man stands in the place of every other man for this other's comrade comfort. But certain are chosen out of the human race to be the consoler of some other. Of these, for example, is Joseph Barker Howe, Ph.D. Of intellects not the first yet of true intellect and lambent instructions, given to that which is intuitive and irrational, not to what is logical in the strict word, what is judged by him is of the heart and not the head. Here is one chosen, in that he chooses himself to stand in the place of another for comfort and consolation. To him more than another I give my gratitude, with all respect to our Dean who reads this, a noble man, but merely dedicated, not consecrated. But not in the aspect of the Paraclete only is Dr. Joseph Barker Howe established, for he must be the Paraclete to another aspect of himself, that which is driven and persecuted by the lack of understanding in the world at large, so that he in himself embodies the full history of man's tribulations and, overflowing upon others, notably the present writer, is the ultimate end."

This was love. There was no escape from it. Try as Howe might to remember that Tertan was mad and all his emotions invalidated, he could not destroy the effect upon him of his student's stern, affectionate regard. He had betrayed not only a power of mind but a power of love. And however firmly he held before his attention the fact of Tertan's madness, he could do nothing to banish the physical sensation of gratitude he felt. He had never thought of himself as "driven and persecuted" and he did not now. But still he could not make meaningless his sensation of gratitude. The pitiable Tertan sternly pitied him, and comfort came from Tertan's never-to-be-comforted mind.

III

In an academic community, even an efficient one, official matters move slowly. The term drew to a close with no action in the case of Tertan, and Joseph Howe had to confront a curious problem. How should he grade his strange student, Tertan?

Tertan's final examination had been no different from all his other writing, and what did one "give" such a student? De Witt must have his A, that was clear. Johnson would get a B. With Casebeer it was a question of a B-minus or a C-plus, and Stettenhover, who had been crammed by the team tutor to fill half a blue-book with his thin feminine scrawl, would have his C-minus which he would accept with mingled indifference and resentment. But with Tertan it was not so easy.

The boy was still in the college process and his name could not be omitted from the grade sheet. Yet what should a mind under suspicion of madness be graded? Until the medical verdict was given, it was for Howe to continue as Tertan's teacher and to keep his judgment pedagogical. Impossible to give him an F: he had not failed. B was for Johnson's stolid mediocrity. He could not be put on the edge of passing with Stettenhover, for he exactly did not pass. In energy and richness of intellect he was perhaps even De Witt's superior, and Howe toyed grimly with the notion of giving him an A, but that would lower the value of the A De Witt had won with his beautiful and clear, if still arrogant, mind. There was a notation which the Registrar recognized—Inc. for Incomplete and in the horrible comedy of the situation, Howe considered that. But really only a mark of M for Mad would serve.

In his perplexity, Howe sought the Dean, but the Dean was out of town. In the end, he decided to maintain the A-minus he had given Tertan at midterm. After all, there had been no falling away from that quality. He entered it on the grade sheet with something like bravado.

Academic time moves quickly. A college year is not really a year, lacking as it does three months. And it is endlessly divided into units which, at their beginning, appear larger than they are—terms, half-terms, months, weeks. And the ultimate unit, the hour, is not really an hour, lacking as it does ten minutes. And so the new term advanced rapidly and one day the fields about the town were all brown, cleared of even the few thin patches of snow which had lingered so long.

Howe, as he lectured on the romantic poets, became conscious of Blackburn emanating wrath. Blackburn did it well, did it with enormous dignity. He did not stir in his seat, he kept his eyes fixed on Howe in perfect attention, but he abstained from using his notebook, there was no mistaking what he proposed to himself as an attitude. His elbow on the writing-wing of the chair, his chin on the curled fingers of his hand, he was the embodiment of intellectual indignation. He was thinking his own thoughts, would give no public offence, yet would claim his due, was not to be intimidated. Howe knew that he would present himself at the end of the hour.

Blackburn entered the office without invitation. He did not smile, there was no cajolery about him. Without invitation he sat down beside Howe's desk. He did not speak until he had taken the blue-book from his pocket. He said, "What does this mean, sir?"

It was a sound and conservative student tactic. Said in the usual way it meant, "How could you have so misunderstood me?" or "What does this mean for my future in the course?" But there were none of the humbler tones in Blackburn's way of saying it.

Howe made the established reply, "I think that's for you to tell me."

Blackburn continued icy. "I'm sure I can't, sir."

There was a silence between them. Both dropped their eyes to the blue-book on the desk. On its cover Howe had pencilled: "F. This is very poor work."

Howe picked up the blue-book. There was always the possibility of injustice. The teacher may be bored by the mass of papers and not wholly attentive. A phrase, even the student's handwriting, may irritate him unreasonably. "Well," said Howe, "let's go through it."

He opened the first page. "Now here: you write, 'In "The Ancient Mariner," Coleridge lives in and transports us to a honey-sweet world where all is rich and strange, a world of charm to which we can escape from the humdrum existence of our daily lives, the world of romance. Here, in this warm and honey-sweet land of charming dreams we can relax and enjoy ourselves.' "

Howe lowered the paper and waited with a neutral look for Blackburn to speak. Blackburn returned the look boldly, did not speak, sat stolid and lofty. At last Howe said, speaking gently, "Did you mean that, or were you just at a loss for something to say?"

"You imply that I was just 'bluffing'?" The quotation marks hung palpable in the air about the word.

"I'd like to know. I'd prefer believing that you were bluffing to believing that you really thought this."

Blackburn's eyebrows went up. From the height of a great and firm-based idea he looked at his teacher. He clasped the crags for a moment and then pounced, craftily, suavely. "Do you mean, Dr. Howe, that there aren't two opinions possible?"

It was superbly done in its air of putting all of Howe's intellectual life into the balance. Howe remained patient and simple. "Yes, many opinions are possible, but not this one. Whatever anyone believes of 'The Ancient Mariner,' no one can in reason believe that it represents a—a honey-sweet world in which we can relax."

"But that is what I *feel,* sir."

This was well done too. Howe said, "Look, Mr. Blackburn. Do you really relax with hunger and thirst, the heat and the sea-serpents, the dead men with staring eyes, Life in Death and the skeletons? Come now, Mr. Blackburn."

Blackburn made no answer and Howe pressed forward. "Now you say of Wordsworth, 'Of peasant stock himself, he turned from the effete life of the salons and found in the peasant the hope of a flaming revolution which would sweep away all the old ideas. This is the subject of his best poems.' "

Beaming at his teacher with youthful eagerness, Blackburn said, "Yes, sir, a rebel, a bringer of light to suffering mankind. I see him as a kind of Prothemeus."

"A kind of what?"

"Prothemeus, sir."

"Think, Mr. Blackburn. We were talking about him only today and I mentioned his name a dozen times. You don't mean Prothemeus. You mean—" Howe waited but there was no response.

"You mean Prometheus."

Blackburn gave no assent and Howe took the reins. "You've done a bad job here, Mr. Blackburn, about as bad as could be done." He saw Blackburn stiffen and his genial face harden again. "It shows either a lack of preparation or a complete lack of understanding." He saw Blackburn's face begin to go to pieces and he stopped.

"Oh, sir," Blackburn burst out, "I've never had a mark like this before, never anything below a B, never. A thing like this has never happened to me before."

It must be true, it was a statement too easily verified. Could it be that other instructors accepted such flaunting nonsense? Howe wanted to end the interview. "I'll set it down to lack of preparation," he said. "I know you're busy. That's not an excuse but it's an explanation. Now suppose you really prepare and then take another quiz in two weeks. We'll forget this one and count the other."

Blackburn squirmed with pleasure and gratitude. "Thank you, sir. You're really very kind, very kind."

Howe rose to conclude the visit. "All right then—in two weeks."

It was that day that the Dean imparted to Howe the conclusion of the case of Tertan. It was simple and a little anticlimactic. A physician had been called in, and had said the word, given the name.

"A classic case, he called it," the Dean said. "Not a doubt in the world," he said. His eyes were full of miserable pity and he clutched at a word. "A classic case, a classic case." To his aid and to Howe's there came the Parthenon and the form of the Greek drama, the Aristotelian logic, Racine and the Well-Tempered Clavichord, the blueness of the Aegean and its clear sky. Classic—that is to say, without a doubt, perfect in its way, a veritable model, and, as the Dean had been told, sure to take a perfectly predictable and inevitable course to a foreknown conclusion.

It was not only pity that stood in the Dean's eyes. For a moment there was fear too. "Terrible," he said, "it is simply terrible."

Then he went on briskly. "Naturally we've told the boy nothing. And naturally we won't. His tuition's paid by his scholarship and we'll continue him on the rolls until the end of the year. That will be kindest. After that the matter will be out of our control. We'll see, of course, that he gets into the proper hands. I'm told there will be no change, he'll go on like this, be as good as this, for four to six months. And so we'll just go along as usual."

So Tertan continued to sit in Section 5 of English 1A, to his classmates still a figure of curiously dignified fun, symbol to most of them of the respectable but absurd intellectual life. But to his teacher he was now very different. He had not changed—he was still the greyhound casting for the scent of ideas and Howe could see that he was still the same Tertan, but he could not feel it. What he felt as he looked at the boy sitting in his accustomed place was the hard blank of a fact. The fact itself was formidable and depressing. But what Howe was chiefly aware of was that he had permitted the metamorphosis of Tertan from person to fact.

As much as possible he avoided seeing Tertan's upraised hand and eager eye. But the fact did not know of its mere factuality, it continued its existence as if it were Tertan, hand up and eye questioning, and one day it appeared in Howe's office with a document.

"Even the spirit who lives egregiously, above the herd, must have its relations with the fellowman," Tertan declared. He laid the document on Howe's desk. It was headed "Quill and Scroll Society of Dwight College. Application for Membership."

"In most ways these are crass minds," Tertan said, touching the paper. "Yet as a whole, bound together in their common love of letters, they transcend their intellectual lacks since it is not a paradox that the whole is greater than the sum of its parts."

"When are the elections?" Howe asked.

"They take place tomorrow."

"I certainly hope you will be successful."

"Thank you. Would you wish to implement that hope?" A rather dirty finger pointed to the bottom of the sheet. "A faculty recommender is necessary," Tertan said stiffly, and waited.

"And you wish me to recommend you?"

"It would be an honor."

"You may use my name."

Tertan's finger pointed again. "It must be a written sponsorship, signed by the sponsor." There was a large blank space on the form under the heading, "Opinion of Faculty Sponsor."

This was almost another thing and Howe hesitated. Yet there was nothing else to do and he took out his fountain pen. He wrote, "Mr. Ferdinand Tertan is marked by his intense devotion to letters and by his exceptional love of all things of the mind." To this he signed his name which looked bold and assertive on the white page. It disturbed him, the strange affirming power of a name. With a business-like air, Tertan whipped up the paper, folded it with decision and put it into his pocket. He bowed and took his departure, leaving Howe with the sense of having done something oddly momentous.

And so much now seemed odd and momentous to Howe that should not have seemed so. It was odd and momentous, he felt, when he sat with Blackburn's second quiz before him and wrote in an excessively firm hand the grade of C-minus. The paper was a clear, an indisputable failure. He was carefully and consciously committing a cowardice. Blackburn had told the truth when he had pleaded his past record. Howe had consulted it in the Dean's office. It showed no grade lower than a B-minus. A canvass of some of Blackburn's previous instructors had brought vague attestations to the adequate powers of a student imperfectly remembered and sometimes surprise that his abilities could be questioned at all.

As he wrote the grade, Howe told himself that his cowardice sprang from an unwillingness to have more dealings with a student he disliked. He knew it was simpler than that. He knew he feared Blackburn: that was the absurd truth. And cowardice did not solve the matter after all. Blackburn, flushed with a first success, attacked at once. The minimal passing grade had not assuaged his feelings and he sat at Howe's desk and again the blue-book lay between them. Blackburn said nothing. With an enormous impudence, he was waiting for Howe to speak and explain himself.

At last Howe said sharply and rudely, "Well?" His throat was tense and the blood was hammering in his head. His mouth was tight with anger at himself for his disturbance.

Blackburn's glance was almost baleful. "This is impossible, sir."

"But there it is," Howe answered.

"Sir?" Blackburn had not caught the meaning but his tone was still haughty.

Impatiently Howe said, "There it is, plain as day. Are you here to complain again?"

"Indeed I am, sir." There was surprise in Blackburn's voice that Howe should ask the question.

"I shouldn't complain if I were you. You did a thoroughly bad job on your first quiz. This one is a little, only a very little, better." This was not true. If anything, it was worse.

"That might be a matter of opinion, sir."

"It is a matter of opinion. Of my opinion."

"Another opinion might be different, sir."

"You really believe that?" Howe said.

"Yes." The omission of the "sir" was monumental.

"Whose, for example?"

"The Dean's, for example." Then the fleshy jaw came forward a little. "Or a certain literary critic's, for example."

It was colossal and almost too much for Blackburn himself to handle. The solidity of his face almost crumpled under it. But he withstood his own audacity and went on. "And the Dean's opinion might be guided by the knowledge that the person who gave me this mark is the man whom a famous critic, the most eminent judge of literature in this country, called a drunken man. The Dean might think twice about whether such a man is fit to teach Dwight students."

Howe said in quiet admonition, "Blackburn, you're mad," meaning no more than to check the boy's extravagance.

But Blackburn paid no heed. He had another shot in the locker. "And the Dean might be guided by the information, of which I have evidence, documentary evidence,"—he slapped his breastpocket twice —"that this same person personally recommended to the college literary society, the oldest in the country, that he personally recommended a student who is crazy, who threw the meeting into an uproar, a psychiatric case. The Dean might take that into account."

Howe was never to learn the details of that "uproar." He had always to content himself with the dim but passionate picture which at that moment sprang into his mind, of Tertan standing on some abstract height and madly denouncing the multitude of Quill and Scroll who howled him down.

He sat quiet a moment and looked at Blackburn. The ferocity had entirely gone from the student's face. He sat regarding his teacher almost benevolently. He had played a good card and now, scarcely at all unfriendly, he was waiting to see the effect. Howe took up the blue-book and negligently sifted through it. He read a page, closed the book, struck out the C-minus and wrote an F.

"Now you may take the paper to the Dean," he said. "You may tell him that after reconsidering it, I lowered the grade."

The gasp was audible. "Oh sir!" Blackburn cried. "Please!" His face was agonized. "It means my graduation, my livelihood, my future. Don't do this to me."

"It's done already."

Blackburn stood up. "I spoke rashly, sir, hastily. I had no intention, no real intention, of seeing the Dean. It rests with you—entirely, entirely. I *hope* you will restore the first mark."

"Take the matter to the Dean or not, just as you choose. The grade is what you deserve and it stands."

Blackburn's head dropped. "And will I be failed at midterm, sir?"

"Of course."

From deep out of Blackburn's great chest rose a cry of anguish. "Oh sir, if you want me to go down on my knees to you, I will, I will."

Howe looked at him in amazement.

"I will, I will. On my knees, sir. This mustn't, mustn't happen."

He spoke so literally, meaning so very truly that his knees and exactly his knees were involved and seeming to think that he was offering something of tangible value to his teacher, that Howe, whose head had become icy clear in the nonsensical drama, thought, "The boy is mad," and began to speculate fantastically whether something in himself attracted or developed aberration. He could see himself standing absurdly before the Dean and saying, "I've found another. This time it's the Vice-president of the Council, the manager of the debating team and secretary of Quill and Scroll."

One more such discovery, he thought, and he himself would be discovered! And there, suddenly, Blackburn was on his knees with a thump, his huge thighs straining his trousers, his hand outstretched in a great gesture of supplication.

With a cry, Howe shoved back his swivel chair and it rolled away on its casters half across the little room. Blackburn knelt for a moment to nothing at all, then got to his feet.

Howe rose abruptly. He said, "Blackburn, you will stop acting like an idiot. Dust your knees off, take your paper and get out. You've behaved like a fool and a malicious person. You have half a term to do a decent job. Keep your silly mouth shut and try to do it. Now get out."

Blackburn's head was low. He raised it and there was a pious light in his eyes. "Will you shake hands, sir?" he said. He thrust out his hand.

"I will not," Howe said.

Head and hand sank together. Blackburn picked up his blue-book and walked to the door. He turned and said, "Thank you, sir." His back, as he departed, was heavy with tragedy and stateliness.

IV

After years of bad luck with the weather, the College had a perfect day for Commencement. It was wonderfully bright, the air so transparent, the wind so brisk that no one could resist talking about it.

As Howe set out for the campus he heard Hilda calling from the back yard. She called, "Professor, professor," and came running to him.

Howe said, "What's this 'professor' business?"

"Mother told me," Hilda said. "You've been promoted. And I want to take your picture."

"Next year," said Howe. "I won't be a professor until next year. And you know better than to call anybody 'professor'."

"It was just in fun," Hilda said. She seemed disappointed.

"But you can take my picture if you want. I won't look much different next year." Still, it was frightening. It might mean that he was to stay in this town all his life.

Hilda brightened. "Can I take it in this?" she said, and touched the gown he carried over his arm.

Howe laughed. "Yes, you can take it in this."

"I'll get my things and meet you in front of Otis," Hilda said. "I have the background all picked out."

On the campus the Commencement crowd was already large. It stood about in eager, nervous little family groups. As he crossed, Howe was greeted by a student, capped and gowned, glad of the chance to make an event for his parents by introducing one of his teachers. It was while Howe stood there chatting that he saw Tertan.

He had never seen anyone quite so alone, as though a circle had been woven about him to separate him from the gay crowd on the campus. Not that Tertan was not gay, he was the gayest of all. Three weeks had passed since Howe had last seen him, the weeks of examination, the lazy week before Commencement, and this was now a different Tertan. On his head he wore a panama hat, broadbrimmed and fine, of the shape associated with South American planters. He wore a suit of raw silk, luxurious but yellowed with age and much too tight, and he sported a whangee cane. He walked sedately, the hat tilted at a devastating angle, the stick coming up and down in time to his measured tread. He had, Howe guessed, outfitted himself to greet the day in the clothes of that ruined father whose existence was on record in the Dean's office. Gravely and arrogantly he surveyed the scene—in it, his whole bearing seemed to say, but not of it. With his haughty step, with his flashing eye, Tertan was coming nearer. Howe did not wish to be seen. He shifted his position slightly. When he looked again, Tertan was not in sight.

The chapel clock struck the quarter hour. Howe detached himself from his chat and hurried to Otis Hall at the far end of the campus. Hilda had not yet come. He went up into the high portico and, using the glass of the door for a mirror, put on his gown, adjusted the hood on his shoulders and set the mortarboard on his head. When he came down the steps Hilda had arrived.

Nothing could have told him more forcibly that a year had passed than the development of Hilda's photographic possessions from the box camera of the previous fall. By a strap about her neck was hung a leather case, so thick and strong, so carefully stitched and so molded to its contents that it could only hold a costly camera. The appearance was deceptive, Howe knew, for he had been present at the Aikens' pre-Christmas conference about its purchase. It was only a fairly good domestic camera. Still, it looked very impressive. Hilda carried another leather case from which she drew a collapsible tripod. Decisively she extended each of its gleaming legs and set it up on the path. She removed the camera from its case and fixed it to the tripod. In its compact efficiency the camera almost had a life of its own, but Hilda treated it with easy familiarity, looked into its eye, glanced casually at its gauges. Then from a pocket she took still another leather case and drew from it a small instrument through which she looked first at Howe, who began to feel inanimate and lost, and then at the sky. She made some adjustment on the instrument, then some adjustment on the camera. She swept the scene with her eye, found a spot and pointed the camera in its direction. She walked to the spot, stood on it and beckoned to Howe. With each new leather case, with each new instrument and with each new adjustment she had grown in ease and now she said, "Joe, will you stand here?"

Obediently Howe stood where he was bidden. She had yet another instrument. She took out a tape-measure on a mechanical spool. Kneeling down before Howe, she put the little metal ring of the tape under the tip of his shoe. At her request, Howe pressed it with his toe. When she had measured her distance, she nodded to Howe who released the tape. At a touch, it sprang back into the spool. "You have to be careful if you're going to get what you want," Hilda said. "I don't believe in all this snap-snap-snapping," she remarked loftily. Howe nodded in agreement, although he was beginning to think Hilda's care excessive.

Now at last the moment had come. Hilda squinted into the camera, moved the tripod slightly. She stood to the side, holding the plunger of the shutter-cable. "Ready," she said. "Will you relax, Joseph, please?" Howe realized that he was standing frozen. Hilda stood poised and precise as a setter, one hand holding the little cable, the other extended with curled dainty fingers like a dancer's, as if expressing to her subject the precarious delicacy of the moment. She pressed the plunger and there was the click. At once she stirred to action, got behind the camera, turned a new exposure. "Thank you," she said. "Would you stand under that tree and let me do a character study with light and shade?"

The childish absurdity of the remark restored Howe's ease. He went to the little tree. The pattern the leaves made on his gown was what Hilda was after. He had just taken a satisfactory position when he heard in the unmistakable voice, "Ah, Doctor! Having your picture taken?"

Howe gave up the pose and turned to Blackburn who stood on the walk, his hands behind his back, a little too large for his bachelor's gown. Annoyed that Blackburn should see him posing for a character study in light and shade, Howe said irritably, "Yes, having my picture taken."

Blackburn beamed at Hilda. "And the little photographer," he said. Hilda fixed her eyes on the ground and stood closer to her brilliant and aggressive camera. Blackburn, teetering on his heels, his hands behind his back, wholly prelatical and benignly patient, was not abashed at the silence. At last Howe said, "If you'll excuse us, Mr. Blackburn, we'll go on with the picture."

"Go right ahead, sir. I'm running along." But he only came closer. "Dr. Howe," he said fervently, "I want to tell you how glad I am that I was able to satisfy your standards at last."

Howe was surprised at the hard insulting brightness of his own voice and even Hilda looked up curiously as he said, "Nothing you have ever done has satisfied me and nothing you could ever do would satisfy me, Blackburn."

With a glance at Hilda, Blackburn made a gesture as if to hush Howe—as though all his former bold malice had taken for granted a kind of understanding between himself and his teacher, a secret which must not be betrayed to a third person. "I only meant, sir," he said, "that I was able to pass your course after all."

Howe said, "You didn't pass my course. I passed you out of my course. I passed you without even reading your paper. I wanted to be sure the college would be rid of you. And when all the grades were in and I did read your paper, I saw I was right not to have read it first."

Blackburn presented a stricken face. "It was very bad, sir?"

But Howe had turned away. The paper had been fantastic. The paper had been, if he wished to see it so, mad. It was at this moment that the Dean came up behind Howe and caught his arm. "Hello, Joseph," he said. "We'd better be getting along, it's almost late."

He was not a familiar man, but when he saw Blackburn, who approached to greet him, he took Blackburn's arm too. "Hello, Theodore," he said. Leaning forward on Howe's arm and on Blackburn's, he said, "Hello, Hilda dear." Hilda replied quietly, "Hello, Uncle George."

Still clinging to their arms, still linking Howe and Blackburn, the Dean said, "Another year gone, Joe, and we've turned out another crop. After you've been here a few years, you'll find it reasonably upsetting—you wonder how there can be so many graduating classes while you stay the same. But of course you don't stay the same." Then he said, "Well," sharply, to dismiss the thought. He pulled

Blackburn's arm and swung him around to Howe. "Have you heard about Teddy Blackburn?" he asked. "He has a job already, before graduation, the first man of his class to be placed." Expectant of congratulations, Blackburn beamed at Howe. Howe remained silent.

"Isn't that good?" the Dean said. Still Howe did not answer and the Dean, puzzled and put out, turned to Hilda. "That's a very fine-looking camera, Hilda." She touched it with affectionate pride.

"Instruments of precision," said a voice. "Instruments of precision." Of the three with joined arms, Howe was the nearest to Tertan, whose gaze took in all the scene except the smile and the nod which Howe gave him. The boy leaned on his cane. The broad-brimmed hat, canting jauntily over his eye, confused the image of his face that Howe had established, suppressed the rigid lines of the ascetic and brought out the baroque curves. It made an effect of perverse majesty.

"Instruments of precision," said Tertan for the last time, addressing no one, making a casual comment to the universe. And it occurred to Howe that Tertan might not be referring to Hilda's equipment. The sense of the thrice-woven circle of the boy's loneliness smote him fiercely. Tertan stood in majestic jauntiness, superior to all the scene, but his isolation made Howe ache with a pity of which Tertan was more the cause than the object, so general and indiscriminate was it.

Whether in his sorrow he made some unintended movement toward Tertan which the Dean checked or whether the suddenly tightened grip on his arm was the Dean's own sorrow and fear, he did not know. Tertan watched them in the incurious way people watch a photograph being taken and suddenly the thought that, to the boy, it must seem that the three were posing for a picture together made Howe detach himself almost rudely from the Dean's grasp.

"I promised Hilda another picture," he announced—needlessly, for Tertan was no longer there, he had vanished in the last sudden flux of visitors who, now that the band had struck up, were rushing nervously to find seats.

"You'd better hurry," the Dean said. "I'll go along, it's getting late for me." He departed and Blackburn walked stately by his side.

Howe again took his position under the little tree which cast its shadow over his face and gown. "Just hurry, Hilda, won't you?" he said. Hilda held the cable at arm's length, her other arm crooked and her fingers crisped. She rose on her toes and said "Ready," and pressed the release. "Thank you," she said gravely and began to dismantle her camera as he hurried off to join the procession.

Sea Raider

BY FRANK LASKIER

To ADD to this series, I've told you exactly what happened to me on board the ship. Perhaps without intending to, because at one time, the memory was so fresh in my mind, that I did not feel inclined to talk about it, or think about it, but now you know, I am the sailor called Frank. One of thousands.

I could tell you my name, but it doesn't matter. It is of no importance. My name might be "Smith" or "Jones" or "Brown" or "Robinson" or anything. I am merely a sailor.

And I have been through things, and I have seen them.

I could give all sorts of messages to you, if I were merely sitting here asking you for money, it would be so dreadfully easy. I know that you would give me anything that I wanted.

But, there is another thing. This is in a world-wide broadcast, and there is one man listening to me to-night, and I have a word for him.

I wonder if you remember me, Mister. I wonder.

You're the Captain of a German raider, and on the 29th January you attacked a merchant ship. Don't you remember? Just when it was dark, you saw me then. You met me. At one time you weren't more than 100 yards from me. You followed us up. You chased us. You kept hidden. You were afraid even of our 4-inch gun, against your 11-inch guns.

You attacked us in the dark, at point-blank range. Don't you remember? Don't you remember shelling us for twenty minutes and then ceasing fire, and coming round to examine the damage.

I was on the starboard bunker hatch, you shone your searchlight on me. You'd shot my foot off. Don't you remember the Fourth Mate making a signal out to you that we were abandoning ship? And you answered the signal. Don't you remember opening fire on us again?

I remember it. We got on to the raft, didn't we? You saw us, you watched our ship sink. And you machine-gunned us. But you didn't do the job properly. Because out of that ship's company ten men are alive, and those ten men know what you did.

Three of us were wounded. Seven of us were not. Those seven are back at sea.

You'd be surprised if you knew the job that the Captain has. You'd be surprised, and I don't think you'd be very happy about it, either.

You murdered my shipmates. You stood by and watched us drown. You machine-gunned us.

But go ahead, Mister. Go right ahead.

Using your yellow, filthy, murderous methods, you may get another couple more ships. You work the same stunt on them. You'll leave them to the sharks, won't you?

But, your time is up.

Sooner or later, and it will be sooner, you will be met by the Navy.

Aircraft from the Fleet Air Arm will come over you, and they'll bomb you and blast you and your bridge will fly to pieces, as ours did, and your decks will burst open as ours did.

And then a battleship will come alongside, and I hope it's the *Warspite*. And with her 15-inch guns she'll fire you, and you will see your crew dead and dying. You will see your ship blowing up, and you yourself will be on a raft.

But we won't machine-gun you. We weren't brought up that way. No, we'll give you a little taste of what it's like in the salt water. Aircraft from the Fleet Air Arm will catch up with you, they'll dive-bomb you, wave after wave after wave, and your guns will be as useless as ours was. And a battleship will come up, and I hope it's the *Warspite,* and you'll be shattered. You'll see your bridge go up in flames, as ours did. You'll see your mates hanging round on the decks, the same as I did. You'll see your ship sink, as I did. And you'll be there in the water, struggling as we were, and your life-jacket won't hold you up, and you'll go down and down and down, and the water will come in your eyes and your ears, and down your mouth, and you'll see death in front of you. And you'll come up to the surface, and the British seamen will get hold of you, and will drag you on board the boat. Because we don't leave men to drown.

But, remember, Mr. Raider, that when we have finished with you —and we won't use blackjacks or castor-oil—you'll wish, and you'll hope, and you'll pray that you had been left to drown, as you left us. But we didn't drown.

Your day is coming. Look out for it.

Zuleika in Cambridge

BY S. C. ROBERTS

> "See if it is possible to go direct from here to Cambridge," said Zuleika. . . . "Stop!" she said suddenly. "I have a much better idea. Go down very early to the station. See the station-master. Order me a special train . . ."
>
> MAX BEERBOHM, *Zuleika Dobson* (p. 350)

I

THE SPECIAL train which Zuleika had instructed Mélisande to order for ten o'clock on the morning following the annihilating tragedy of Eights Week did not start punctually. The station-master was not prepared to accept the order as a matter of the day's routine. Of course he had arranged special trains before; there had been a year when he had facilitated the departure of a Royal Personage returning from the glories of the Encaenia and a pair of cuff-links engraved with the august monogram remained, unworn, in its case on his drawing-room table. But a peremptory order from a young woman given at 8.30 in the morning in a suspiciously foreign accent was unprecedented.

"Who's the train for?" asked the station-master with ungrammatical directness.

"For Miss Dobson."

"Never heard of her."

"You never hear of Miss Dobson, Miss Zuleika Dobson! But she is the grand-daughter of the Warden of Judas College, yes."

At this the station-master showed some interest. He took the precaution, however, of consulting the Proctor by telephone. The Proctor replied, feverishly, that the sooner Miss Dobson left Oxford, the better. When he heard that her destination was Cambridge, his enthusiasm rose still higher.

So Zuleika's train was prepared and perhaps the Roman Emperors sighed wistfully. Lately they had seen so much—it had been like old times.

Slowly the special train passed through the cavalier country and approached the puritan plains of East Anglia.

Zuleika's spirits drooped. She knew little of English history, but by some premonition she was aware that the country in which a Knight of the Garter would die for an idea was receding from her. . . . Could it be, she wondered, that she was being guilty of an impossible disloyalty?

At Bletchley there was some delay. Special or no special, it was too much to expect that the train should pass every signal-box unchallenged. Zuleika fumed and Mélisande still showed a tendency to sulk.

At length the train drew up at the Cambridge platform. Already, it appeared, several other trains—ordinary trains—were halted at it; but as the platform stretched far, far beyond the limits of human vision, it seemed to matter little—except to Zuleika. Why had not Mélisande arranged things better?

"But, mademoiselle, I order a special train where we begin. I could order not a special *voie* where we finish."

"We are not finishing," said Zuleika, "we are beginning again."

Alas, there was no Warden to meet Zuleika at the station. In Cambridge, of course, they do not have Wardens, but Zuleika could not know that. But at least there were porters and Mélisande quickly secured, and fully employed, three of them. The cab-rank was, to Zuleika, uninviting, but a hansom for herself, another for Mélisande and the light luggage, and two others for the heavy luggage proved to be an adequate, if not very convenient, means of transport.

"Where to, Miss?" enquired the leading cabman.

To this Zuleika was unable to give a ready answer. She had, so far as she knew, no relatives or friends in Cambridge. But Cambridge, she assumed, had, like Oxford, a number of colleges. Did the granddaughter of the head of an Oxford college acquire any status, by affiliation or otherwise, in Cambridge? It was long before the days of "friendly alliances" between Oxford and Cambridge colleges and Zuleika was puzzled.

"Which is the best college?" she asked the cabman.

"That's not for me to say, Miss. Of course, some's better class than others, but nowadays there's all sorts in most of 'em. Now if you just tell me which one your brother or friend is in, I'll take you there."

But Zuleika, alas, could not.

"Are there hotels?" she asked.

"Yes, plenty, Miss."

"Take me to the best."

"Very good, Miss."

So the cavalcade set off.

The first part of the journey did not impress, or amuse, Zuleika. The Station Road was like all Station Roads in the world—perhaps more so, since when the railway had first come to Cambridge, it had been the particular care of the University authorities to remove its distracting influence as far as possible from the centre of academic calm. A one-horse tram, which occasionally interfered with the orderly sequence of the four hansoms, seemed to be the only distinguishing feature of Cambridge transport. Even when the cabs swung round into another street, Zuleika could see no evidence of collegiate grandeur. No Roman Emperors looked down upon her, though shortly an imposing spire came into view. Zuleika surmised that it might be the cathedral. How could she know that it was but a modern church, alien alike from Anglican and Cantabrigian tradition? The hansoms swung to the left and passed a row of villas which might well have reminded Zuleika of Oxford had her knowledge of that city extended to its northern area and not been confined to Judas College and the meadows.

But the last swerve of the cab brought her to something better—a street of gentle but repeated curves with solid terraced houses, a running stream in each gutter and, later, a jumble of shops and colleges.

Just as Zuleika was contemplating this medley, the hansoms drew up alongside the hotel. Mélisande dealt with the four cabmen while Zuleika issued an order for the best suite available. The bathroom arrangements seemed to her inadequate, but she supposed that they must suffice—at least until she should be able to establish herself under a more dignified and appropriate roof. Meanwhile she was hungry. It was after two o'clock and as she approached the dining-room, she saw that it was empty, save for a young man who was lingering over his coffee. Zuleika inferred that he was an undergraduate, though probably not a duke. Nevertheless, a slight thrill shot through her tired frame. It was a meeting not comparable with her initial encounter with the Duke of Dorset, but here was Zuleika face to face for the first time with a Cambridge undergraduate; and undergraduates, she assumed (as Dr Johnson assumed of the waters of the sea), were much the same everywhere. She hoped that the young man would not fall in love with her too violently before she had had her lunch.

As she entered the room, the victim, as it seemed, leapt violently to his doom.

"Ah, at last you've come."

Zuleika recognised the tone. It was a lover's welcome. So, she mused, it was inevitable. The greeting was freer, gayer, less dignified, perhaps; but the magic was still working. Quickly Zuleika began to speculate on the probable course of events. Had they a river at Cambridge? Yes, she thought she had heard of Cambridge boating and boat-races, but what was the capacity of the Cambridge river? What of the reeds and mud to which she had heard vaguely scornful reference made in Oxford? If young men must die for her, she liked them to die cleanly. . . . Her reverie was harshly interrupted.

"Oh, I beg your pardon," said the young man, "I'm frightfully sorry. . . . I thought you were——"

"You thought I was——?" murmured Zuleika.

"I thought you were my—er—friend. You see, I was just waiting for her and—well, here she is. I'm awfully sorry."

The friend had round blue eyes and fluffy fair hair. Zuleika sat down to her lunch.

II

Sipping her *café noir,* Zuleika reviewed the situation. The encounter with the young man was puzzling. Yet it might well be that he was not an undergraduate; possibly he was just a visitor passing through the town. The hotel seemed now to be empty except for two elderly ladies dozing over illustrated papers in the lounge. Zuleika was wondering how to approach the problem of Cambridge. With no grandfather and, so far, no duke to guide or shelter her, she found it difficult. But at least the sun was shining and she stepped out into the street.

The pinnacles of King's were silhouetted against the cerulean blue of the summer sky and Zuleika contemplated them with quizzical awe. So far as she could remember, she had seen nothing quite like them in Oxford. But she had not come to Cambridge to contemplate pinnacles. How, she reflected, was she to make acquaintance with a Cambridge college from within? At that moment the hotel-porter approached her.

"You're wanted, please, Miss," he said.

"By whom?"

"It's the manager, Miss. I think he's got a message for you."

Zuleika turned back into the hotel. The manager seemed to be slightly perturbed.

"I'm sorry to trouble you, Miss Dobson," he said politely, "but the Senior Proctor wishes to see you at once."

"What is a Proctor?" asked Zuleika. "Is it the same as a Warden?"

The question confused the manager a little. The only kind of warden with which he was familiar was a church-warden. He knew, of course, that the Proctors attended divine service, compulsorily, on certain occasions; but he rightly associated them with disciplinary, rather than with spiritual, responsibility.

"The Proctors," he said, "keep an eye on the undergraduates."

Zuleika brightened at this.

"I see," she said, "and what is the message?"

The manager read from a piece of paper:

"The Senior Proctor presents his compliments to Miss Dobson and would be obliged if she would call upon him in his rooms at her earliest convenience."

"Why doesn't he call upon me?" asked Zuleika.

"I expect it's easier to talk privately in his rooms," said the manager tactfully.

Zuleika was mollified. The message was not rapturous, but it was polite and would at least give her contact with a university personage.

"Where does the Proctor live?" she asked.

"In St Benedict's."

"Then order a cab."

"But, excuse me, Miss Dobson. St Benedict's is only just across the road."

"Oh very well, but it is tiring to walk across roads in the strong sunshine. . . . Where is Mélisande?"

On the subject of proctors Mélisande was not helpful. If they bore any resemblance to a *procurateur,* she recommended avoidance.

Zuleika crossed the road and found herself at the main gate of the college of St Benedict. A dignified porter, wearing a silk hat, looked at her with the half-suspicious, half-tolerant expression with which he greeted all May Term visitors.

"The Proctor wishes to see me," said Zuleika simply.

"You mean Mr Mackenzie, Miss. K Old Court."

Zuleika was not enlightened. The description reminded her vaguely of a move at chess.

"Through the screens, Miss," said the porter helpfully. But still Zuleika was at a loss. The porter realised that he had to deal with the really hopeless May Term type. He walked far enough with Zuleika to show her the precise approach to Mr Mackenzie's staircase.

Brian Mackenzie, formerly of the University of Aberdeen, and now Fellow and Mathematical Lecturer of St Benedict's and Senior Proctor in the University, was a man of tidy mind and tidy habits. He had no love of the office of Proctor, but he had recognised the obligation to serve and he had come through the greater part of his year of office without any major scandal or disturbance. He had a reputation for courtesy, dignity and efficiency.

What he had heard from Oxford in the preceding twenty-four hours had filled him with incredulous astonishment. He had been convinced that the daily press, following its invariable practice of putting Oxford in the headlines and Cambridge in the University Intelligence, had grossly exaggerated the devastation produced by the visit of Zuleika to Judas College. Nevertheless, when the news of her migration to Cambridge reached him, he felt that he must act and act promptly. He had called upon the Vice-Chancellor and suggested that he should summon a special meeting of the Proctorial Syndicate. The Vice-Chancellor was disturbed. As Full Term drew to an end, he liked to resume his collation of certain Syriac fragments which seemed to embody a dialect hitherto unknown to scholars and he hoped shortly to complete an article on the subject for *The Journal of Oriental Studies*. He, too, had heard something about strange happenings at the other university, but when he had caught sight of a headline "Oxford Sensation" he had shuddered slightly and put the newspaper down. The description of an event as a "sensation" always produced in him a feeling of incipient nausea. However, he trusted Mackenzie's judgment and a meeting of the Proctorial Syndicate had been convened for five o'clock.

Mackenzie's aim was clear. He wanted to remove Zuleika from Cambridge as quickly and as quietly as possible. Sceptical as he was about the measure of disaster which she had brought upon Oxford, he desired above all things to see her safely in a Liverpool Street train. It was a policy he had pursued with some success, during his year of office, in relation to female immigrants of a different type. "Let us have a minimum of fuss," he used to say at proctorial conferences. As a mathematician, Mackenzie had a reputation for neatness rather than for elegance.

He rose to greet Zuleika.

"Ah, Miss Dobson, this is very kind of you. Won't you sit down?"

Zuleika sat down slowly and looked round the room, at its bookshelves heavy with treatises on Octonions and Invariants and Periodic Functions and Sets of Points and Twisted Cubics, all in massive dark blue bindings; at the mantelpiece with its neat array of pipes and fixture-cards; at the pile of *Proceedings* of the London Mathematical Society on a side table; at the faded Persian hearth-rug and the deep padded chairs on each side of it.

"So you are the Proctor," said Zuleika.

"I am."

"You sent for me. Why do you want me?"

"I wished to have a talk with you."

"And you could not brook delay?"

"Miss Dobson, it was important that I should have an opportunity of speaking to you and, in particular, that I should take the opportunity before five o'clock this afternoon."

"So soon? Do you wish to die for me at five o'clock?"

Mackenzie was irritated. Either the girl was a lunatic or she was trying to make a fool of him. In either case she was wasting time.

"I have no wish," he began, "to enter into unnecessary detail. But as an official of the University responsible for the discipline and good behaviour of undergraduates——"

"Oxford undergraduates behave divinely."

"Outside Cambridge I have no jurisdiction," said Mackenzie a little sharply.

"Has the college ghost walked?" asked Zuleika.

Mackenzie was for a moment thrown out of his official stride. In any other college the question might have been disregarded as a piece of frivolous irrelevance. But the St Benedict's ghost was famous. It was the only one which had crept into the guide-books.

"An ancient college like this accumulates much curious tradition," said Mackenzie, temporising.

"Will it walk at five o'clock?" asked Zuleika, disregarding the generalisation.

"I have never seen it," said Mackenzie curtly.

"And did the black owls perch on the battlements last night, hooting until the dawn?"

Again, Mackenzie was unfortunate. The owls which favoured the elm-trees within the precincts of the college on the opposite side of the street were becoming an intolerable nuisance to light sleepers in St Benedict's. At a recent college meeting Mackenzie had urged that a strong letter of protest should be addressed to the governing body of the offending college.

"May we not return to the subject of our discussion?" he said politely.

"But what is the subject?" asked Zuleika.

"In a word—yourself," said Mackenzie with great suavity.

"At Oxford they did not summon me to discussions. They just died for me. Do *you* wish to die for me—at five o'clock?"

"For that hour, my dear Miss Dobson, I already have a more vital engagement. The Vice-Chancellor has agreed to preside over a special meeting of the Proctorial Syndicate."

"What is the meeting for?"

Mackenzie took up a piece of paper from his writing-table.

"The draft of the terms of reference which I have ventured to propose to the Vice-Chancellor is here. I will read it to you: 'To consider the steps to be taken to meet the situation arising out of the arrival in Cambridge of a stranger alleged to have caused grave disturbance in another university.' That, of course, is a draft and subject to amendment. But it may serve to show that the University is likely to take a serious view."

"But aren't Universities always serious?" asked Zuleika humbly.

"The University has a variety of functions to perform," replied Mackenzie.

"And what does a Syndicate perform?"

"I have no wish to weary you, Miss Dobson, with the detail of academic procedure. But if I can inform the Vice-Chancellor and the Syndicate at five o'clock that you agree with the course I am about to propose——"

"You are about to propose?" repeated Zuleika with wide-open eyes.

"I am about to propose that you should leave Cambridge by the 6.25 train."

"But I have only just arrived."

"My dear Miss Dobson, I will refrain from the obvious retort, which no doubt would have been made in Oxford, of the greater benefit of travelling hopefully. I have no wish to indulge in exaggerated censure, but in my position I am bound to safeguard the University against risk."

"Risk of what?"

"Risk of—er—disturbance of the undergraduate population."

Zuleika was growing weary. The conversation had taken on a staccato quality.

"Are you going to offer me tea?" she enquired.

Momentarily taken aback, Mackenzie made a quick recovery. He had no wide experience of negotiations with females, for, in Edvardian times, ladies did not sit upon Faculty Boards. But he knew that, just as valuable concessions in academic negotiation could be most successfully secured after the port had travelled twice round the table, so, with women, it was necessary to conduct really important business over the tea-cups.

Normally he did not take afternoon tea himself. His gyp did not report to him until 6 o'clock. It would be necessary for him to visit the buttery himself. "But, of course," he said amiably, "excuse me for a moment."

When he reached the buttery, he found the main door locked. He tried the side door to the butler's private room, but the room was empty. Shortly a buttery-boy, only recently engaged, appeared. Mackenzie stated his wants. The boy stated in reply that the buttery staff would "come on" in about ten minutes' time.

"I want tea for two and cakes—in my rooms at once," said Mackenzie.

"What sort of cakes?" asked the boy.

"Oh—the best sort," said Mackenzie.

"I'll tell them," said the boy. It was all he could do. Meanwhile Zuleika sat in Mackenzie's rooms. She was bored. She could not follow very clearly all the talk about Vice-Chancellors and Syndicates and she certainly did not intend to leave by the 6.25. She wanted to learn what Cambridge men were like and poor Mackenzie seemed to her to be not so much a man as a piece of official mechanism. A phrase came into her head. It had been spoken to her in her early days of struggle by an unsympathetic employer: "No good purpose will be served by prolonging this interview." Zuleika felt that it was apt. She went out.

"Find Mr Mackenzie all right, Miss?" said the porter cheerfully.

"Yes, thank you—and lost him."

III

Zuleika stood at the gate of St Benedict's and turned her steps towards the hotel. Then she changed her mind and turned in the opposite direction. The hotel held no attraction for her. Instead, she gazed wonderingly at a Gothic pile which faced her on the opposite side of the street. She was unable to determine whether it was a college or a church. There was no one to tell her that it was just a printing-house.

So she went on and came to a gateway which must surely betoken another college. Was it full of more Mackenzies, she wondered. At that moment a young man came out of the college. He caught sight of Zuleika and stopped. A light of thrilled recognition came into his eye.

"Excuse me," he said, "but aren't you Miss Dobson, Miss Zuleika Dobson?"

Zuleika looked at the young man through her long lashes. Who could he be? Someone who had escaped from Oxford and followed her across? Or had he merely seen her picture in the illustrated papers? If so, his effrontery must be crushed.

"That is my name," she said, "but I do not think I have the pleasure——"

"Oh, of course, you wouldn't remember me. But you might conceivably remember giving a sort of semi-private show at the Jacobean Club at Yale last year. I was living at Yale at the same time and shook hands with you after the show. But of course you don't remember. Why should you?"

"Why should you remember me?"

"Because . . . well, you're Zuleika Dobson and I'm just Desmond Hawkins of Valence Hall."

"Are you a Proctor?"

Hawkins burst into laughter.

"Heavens, no! I've just come back for a fifth year, trying to write a thesis for a fellowship, you know."

But Zuleika didn't know anything about fellowship theses.

"Five years seems a long time," she said, "I haven't been in Cambridge for five hours yet."

"Where are you staying?"

"I'm not sure that I am staying. They want to send me away by the 6.25 train."

"Who wants to?"

"The Syndicate."

"What Syndicate?"

"I don't know," said Zuleika wearily. "I don't know anything about Cambridge. It seems so different from——"

"Yes, I know what you're going to say. It *is* different, I know. But, Miss Dobson, do tell me. There's an absurd rumour going round about everyone at Oxford dying for you. I suppose it's just another Oxford legend written up by some clever journalist. Do tell me about it."

Zuleika looked in some astonishment at the amused, enquiring, and ingenuous countenance of Desmond Hawkins. He was recovering from his initial shyness and was now nearly at his ease. It was evident that he admired her, but it was equally evident that he did not believe in the Oxford stories. He was polite and charming, but he was not prostrate before her.

"Oxford indeed has died for me," she said in the voice of a tragedy-queen, "in Cambridge I am dying for a cup of tea."

Hawkins was startled. Had the fierce afternoon sunshine been too much for Zuleika? Or was she merely thirsty?

"Miss Dobson," he said eagerly, "if you'd really do me the honour of having tea in my rooms, I should be proud, of course, and delighted."

"Lead me to them," said Zuleika.

They went over the cobbles, which Zuleika disliked very much, and turned into a tiny cloister. Hawkins led the way up a narrow staircase and Zuleika followed him. She found herself in an untidy, but cosy room. There were several comfortable chairs. One of them was burdened with a pile of books, another with a tennis racket, another with a pair of flannel trousers, which Hawkins flung hastily into his bedroom.

Zuleika sank into the chair thus disencumbered.

"This is grand," said Hawkins.

Whatever other qualities the scene might hold, Zuleika felt that the element of grandeur was lacking.

"What is grand?" she murmured.

"Why, being able to persuade you to come and have tea with me like this."

"Like what?"

"Well, informally and . . . (Hawkins blushed slightly) alone."

"Then you are not afraid?"

"Afraid? Oh, you're harking back to that Oxford rumour? No, I'm sorry, Miss Dobson, but candidly I don't feel a bit like dying. I'd much rather go on living and——"

"And——?" Zuleika's lips were parted.

"And get you some tea."

Zuleika sank back into the chair.

"That," she said, "would be a very admirable thing to do."

Hawkins began operations upon his Primus stove. It was, fortunately, in good order.

"If you don't mind waiting half a minute, I'll just pop across to the buttery and get something to eat."

For the second time in half an hour Zuleika was left alone in college rooms. This time she had no desire to escape. Her host offered little of excitement or romance, but at least he did not talk gibberish about syndicates and terms of reference.

Hawkins re-appeared in a few minutes. He had given some quite precise orders about the food to be sent to his rooms. In particular he had made certain that the toast should be what was known in the college as "fellows' toast," neat little crustless triangles with just the right amount of butter evenly spread, not the solid slabs moistened in the middle which were commonly served to undergraduates. Also he made a point of ordering a few slices of lemon.

"Ah, the kettle is nearly boiling," he said cheerfully. "As it happens, I have some China tea. You'd prefer that, wouldn't you?"

"Yes, I think I should."

"And you also prefer a slice of lemon to milk?"

"Yes. Don't you?"

"No, I can't stand it, but I felt sure you would."

"Why?"

"Well, you're that sort."

"What sort?"

"Well, shall we say, a little . . . exotic?"

"And what precisely does the word 'exotic' signify?"

"Oh, I say, you mustn't press me too hard. Anyhow, it's the opposite of 'dowdy.'"

"I am relieved," said Zuleika, "to find that I am not dowdy."

The kettle boiled, Hawkins made the tea, and a buttery-boy entered with a number of dishes.

"What will you have to eat? Toast?" asked Hawkins.

"A tiny piece," said Zuleika. But in fact she ate four.

"How about a sandwich now?" said Hawkins.

"A sandwich?" cried Zuleika, visualising the crude layers of ham dear to masculine appetite.

"Oh, come," said Hawkins, "these are really rather tasty." He held before her a plate of diminutive confections at the heart of which was Gentleman's Relish or, alternatively, *pâté de foie gras.*

"Or there are these little things if you prefer them," Hawkins went on, indicating coffee éclairs of small size but agreeable texture.

Zuleika made a triple surrender.

"To take tea with you, Mr. Hawkins," she said, "is an agreeable experience, but to repeat it would be to ruin my figure."

"I don't believe it, Miss Dobson–, I mean about your figure. But it's been wonderful to be able to entertain you for a few minutes like this."

Zuleika rose.

"Can I escort you anywhere, Miss Dobson? I expect you may want to rest a bit. No doubt you have a lot of engagements here."

"I know no one in Cambridge," said Zuleika.

"No one? Then why——"

"Why indeed did I come to Cambridge? Yes, you are entitled to ask that. They did wonderful things for me in Oxford, but in retrospect I cannot help feeling that they overdid them. The art of dying for me ceased, I fear, to be an art. It degenerated into a stampede. Nothing, as they say in Oxford, impedes like excess."

"D'you really mean, Miss Dobson, that you're free of engagements for this evening, for instance?"

"I am free of everything except my memories," said Zuleika. "Up to now I have looked forward always, but now there is nothing left but retrospect."

"Then, if it isn't too bold on my part to suggest it, would you care to dine with me?"

"Here?" asked Zuleika.

"Well, no. You see, my rooms are not really large enough for a party, but to-night, as it happens, Duxberry (one of the younger dons here) and his wife and a few others are dining with me in the Guest Room and after dinner we're going to move across to another man's rooms. Quite a friendly and informal affair. No fuss. It would be wonderful if you could join us."

Zuleika looked across at Hawkins. His enthusiasm was obvious, but it was the enthusiasm of youth in anticipation of a good lark. She reflected quietly which frock in her wardrobe would most suitably accord with the atmosphere of "no fuss." The dove-grey, perhaps? Or should she heighten the effect by wearing the flame-coloured dress with . . . ? But suddenly she realised that she was choosing her dress before she had decided whether to accept the invitation.

"But your party, surely, is made up?" she temporised.

"It *was*. But it will be eternally incomplete unless——"

"I will come," said Zuleika.

IV

When Mackenzie returned to his rooms and found them empty, he was annoyed. He could not really believe that Zuleika was prowling round his bedroom, but he looked in to make sure and came to the conclusion, quite correctly, that Zuleika had quietly given him the slip. He hurried down to the porter's lodge.

"Has a lady just left the college, Barnicott?"

"Yes, Sir."

"Which way did she go?"

"Went along to the right, Sir."

For a moment Mackenzie thought of dashing off in pursuit, since it seemed clear that Zuleika had returned to her hotel. But he noted a rather curious look on the porter's face and refrained.

"Anything I can do, Sir?"

"Not at present, thank you, Barnicott. I may want to send a message later."

"Very good, Sir."

On his way back to his rooms Mackenzie remembered to cancel his order at the buttery.

It would, he reflected, be undignified to pursue Zuleika at the moment. Her disappearance suggested either that she was frightened or that she was up to some mischief. He confessed to himself that he thought the latter alternative more probable. However, he had at any rate succeeded in interviewing her and in giving her warning; he would be in a reasonably strong position at the meeting of the Proctorial Syndicate.

The Vice-Chancellor took the chair punctually, but with an air of mild grievance, at five o'clock.

He must apologise, he said, for summoning a meeting of the Syndicate at such an unusual time and at such short notice. But circumstances of a peculiar nature had arisen which had given rise to grave apprehension in the mind of the Senior Proctor. Such apprehensions were due to reports, not at present wholly substantiated, of events of a somewhat alarming character which had occurred, or were alleged to have occurred, within the precincts of the sister university. In thus adumbrating the general situation the last thing he would wish to do would be to prejudge, in any particular, the issues which lay before the Syndicate. He would therefore call upon the Senior Proctor.

The Senior Proctor bowed slightly to the Vice-Chancellor and cleared his throat. He had no wish to take up the time of the Syndicate and would be as brief as possible. Information had reached him in the course of the morning concerning the recent visit of a Miss Zuleika Dobson to the University of Oxford—a lady rumoured, though he could with difficulty credit the rumour, to be closely related to one of the best known and most widely esteemed Heads of Houses in that university. Detailed reports, as the Vice-Chancellor had observed, were not at present forthcoming, but on the evidence available it appeared that the lady's influence among the junior members of the university had been of the most extraordinary and devastating character. After every allowance had been made for journalistic exaggeration it appeared tolerably certain that not a few undergraduate members of Oxford colleges, following the lead of a somewhat eccentric nobleman, had deliberately drowned themselves on account of this young woman.

"Don't believe a word of it!" interrupted Simpkins, a young classical don from Jesus, who was coaching one of his college boats and resented being dragged to the meeting at a most inconvenient hour.

Mackenzie, continuing, recognised that such an attitude of hasty incredulity could well be understood, but suggested that Mr Simpkins might suitably suspend judgment for the moment. The Syndicate, indeed, might feel at this point that however deeply they might commiserate with the sister university in her misfortune, the matter was officially no concern of theirs (*Hear, hear*). Unfortunately, it was impossible for the University to take up such a position of detachment.

Mackenzie paused. The Syndicate was listening to him now.

"I regret to have to inform the Syndicate," he concluded, "that the young lady in question is now in our midst."

"How do you know?" blurted Simpkins.

Mackenzie played his trump card.

"Because I interviewed her in my rooms two hours ago."

"Then why——" Simpkins began.

The Vice-Chancellor interposed.

"I am sure the Syndicate and indeed the University will be most grateful to the Senior Proctor for the great care and promptitude which he has shown in approaching this difficult problem. As to any further course of action to be followed, I am of course in the hands of the Syndicate."

"Could we be informed, Mr Vice-Chancellor, of our precise terms of reference?" asked the Vice-Master of Emmanuel.

The Vice-Chancellor looked a little perplexed, but Mackenzie promptly handed him a slip of paper.

"It is suggested," said the Vice-Chancellor, "that our business might be summarised in the following terms: 'To consider the steps to be taken to meet the situation arising out of the arrival in Cambridge of a stranger alleged to have caused grave disturbance in another university.' "

"Could the Senior Proctor tell us where the stranger is now?" asked Simpkins.

Mackenzie looked a little uncomfortable.

"She is staying at a hotel not far from my own college," he replied.

"Is she there now?"

"I believe so."

"Mr Vice-Chancellor," said Simpkins, "may we have this point cleared up a little? We know that two hours ago the lady was in the Senior Proctor's rooms. But where is she now? For all we know, while we are talking, she may be submerging freshmen right and left!"

"Mr Simpkins, please," said the Vice-Chancellor reproachfully.

"I have already made it clear," said Mackenzie, "that the lady is in all probability in her hotel."

"Probabilities," said the Junior Proctor, a logician from Sidney Sussex, "seem to be an unsatisfactory basis for a policy of action. But, assuming for the moment that the Proctors are successful in getting hold of the lady, may I enquire what we are to do with her?"

"Put her into the train for Liverpool Street," said Mackenzie.

"Under what Ordinance?" asked the Registrary, who had attended the meeting at the Vice-Chancellor's request.

"Surely the Proctors have summary powers in dealing with certain kinds of women?" said Mackenzie.

"This seems to be an uncertain kind," replied the Registrary tonelessly.

"Aren't we beating about the bush?" interposed Simpkins. "What I want to know is this: is the woman a bad lot or not?"

The Vice-Chancellor coughed.

"Perhaps," he said wanly, "the Senior Proctor would . . ." His voice faded.

"I really cannot undertake to give a categorical answer to Mr Simpkins' question," said Mackenzie.

"But you have talked to her in your own rooms, alone, haven't you?" retorted Simpkins.

Doctor Blenkinsop, Maitland Professor of Civil Law, spoke for the first time:

"With respect, Mr Vice-Chancellor, I venture to think the discussion has strayed a little from the main issue. While I would not suggest that the character of the lady is wholly irrelevant to the argument, it appears to me that there are two main questions to be determined: first, whether it is desirable that action should be taken to remove the lady from the precincts; and secondly, if the desirability of such action should be established, under what authority it should be taken. It is clearly not a case, in my submission, for the Sex Viri or for the Court of Discipline and, as at present advised, I should hesitate to subscribe to the view that the Proctors have any right of summary jurisdiction in such a case."

The Vice-Master of Emmanuel said that everything Professor Blenkinsop had said ought to be very carefully weighed. For his own part he was beginning to doubt whether the question before them could be satisfactorily examined by a body like the present Syndicate and, notwithstanding the very natural desire of the responsible officials to proceed without undue delay, he could not help wondering whether the most satisfactory course might not be the appointment of a small committee.

"A committee of this Syndicate or a body appointed *ad hoc?*" asked the Registrary.

"*Ad hoc* and *de novo,* I suggest," replied the Vice-Master, though he was at pains to add that he had not fully thought out the most appropriate constitution for the suggested committee.

"Mr Vice-Chancellor," said Greville of Trinity, who was sitting next to Simpkins and had had much whispered conversation with him, "may I with great respect enquire whether we are really getting anywhere?"

"I had understood," replied the Vice-Chancellor, "though of course I am open to correction by the Syndicate, I had understood that the Vice-Master of Emmanuel desired to formulate a motion. If such a motion should be seconded, perhaps Professor Blenkinsop might find it convenient to express his views in the form of an amendment."

But the Professor was understood to reply that, on reconsideration, he felt that, as major questions of academic policy might now be involved, it would be better to refer the whole question to the Council of the Senate.

"Mr Vice-Chancellor," Simpkins broke in, "if this matter is really urgent, can't we *do* something instead of just talking about committees?"

"Do I now understand," asked the Vice-Chancellor plaintively, "that the Vice-Master of Emmanuel's motion is not seconded?"

"In view of the turn the discussion has taken," replied the Vice-Master, "I am hardly prepared to make a formal motion."

"In that case," said Simpkins, "I beg to move that as the Senior Proctor has apparently caught the lady once and then let her slip through his fingers, he had better try again, with the aid of his bulldogs if necessary, and then tell us more about it."

"I second that," said Greville quickly.

"Mr Simpkins moves, and Mr Greville seconds, that— Perhaps the Registrary will give us the exact wording."

The Registrary read from his notes:

"That the Senior Proctor be requested to take immediate steps to gain further information, at first-hand, of a certain visitor; and to report to the Syndicate thereon."

"May I ask for a show of hands?" said the Vice-Chancellor.

Three hands went up.

"Those against?"

No hands were raised.

"Hardly a majority of the Syndicate, I am afraid," said the Vice-Chancellor sadly, "but nevertheless *nemine contradicente*. No doubt the Senior Proctor is now fully seized of the sense of the meeting, and I feel sure that he will very kindly undertake to report to us in due course. The Syndicate will adjourn."

V

Zuleika's hansom drew up at the front gate of Valence Hall. Mélisande was with her, carrying a pair of goloshes (or, more accurately, overshoes) that had been a gift from a Rubber King after her final performance in Milwaukee. They were lined with swan's down and bore Zuleika's initials studded in diamonds. Mélisande slipped them over her mistress's shoes and accompanied her over the cobblestones to the foot of the staircase which led to the Guest Room.

After much reflection Zuleika had decided to wear a dress of deep wine-colour. It clung closely to her lithe figure and was wholly lacking in trimming or ornament. Amongst the May Term muslins its rich and sombre plainness produced a startling effect. Zuleika wore no jewelry save a snake-bracelet with deep ruby eyes. (It had been a parting tribute from the Maharajah of Kurrigalore.)

Hawkins greeted Zuleika with an air of subdued excitement, and introduced his other guests—Duxberry and his wife, Davidson (an undergraduate) and his sister, and a Newnham history don.

"I'll be frank with you, Miss Dobson," he said. "I had to get a man in a great hurry to make the party even. He's a bit late, I'm afraid, but he's coming all right."

Zuleika was not pleased. She had deliberately ordered her cab ten minutes late; she took no pleasure in making a penultimate entrance.

"Mr Simpkins, Sir," announced the gyp at the doorway.

"Ah, Simmy," said Hawkins, "that's splendid."

"Sorry I'm so late," said Simpkins, "but I've had to waste hours at a ridiculous meeting about some woman who's supposed to have——"

"May I introduce Miss Dobson," said Hawkins, quickly.

Simpkins gasped.

"Miss Zuleika Dobson?" he asked.

"Is it so strange a name?" said Zuleika.

"No, no. Not strange exactly. Just a little—what shall I say—coincidental."

They sat down. Zuleika was, of course, on the right of her host; on the other side of her was Simpkins. Inevitably Zuleika compared the scene in her mind's eye with her initial entertainment by the Warden of Judas. How different was the familiar gaiety of this party round the oval table from the superb and icy neglect with which the Duke had treated her at that first meeting. This was a party *sans cérémonie,* but, as the dinner progressed, Zuleika noted with satisfaction that there was no nonsense about "pot luck": the *vol-au-vent financière* was exquisite and the *crème brûlée* was something new in Zuleika's culinary experience.

Hawkins did not say much to Zuleika. In the first place he was conscious of his obligation to Mrs Duxberry whose chaperonage had facilitated the making of the party; also, the cares of the host were upon him and on this evening he felt that he had incurred no ordinary responsibilities. Further, he had a slight feeling of guilt, since, but for Zuleika's irruption, he would have had next to him Davidson's pretty sister. Zuleika, no doubt, would have been quick to observe something of this, had she not been continuously engaged in conversation by Simpkins.

Simpkins knew little more of Zuleika than what he had heard at the meeting of the Proctorial Syndicate; but this party was going to be the best joke of the term for him.

"D'you know Cambridge well, Miss Dobson?" he asked innocently.

"Can one know a place well in a few hours?"

"Hardly, perhaps. But people are more interesting than places, don't you think?"

"I am weary of both," said Zuleika, mournfully.

"Oh, come, Miss Dobson, don't judge us too hastily. People take their colour from places to some extent, I admit. In Oxford, for instance, a party like this might look very much the same at first glance, but in fact the people would be fundamentally different."

"I agree," said Zuleika, coldly.

"Oh, you know Oxford?" said Simpkins.

Hawkins had caught a little of this and broke in:

"You're barking up the wrong tree, Simmy. You can't teach Miss Dobson anything about Oxford."

The other little conversations round the table broke off. Simpkins was about to retort, but Duxberry slipped in a word from the end of the table.

"I hope," he said gallantly, "that we shan't try to teach Miss Dobson anything."

"The Warden of Judas is your grandfather, is he not, Miss Dobson?" said the Newnham don.

"He is," said Zuleika.

"A charming old gentleman, I believe," said Mrs Duxberry. "My brother-in-law stayed with him last term when he was preaching the University Sermon."

Simpkins was enjoying his second glass of Ruppertsberger.

"I daresay my conversational gambits are clumsy enough," he said, "but of course we all know that having devastated Oxford, Miss Dobson is now rapidly making us her slaves in Cambridge."

"Do you know the Senior Proctor?" asked Zuleika.

Simpkins laughed.

"Poor old Mac," he said. "Yes, you've captivated him."

"But he didn't seem to like me at all," said Zuleika. "He wanted to send me to Liverpool Street."

"He might at least have chosen King's Cross," said the Newnham don.

"Miss Dobson," said Hawkins, "I think what Mr Simpkins is trying to say is that we're all delighted to have you with us in Cambridge."

"I can say it much better than that," said Simpkins. "I'll give you a toast. The divine Zuleika and may we all live for ever to do her honour!"

The toast was drunk and they moved across to Davidson's rooms. To sit down in re-arranged pairs seemed something of an anti-climax.

"What do we do now?" said Simpkins, irrepressibly. "Sing? Dance? Play Consequences? Have you any parlour-tricks, Miss Dobson?"

For a moment Zuleika suspected a further attempt at leg-pulling. Furious, she gazed at Simpkins. Simpkins felt that he had never seen anyone half so beautiful. He even blushed, but Zuleika perceived that it was not a blush of shame. He was, in fact, unaware of Zuleika's professional activities and Zuleika, as she noted his rubicund adoration, knew that she had nothing to forgive. Why, after all, should she worry overmuch about young men dying for her if there were others with whom she could enjoy herself? Surprised, she heard herself saying:

"Let's play charades."

"Splendid," said Hawkins, much relieved.

"We're not a very large party," said Mrs Duxberry. "All you young people must act and Frank and I will be the audience."

The Newnham don brightened a little at this and they trooped into Davidson's bedroom.

The usual Babel of murmurs about the choice of word arose. Simpkins cut the discussion short.

"Of course, there's only one possible word—Zu–leika!"

"Two syllables or three?" asked Hawkins.

"Oh, don't bother about details now. Let's find some costumes."

Davidson's wardrobe was ransacked.

"Now, for the first syllable——" Simpkins began.

Heavy footsteps were heard and then a knock at the door.

"You can't come in here. We're dressing up," shouted Simpkins.

"Is Mr Hawkins there?" said a voice.

Hawkins opened the door and found himself facing the college porter.

"I'm sorry to disturb your party, Sir, but the Proctor's down below. He wants to know if there's a Miss Dobson with you."

Hawkins looked embarrassed.

"Tell him to come up," said Simpkins, "tell him he's just in time for the fun, tell him he can choose what part he likes, tell him——"

"Very good, Sir," said the porter.

Mackenzie arrived.

"Hello, Mac," cried Simpkins, "you're just in time for a little green room gossip. Come and help me to dress as the King of Beasts."

Mackenzie blinked.

"I wish to see a Mr Hawkins," he said.

"No, you don't, Mac," said Simpkins. "What you've come for is to renew your acquaintance with Miss Dobson. Here she is, Mac, divinely beautiful and divinely ready to forgive you."

"Really," began Mackenzie, "I have no wish to intrude upon a private gathering, but in accordance with the Vice-Chancellor's instructions I am obliged to——"

"Don't worry, Mac. You've nothing to do. I've made all the further enquiries myself. Now you go into the next room and help to swell the audience."

Mackenzie stared helplessly at the group of half-dressed figures. Hawkins came forward.

"Yes, do go in, Sir. You'll find Mr and Mrs Duxberry there."

So Mackenzie found himself talking politely to Mrs Duxberry about his plans for the Long Vacation and the vacant professorship of Hebrew and the forthcoming concert of the Fugue Society and other seasonable topics. In a few minutes they were watching the First Scene of the charade in which an August Personage, attended by her suite, was conducted round the Zoo to see a newly-arrived lion of great ferocity; the Second Scene in which the same Personage from a stand at Ditton Corner witnessed the sinking of a clinker four (it sank because it was a "leaker"); and the Final Scene in which the Personage, seated on an improvised throne and wearing an improvised crown, received the homage of her faithful subjects. Duxberry and his wife applauded in rapture, and Mackenzie clapped uncomfortably.

"I think perhaps," he said, "that I had better be going now. It is clearly not an appropriate time for the discussion of official business."

"Of course it isn't," said Simpkins. *"Dulce est desipere,* Mac, and we're certainly *in loco* to-night."

"I'm glad we didn't have to play the charade in Latin," said Zuleika to Mrs Duxberry.

"Ah, these classical dons," said Mrs Duxberry indulgently, "it's second nature to them, I suppose."

"Well, second nature's better than original sin," retorted Simpkins. "Don't you think so, Miss Dobson?"

"I prefer Art to both," said Zuleika.

"I'm bound to say that I agree with Miss Dobson," said Mackenzie unexpectedly.

"Of course you do, Mac," said Simpkins. "Miss Dobson," he went on, turning to Zuleika, "we have an institution in Cambridge known as May Week. As many commentators have explained, it isn't exactly a week and it isn't in May, but it can be quite pleasant. Concerts, you know, and balls and boat-races and——"

"I know," said Zuleika quietly.

"Well, a sister-in-law of mine is bringing a few friends this year to be my guests. Couldn't I induce you to join us?"

Zuleika pondered. She had to confess to herself that the evening had been enjoyable, though she did not quite know why. To be admired and adored by men was nothing new to her; but Cambridge men gave no sign of wanting to lie down and die for love of her. Instead, they stood about and made harmless jokes. Zuleika still knew what she liked; and she was growing a little tired of innocent fun.

"Who'll have some Moselle cup?" said Hawkins, from the other end of the room.

"All of us," shouted Simpkins, "except Mackenzie. He'd prefer a whiskey and soda."

"Simpkins," said Mackenzie, embarrassed, "you might at least let me state my own preferences."

"Certainly, Mac. Just tell Miss Dobson how much you'd prefer it if she came up for May Week."

"Of course," said Mackenzie, still more confused, "but it's hardly for me to . . ."

Zuleika came to his rescue.

"Thank you," she said slowly. "It has certainly been interesting to learn something of Cambridge. But Mr Mackenzie need have no fear; I should not dream of bringing fresh embarrassment upon his Syndicate."

The Struggle for North America

BY ARNOLD J. TOYNBEE

THE CLASSIC illustration of our present theme in our Western history is the outcome of the competition between half a dozen different groups of Western colonists for the mastery of North America. The victors in this contest were the New Englanders; and at an earlier point in this chapter, * apropos of the reversion of Town Hill, Connecticut, to its pristine state of Nature, we have taken note of the unusual difficulty of the local American environment which first fell to the lot of the ultimate masters of the whole continent. Let us now compare this New England environment, of which the site of Town Hill is a specimen, with the earliest American environments of the New Englanders' unsuccessful competitors: the Dutch, the French, the Spaniards, and the New Englanders' own kinsmen and neighbours from England who established themselves along the southern section of the Atlantic seaboard.

In the middle of the seventeenth century of the Christian Era, when all these settlers had already found their first footing on the fringes of the North American mainland, it would have been quite easy to predict the coming conflict between them for the possession of the interior; but the most acute and far-sighted observer then alive would hardly have been likely to hit the mark if he had been asked, at the time, to designate the ultimate victor. He might conceivably have had the acumen to rule out the Spaniards in spite of their two obvious assets: their ownership, in Mexico, of the only region in or adjoining North America which had been broken-in and developed economically, before the European colonists' arrival, by an indigenous civilization; and the primacy of Spain, in our hypothetical observer's own day, among the Great Powers of the Western World. Our observer might have discounted the high development of Mexico in view of its outlying position—cut off, as it was, from

---

* Reference is to earlier pages of *A Study of History* [editor's note].

the main body of North America by a broad belt of inhospitable plateau and desert; and have discounted the political strength of Spain by reading the political signs of the times as they were written between the lines of the Treaty of Westphalia.

'The Spanish Empire', he might have pronounced, 'is already a carcass round which the vultures are gathering. France will succeed to the military hegemony of Spain in Europe, Holland and England will succeed to her naval and commercial supremacy on the seas. The competition for North America lies now between these three countries. Let us estimate their respective chances in the double light of their general positions in the World and of their local holdings in America. On a short view, Holland's chances might appear to be the most promising. She is mistress of the seas (England being no match for her on this element, and France not seriously competing); and in America she holds a splendid water-gate opening into the interior: the valley of the Hudson. On a longer view, however, France seems more likely to be the winner; for the French St. Lawrence offers still better means of access to the interior of North America than the Dutch Hudson, while it is in the power of the French to immobilize and exhaust the Dutch by bringing to bear against them the overwhelming military superiority of France on the Continent of Europe. All the same, as between French and Dutch prospects, I hesitate' (we hear him saying) 'to decide. The one prophecy that I make with confidence is that the English are not in the running. Possibly the more southerly of the English colonies, with their relatively genial soil and climate, will manage to survive—though at best they will find themselves hemmed in between the Dutch along the Hudson in the north and the Spaniards in Florida on the south and the Dutch or the French, whichever it may be that cuts off their hinterland on the west by securing the control of the Mississippi. One thing, however, is certain. The little group of settlements in the bleak and barren country which the colonists have christened "New England" is bound to disappear. They are cut off from the other English settlements by the Dutch in the Hudson Valley, while the French in the St. Lawrence Valley press them close on the opposite flank. The destinies of these New Englanders, at any rate, are not in doubt!'

Let us now suppose that our hypothetical observer lives to see the turn of the century. By the year 1701 he will be congratulating himself on his discernment, fifty years earlier, in rating French prospects higher than Dutch; for in the course of these last fifty years the St. Lawrence has vanquished the Hudson. The French explorers have pushed up the St. Lawrence on to the Great Lakes, and over the portage into the Basin of the Mississippi, and down these Western Waters to the delta of the great river, where they have established the new French colony of Louisiana to match the older French colony of Canada at the other end of the trans-continental waterway. As for the Dutch, our observer must admit that he had rated their prospects much too high. They might have made themselves masters of the Great Lakes before the French arrived there. Indeed, for the ocean-going vessels of the century, the head of navigation was rather less distant up the Hudson than it was up the St. Lawrence from the shores of Lake Ontario. Yet, far from that, the Dutch have tamely allowed the Hudson Valley itself to be taken from them by their weaker maritime rivals the English. Well, the Dutch are out of the running now in North America, and the French and the English are left there *tête à tête;* but the English can hardly be regarded as serious competitors. The events of the last half-century assuredly do not call for any revision of forecasts on this head—notwithstanding the unlooked-for success which the English have gained in the Hudson Valley. Certainly the New Englanders are making the most of this windfall. Already they are colonizing the back-country of the Dutch province and are linking New England up with the rest of the English settlements on the Atlantic coast. Possibly the New Englanders have been saved from extinction—but this only to share the modest prospects of their southern kinsfolk. For the English feat of conquering the Hudson Valley from the facile Dutch has been utterly surpassed by the simultaneous French feat of conquering from the formidable virgin wilderness the whole extent of the magnificent inland waterway between Quebec and New Orleans. While the English colonies have been consolidated, the French colonies have effectively hemmed them in. The future of the Continent is decided! The victors are the French!

Shall we endow our observer with superhuman length of life, in order that he may review the situation once more in the year 1803? If we do preserve him alive till then, he will be forced to confess that his wits have not been worthy of his longevity. By the end of 1803, the French flag has actually disappeared off the political map of North America altogether. For forty years past, Canada has been a possession of the British Crown, while Louisiana, after being ceded by France to Spain and retroceded again, has just been sold on the 20th December, 1803, by Napoleon to the United States—the new Great Power which has emerged out of the thirteen English colonies by a most extraordinary metamorphosis.

'The United States of America!' Who would have prophesied it? Yet the ambitious title is justified by the accomplished facts. In this year 1803, the United States have the continent in their pockets, and the scope for prophecy is reduced. It only remains to forecast which section of these United States is going to pocket the larger share of this vast estate—the breadth of a continent—that has come into their joint possession. And surely this time there can be no mistake? The Southern States are the manifest masters of the Union and residuary legatees in North America of Great Britain and France. Look how the Southerners are leading in this final round of the competition—in this inter-American race for the Winning of the West. It is the backwoodsmen of Virginia who have founded Kentucky—the first new state to be established west of those mountains which have so long conspired with the French to keep the English-speaking settlers on the Atlantic coast from penetrating into the interior. And take note of the key-position which Kentucky occupies, extending right down the left bank of the Ohio to the confluence of the Mississippi's principal tributary with the Mississippi himself. The West is in the Southerners' grasp, and mark how all things work together for their good. The statesmanship of an English Chatham and a Pennsylvanian Franklin and a Corsican Buonaparte has endowed them with an immeasurable supply of land; and, as fast as they can put this new land under the hoe, the new-fangled mills of distant Lancashire are offering them an ever-expanding market for the cotton-crop which the soil and climate of the South enable them to raise. The Negro provides the labour and the Mississippi the means of transporting the produce to the quays of New Orleans, where the ships from Liverpool are waiting to bear it away. Even the New Englander is a useful auxiliary, as the Southerner superciliously points out.

'Our Yankee cousin,' the Southerner observes in 1807, 'has just invented a "steam-boat" which will navigate our Mississippi upstream; and he has made a practical success of a machine for carding and cleaning our cotton-bolls. Those unlovable, unfortunate fellow-citizens of ours in that out-of-the-way corner, down east! Their "Yankee notions" are more profitable to us than they are to the ingenious inventors! For what are New England's prospects? Her prospects are no better in this year 1807 than they were a century since. To-day, when the wide West has been thrown open to Southern enterprise at last, it still remains closed to the New Englander. New England is still barred in on the landward side by the barrier of Canada, which has not ceased to be a foreign country in passing from the French to the British Crown. So there our poor relation still sits in his out-of-the-way corner, cooped up on the "bad lands" of Town Hill; and there, presumably, he will go on sitting till Doomsday! "Sedet, aeternumque sedebit!" ' *

If our unlucky prophet takes Southern prospects on the morrow of the Louisiana Purchase at the Southerner's own valuation, he must indeed be in his dotage; for in the last round of the two-centuries-long contest for the mastery of the North American Continent, the Southerner is destined to meet a swifter and more crushing defeat than those that have been met heretofore by the Spaniard and the Dutchman and the Frenchman. To witness his discomfiture, we shall not have to wait as long as a century. We shall see the relative positions of South and North reversed in less than a lifetime.

In the year 1865, the situation is already transformed, out of all recognition, from what it was in 1807. In the Winning of the West, the Southern pioneer had been outstripped and outflanked by his Northern rival. After almost winning his way to the Great Lakes through Indiana and after getting the best of the bargain in Missouri, the Southerner has been decisively defeated in Kansas, and he has never reached the Pacific. The descendants of the men who mastered the difficulties of Town Hill, Connecticut, have now become masters of the Pacific coast along the whole front from Seattle to Los Angeles. Nor has the Southerner's command of the Mississippi much availed him. He had counted on the network of the Western Waters to draw the whole of the West into a Southern system of economic and political relations; and when the Yankee presented him with steam-boats to ply on the Western Waters, he imagined that the Yankee had delivered the West into his hands. But 'Yankee notions' have not ceased. The inventor of the steamer has gone on to invent the locomotive; and the locomotive has taken away more from the Southerner than the steamer ever gave him; for the potential function of the Hudson Valley in the human geography of North America as the main gateway from the Atlantic to the West—a potentiality which the Dutch had failed to turn to account in competition with the French—has been actualized at last in the railway age. The railway-traffic which now passes up the valley of the Hudson and the valley of the Mohawk and then along the lake-side to link New York with Chicago has superseded the river-traffic on the Mississippi between New Orleans and St. Louis. Therewith, the internal lines of communication of the North American Continent have been turned at right angles from south and north to east and west;

* Virgil: *Aeneid,* Book VI, 1. 617.

and the North-West has been detached from the South, to be welded on to the North-East in interest and in sentiment. Indeed, the Easterner, who once made the South-West a present of the river-steamer, has now won the heart of the North-West with a double gift: he has come to the North-Western farmer with the locomotive in one hand and with the reaper-and-binder in the other, and so has provided him with solutions for both the problems with which the West is confronted. In order to develop its potential economic capacities, the whole West has need of two things: transport and labour; but the South-Western planter—believing that his labour-problem has been solved for ever by the institution of Negro slavery—has sought a solution for his transport-problem, and for this only, from the Yankee's mechanical ingenuity. The North-Western farmer is in a different case. He disposes of no servile man-power, and his free-labour force is recruited by the casual process of immigration from Europe all too slowly to till his fast-expanding fields. So he finds the agricultural machinery which is turned out by the Eastern factories as great a godsend as the Eastern railways. By these two 'Yankee notions', together, the allegiance of the North-West has been decided; and thus the Civil War has been lost by the South before it has been fought. In taking up arms in the hope of redressing her economic reverses by a military counterstroke, the South has merely precipitated and consummated a *débâcle* that was already inevitable.

This ultimate victory of the New Englanders, in a competition for the mastery of North America in which their Spanish, Dutch, French, and Southern competitors were successively discomfited, is illuminating for the study of the question with which we are concerned at the moment: the question of the relative stimulating effects of different degrees of difficulty in the physical environment of human life. For, unusually difficult though the New Englanders' environment was, it is manifest that the rival colonists' environments were none of them easy. To begin with, all alike had undergone the initial ordeal of plucking up their social roots in Europe and crossing the Atlantic and striking fresh roots in the soil of a New World; and, when they had succeeded in re-establishing themselves, it was not only the New Englanders who found permanent difficulties to contend with in their new American home. The French settlers in Canada had to contend with an almost arctic cold; and the French settlers in Louisiana had to break in a great river. The Mississippi was as wayward in changing his course, and as devastating in his inundations, as the Yellow River or the Nile or the Tigris; and the *levées* with which the Creoles protected their hard-won fields and villages cost no less human effort to build and maintain than the earthen bulwarks of the Egyptiac and the Sumeric and the Sinic Civilization. In fact, the difficulties presented by the physical environment in Canada and in Louisiana were only less formidable than those which the New Englanders encountered on Town Hill itself. Thus this North American illustration, as far as it goes, tells in favour of the proposition that the difficulty and the stimulus of an environment are apt to increase *pari passu*. It will tell the same tale if we push it even farther.

Can we push it farther? Can we venture, in 1933, to prophesy in whose hands the mastery of North America will lie a century hence? Can we hope to come any nearer to the mark ourselves than our imaginary prophet in 1650 and 1701 and 1803? Can we do more than ring down the curtain on the present scene, in which the offspring of the New Englanders dominates the stage? Difficult though divination may be, there are already certain signs that the drama is not yet played out and the final victory in the struggle not yet decided. One small sign once came to the notice of the author of this Study.

A few days after the occasion, mentioned above,* when I passed by the deserted site of Town Hill, Connecticut, I found myself with an hour to spend between trains in one of the small back-country manufacturing towns of New England, on the Massachusetts side of the Connecticut-Massachusetts state-line. Since the General War of 1914–18, the industrial districts of New England have fared as badly as those of the mother country. They have fallen on evil days, and they show it in their aspect. In this town, however, on this day, the atmosphere was not at all forlorn or lifeless. The town was in fête, and the whole population was abroad in the streets. Threading my way through the crowds I noticed that one person out of every two was wearing a special badge, and I inquired what the colours signified. I was told that they were the colours of the local French Canadian club; and I ascertained that my rough impression of their frequency in the streets was borne out by statistics. In that year 1925, in that New England manufacturing town, the French Canadians were by far the strongest contingent in the local labour-force. The indigenous New Englanders had left these factories, as they had left the fields of Town Hill, to find their fortunes in the West; but the town, unlike the village, had not been deserted. As

* Reference is to earlier pages of *A Study of History* [editor's note].

fast as the indigenous population had ebbed out, a tide of French Canadian immigrants had flooded in. Conditions of work and life which had ceased to be attractive to the descendants of the Pilgrim Fathers seemed luxurious to these Norman peasants' children from the sub-arctic hinterland of Quebec. Moreover, I was told, the French Canadian immigrants were spreading from the towns of New England on to the land, where, as peasants, they found themselves truly at home. On their frugal standard of living, American rates of industrial wages left them with a surplus which quickly mounted up to the purchase-price of a derelict New England farm. The immigrants were actually re-populating the deserted countryside. Perhaps, on my next visit, I should find Town Hill itself no longer desolate. Yet if, on that forbidding spot, the works of Man overcame the wilderness for the second time, it could be foreseen that history would repeat itself with a difference. The fields and orchards and even the houses might wear again in 1950 the aspect which they had worn two centuries before; but this time the blood in the veins of the farmers would be French and not English, and divine worship in the antique wooden church would be conducted no longer by a Presbyterian minister but by a Catholic priest!

Thus it seems possible that the contest between the French Canadian and the New Englander for the mastery of North America may not, after all, have been concluded and disposed of finally by the outcome of the Seven Years' War. For, when the French flag was hauled down, the French peasant did not disappear with the emblem of the French Government's sovereignty. Under the tutelage of the Roman Catholic Church, this peasantry continued, undisturbed, to be fruitful and multiply and replenish the Earth; and now in the fullness of time the French Canadian is making a counter-offensive into the heart of his old rival's homeland. He is conquering New England in the peasant's way—by slower but surer methods than those which Governments have at their command. He is conducting his operations with the ploughshare and not with the sword, and he is asserting his ownership by the positive act of colonizing the countryside and not by the cartographical conceit of painting colours and drawing lines on a scrap of paper. Meanwhile, law and religion and environment are combining to assist him. The environment of a harsh countryside keeps him exposed to a stimulus which no longer invigorates his rival in the softer atmosphere of the distant Western cities. His religion forbids him to restrict the size of his family by contraceptive methods of birth-control. And United States legislation, which has restricted immigration from countries overseas but not from countries on the American Continent, has left the French Canadian immigrant in a privileged position which is shared with him by none but the Mexican.* Perhaps the present act in the drama of North American history may end, after a century of peaceful penetration, in a triumphal meeting between the two resurgent Latin peasantries in the neighbourhood of the Federal Capital of the United States! Is this the denouement that our great-grandchildren are destined to witness in A.D. 2033? There have been reversals of fortune every bit as strange as this in North American history before.

* This restriction of immigration into the United States has been effected by the Immigration (Restriction) Acts of 1921 and 1924. It should be noted that the wide door left open for immigration into the United States across the land-frontiers is only open for native-born inhabitants of the adjoining American countries. A European or Asiatic who attempts to enter the United States through Canada or Mexico, without having secured a place in the annual quota of immigrants assigned to his own country of origin, finds himself excluded. In this matter, the United States Bureau of Immigration has adopted the British Admiralty's doctrine of 'continuous voyage'.

Monologue D'Outre Tombe
(Pantoum)

ANONYMOUS

Morn and noon and night,
Here I lie in the ground;
No faintest glimmer of light,
No lightest whisper of sound.

Here I lie in the ground;
The worms glide out and in;
No lightest whisper of sound,
After a life-long din.

The worms glide out and in;
They are fruitful and multiply;
After a life-long din,
I watch them quietly.

They are fruitful and multiply,
My body dwindles the while;
I watch them quietly;
I can scarce forbear a smile.

My body dwindles the while,
I shall soon be a skeleton;
I can scarce forbear a smile
They have had such glorious fun.

I shall soon be a skeleton,
The worms are wriggling away;
They have had such glorious fun,
They will fertilise my clay.

The worms are wriggling away,
They are what I have been,

They will fertilise my clay.
The grass will grow more green.

They are what I have been.
I shall change, but what of that?
The grass will grow more green,
The parson's sheep grow fat.

I shall change, but what of that?
All flesh is grass, one says,
The parson's sheep grow fat,
The parson grows in grace.

All flesh is grass, one says,
Grass becomes flesh, one knows,
The parson grows in grace;
I am the grace he grows.

Grass becomes flesh, one knows,
He grows like a bull of Bashan.
I am the grace he grows;
I startle his congregation.

He grows like a bull of Bashan,
One day he'll be Bishop or Dean,
I startle his congregation:
One day I shall preach to the Q—n.

One day he'll be Bishop or Dean,
One of those science-haters;
One day I shall preach to the Q—n,
To think of my going in gaiters!

One of those science-haters,
Blind as a mole or bat;
To think of my going in gaiters,
And wearing a shovel hat!

Blind as a mole or bat,
No faintest glimmer of light,
And wearing a shovel hat,
Morning and noon and night.

The Celestial Omnibus

BY E. M. FORSTER

I

THE BOY who resided at Agathox Lodge, 28, Buckingham Park Road, Surbiton, had often been puzzled by the old sign-post that stood almost opposite. He asked his mother about it, and she replied that it was a joke, and not a very nice one, which had been made many years back by some naughty young men, and that the police ought to remove it. For there were two strange things about this sign-post: firstly, it pointed up a blank alley, and, secondly, it had painted on it, in faded characters, the words, "To Heaven."

"What kind of young men were they?" he asked.

"I think your father told me that one of them wrote verses, and was expelled from the University and came to grief in other ways. Still, it was a long time ago. You must ask your father about it. He will say the same as I do, that it was put up as a joke."

"So it doesn't mean anything at all?"

She sent him up-stairs to put on his best things, for the Bonses were coming to tea, and he was to hand the cake-stand.

It struck him, as he wrenched on his tightening trousers, that he might do worse than ask Mr. Bons about the sign-post. His father, though very kind, always laughed at him—shrieked with laughter whenever he or any other child asked a question or spoke. But Mr. Bons was serious as well as kind. He had a beautiful house and lent one books, he was a churchwarden, and a candidate for the County Council; he had donated to the Free Library enormously, he presided over the Literary Society, and had Members of Parliament to stop with him—in short, he was probably the wisest person alive.

Yet even Mr. Bons could only say that the sign-post was a joke—the joke of a person named Shelley.

"Of course!" cried the mother; "I told you so, dear. That was the name."

"Had you never heard of Shelley?" asked Mr. Bons.

"No," said the boy, and hung his head.

"But is there no Shelley in the house?"

"Why, yes!" exclaimed the lady, in much agitation. "Dear Mr. Bons, we aren't such Philistines as that. Two at the least. One a wedding present, and the other, smaller print, in one of the spare rooms."

"I believe we have seven Shelleys," said Mr. Bons, with a slow smile. Then he brushed the cake crumbs off his stomach, and, together with his daughter, rose to go.

The boy, obeying a wink from his mother, saw them all the way to the garden gate, and when they had gone he did not at once return to the house, but gazed for a little up and down Buckingham Park Road.

His parents lived at the right end of it. After No. 39 the quality of the houses dropped very suddenly, and 64 had not even a separate servants' entrance. But at the present moment the whole road looked rather pretty, for the sun had just set in splendour, and the inequalities of rent were drowned in a saffron afterglow. Small birds twittered, and the breadwinners' train shrieked musically down through the cutting—that wonderful cutting which has drawn to itself the whole beauty out of Surbiton, and clad itself, like any Alpine valley, with the glory of the fir and the silver birch and the primrose. It was this cutting that had first stirred desires within the boy—desires for something just a little different, he knew not what, desires that would return whenever things were sunlit, as they were this evening, running up and down inside him, up and down, up and down, till he would feel quite unusual all over, and as likely as not would want to cry. This evening he was even sillier, for he slipped across the road towards the sign-post and began to run up the blank alley.

The alley runs between high walls—the walls of the gardens of "Ivanhoe" and "Belle Vista" respectively. It smells a little all the way, and is scarcely twenty yards long, including the turn at the end. So not unnaturally the boy soon came to a standstill. "I'd like to kick that Shelley," he exclaimed, and glanced idly at a piece of paper which was pasted on the wall. Rather an odd piece of paper, and he read it carefully before he turned back. This is what he read:

S. AND C. R. C. C.

Alteration in Service.

Owing to lack of patronage the Company are regretfully compelled to suspend the hourly service, and to retain only the

Sunrise and Sunset Omnibuses,

which will run as usual. It is to be hoped that the public will patronize an arrangement which is intended for their convenience. As an extra inducement, the Company will, for the first time, now issue

Return Tickets!

(available one day only), which may be obtained of the driver. Passengers are again reminded that *no tickets are issued at the other end,* and that no complaints in this connection will receive consideration from the Company. Nor will the Company be responsible for any negligence or stupidity on the part of Passengers, nor for Hailstorms, Lightning, Loss of Tickets, nor for any Act of God.

☼ For the Direction.

Now he had never seen this notice before, nor could he imagine where the omnibus went to. S. of course was for Surbiton, and R.C.C. meant Road Car Company. But what was the meaning of the other C.? Coombe and Malden, perhaps, or possibly "City." Yet it could not hope to compete with the South-Western. The whole thing, the boy reflected, was run on hopelessly unbusiness-like lines. Why no tickets from the other end? And what an hour to start! Then he realized that unless the notice was a hoax, an omnibus must have been starting just as he was wishing the Bonses good-bye. He peered at the ground through the gathering dusk, and there he saw what might or might not be the marks of wheels. Yet nothing had come out of the alley. And he had never seen an omnibus at any time in the Buckingham Park Road. No: it must be a hoax, like the signposts, like the fairy tales, like the dreams upon which he would wake suddenly in the night. And with a sigh he stepped from the alley—right into the arms of his father.

Oh, how his father laughed! "Poor, poor Popsey!" he cried. "Diddums! Diddums! Diddums think he'd walky-palky up to Evvink!" And his mother, also convulsed with laughter, appeared on the steps of Agathox Lodge. "Don't, Bob!" she gasped. "Don't be so naughty! Oh, you'll kill me! Oh, leave the boy alone!"

But all that evening the joke was kept up. The father implored to be taken too. Was it a very tiring walk? Need one wipe one's shoes on the door-mat? And the boy went to bed feeling faint and sore, and thankful for only one thing—that he had not said a word about the omnibus. It was a hoax, yet through his dreams it grew more and more real, and the streets of Surbiton, through which he saw it driving, seemed instead to become hoaxes and shadows. And very early in the morning he woke with a cry, for he had had a glimpse of its destination.

He struck a match, and its light fell not only on his watch but also on his calendar, so that he knew it to be half-an-hour to sunrise. It was pitch dark, for the fog had come down from London in the night, and all Surbiton was wrapped in its embraces. Yet he sprang out and dressed himself, for he was determined to settle once for all which was real: the omnibus or the streets. "I shall be a fool one way or the other," he thought, "until I know." Soon he was shivering in the road under the gas lamp that guarded the entrance to the alley.

To enter the alley itself required some courage. Not only was it horribly dark, but he now realized that it was an impossible terminus for an omnibus. If it had not been for a policeman, whom he heard approaching through the fog, he would never have made the attempt. The next moment he had made the attempt and failed. Nothing. Nothing but a blank alley and a very silly boy gaping at its dirty floor. It *was* a hoax. "I'll tell papa and mamma," he decided. "I deserve it. I deserve that they should know. I am too silly to be alive." And he went back to the gate of Agathox Lodge.

There he remembered that his watch was fast. The sun was not risen; it would not rise for two minutes. "Give the bus every chance," he thought cynically, and returned into the alley.

But the omnibus was there.

II

It had two horses, whose sides were still smoking from their journey, and its two great lamps shone through the fog against the alley's walls, changing their cobwebs and moss into tissues of fairyland. The driver was huddled up in a cape. He faced the blank wall, and how he had managed to drive in so neatly and so silently was one of the many things that the boy never discovered. Nor could he imagine how ever he would drive out.

"Please," his voice quavered through the foul brown air, "Please, is that an omnibus?"

"Omnibus est," said the driver, without turning round. There was a moment's silence. The policeman passed, coughing, by the entrance of the alley. The boy crouched in the shadow, for he did not want to be found out. He was pretty sure, too, that it was a Pirate;

nothing else, he reasoned, would go from such odd places and at such odd hours.

"About when do you start?" He tried to sound nonchalant.

"At sunrise."

"How far do you go?"

"The whole way."

"And can I have a return ticket which will bring me all the way back?"

"You can."

"Do you know, I half think I'll come." The driver made no answer. The sun must have risen, for he unhitched the brake. And scarcely had the boy jumped in before the omnibus was off.

How? Did it turn? There was no room. Did it go forward? There was a blank wall. Yet it was moving—moving at a stately pace through the fog, which had turned from brown to yellow. The thought of warm bed and warmer breakfast made the boy feel faint. He wished he had not come. His parents would not have approved. He would have gone back to them if the weather had not made it impossible. The solitude was terrible; he was the only passenger. And the omnibus, though well-built, was cold and somewhat musty. He drew his coat round him, and in so doing chanced to feel his pocket. It was empty. He had forgotten his purse.

"Stop!" he shouted. "Stop!" And then, being of a polite disposition, he glanced up at the painted notice-board so that he might call the driver by name. "Mr. Browne! stop; O, do please stop!"

Mr. Browne did not stop, but he opened a little window and looked in at the boy. His face was a surprise, so kind it was and modest.

"Mr. Browne, I've left my purse behind. I've not got a penny. I can't pay for the ticket. Will you take my watch, please? I am in the most awful hole."

"Tickets on this line," said the driver, "whether single or return, can be purchased by coinage from no terrene mint. And a chronometer, though it had solaced the vigils of Charlemagne, or measured the slumbers of Laura, can acquire by no mutation the double-cake that charms the fangless Cerberus of Heaven!" So saying, he handed in the necessary ticket, and, while the boy said "Thank you," continued: "Titular pretensions, I know it well, are vanity. Yet they merit no censure when uttered on a laughing lip, and in an homonymous world are in some sort useful, since they do serve to distinguish one Jack from his fellow. Remember me, therefore, as Sir Thomas Browne."

"Are you a Sir? Oh, sorry!" He had heard of these gentlemen drivers. "It *is* good of you about the ticket. But if you go on at this rate, however does your bus pay?"

"It does not pay. It was not intended to pay. Many are the faults of my equipage; it is compounded too curiously of foreign woods; its cushions tickle erudition rather than promote repose; and my horses are nourished not on the evergreen pastures of the moment, but on the dried bents and clovers of Latinity. But that it pays!—that error at all events was never intended and never attained."

"Sorry again," said the boy rather hopelessly. Sir Thomas looked sad, fearing that, even for a moment, he had been the cause of sadness. He invited the boy to come up and sit beside him on the box, and together they journeyed on through the fog, which was now changing from yellow to white. There were no houses by the road; so it must be either Putney Heath or Wimbledon Common.

"Have you been a driver always?"

"I was a physician once."

"But why did you stop? Weren't you good?"

"As a healer of bodies I had scant success, and several score of my patients preceded me. But as a healer of the spirit I have succeeded beyond my hopes and my deserts. For though my draughts were not better nor subtler than those of other men, yet, by reason of the cunning goblets wherein I offered them, the queasy soul was ofttimes tempted to sip and be refreshed."

"The queasy soul," he murmured; "if the sun sets with trees in front of it, and you suddenly come strange all over, is that a queasy soul?"

"Have you felt that?"

"Why yes."

After a pause he told the boy a little, a very little, about the journey's end. But they did not chatter much, for the boy, when he liked a person, would as soon sit silent in his company as speak, and this, he discovered, was also the mind of Sir Thomas Browne and of many others with whom he was to be acquainted. He heard, however, about the young man Shelley, who was now quite a famous person, with a carriage of his own, and about some of the other drivers who are in the service of the Company. Meanwhile the light grew stronger, though the fog did not disperse. It was now more like mist than fog, and at times would travel quickly across them, as if it was part of a cloud. They had been ascending, too, in a most puzzling way; for over two hours the horses had been pulling against the collar, and even if it were Richmond Hill they ought to have been at the top long ago. Perhaps it was Epsom, or even the North Downs; yet the air seemed keener than that which blows on either. And as to the name of their destination, Sir Thomas Browne was silent.

Crash!

"Thunder, by Jove!" said the boy, "and not so far off either. Listen to the echoes! It's more like mountains."

He thought, not very vividly, of his father and mother. He saw them sitting down to sausages and listening to the storm. He saw his own empty place. Then there would be questions, alarms, theories, jokes, consolations. They would expect him back at lunch. To lunch he would not come, nor to tea, but he would be in for dinner, and so his day's truancy would be over. If he had had his purse he would have bought them presents—not that he should have known what to get them.

Crash!

The peal and the lightning came together. The cloud quivered as if it were alive, and torn streamers of mist rushed past. "Are you afraid?" asked Sir Thomas Browne.

"What is there to be afraid of? Is it much farther?"

The horses of the omnibus stopped just as a ball of fire burst up and exploded with a ringing noise that was deafening but clear, like the noise of a blacksmith's forge. All the cloud was shattered.

"Oh, listen, Sir Thomas Browne! No, I mean look; we shall get a view at last. No, I mean listen; that sounds like a rainbow!"

The noise had died into the faintest murmur, beneath which another murmur grew, spreading stealthily, steadily, in a curve that widened but did not vary. And in widening curves a rainbow was spreading from the horses' feet into the dissolving mists.

"But how beautiful! What colours! Where will it stop? It is more like the rainbows you can tread on. More like dreams."

The colour and the sound grew together. The rainbow spanned an enormous gulf. Clouds rushed under it and were pierced by it, and still it grew, reaching forward, conquering the darkness, until it touched something that seemed more solid than a cloud.

The boy stood up. "What is that out there?" he called. "What does it rest on, out at that other end?"

In the morning sunshine a precipice shone forth beyond the gulf. A precipice—or was it a castle? The horses moved. They set their feet upon the rainbow.

"Oh, look!" the boy shouted. "Oh, listen! Those caves—or are they gateways? Oh, look between those cliffs at those ledges. I see people! I see trees!"

"Look also below," whispered Sir Thomas. "Neglect not the diviner Acheron."

The boy looked below, past the flames of the rainbow that licked against their wheels. The gulf also had cleared, and in its depths there flowed an everlasting river. One sunbeam entered and struck a green pool, and as they passed over he saw three maidens rise to the surface of the pool, singing, and playing with something that glistened like a ring.

"You down in the water——" he called.

They answered, "You up on the bridge——" There was a burst of music. "You up on the bridge, good luck to you. Truth in the depth, truth on the height."

"You down in the water, what are you doing?"

Sir Thomas Browne replied: "They sport in the mancipiary possession of their gold"; and the omnibus arrived.

III

The boy was in disgrace. He sat locked up in the nursery of Agathox Lodge, learning poetry for a punishment. His father had said, "My boy! I can pardon anything but untruthfulness," and had caned him, saying at each stroke, "There is *no* omnibus, *no* driver, *no* bridge, *no* mountain; you are a *truant,* a *gutter snipe,* a *liar.*" His father could be very stern at times. His mother had begged him to say he was sorry. But he could not say that. It was the greatest day of his life, in spite of the caning and the poetry at the end of it.

He had returned punctually at sunset—driven not by Sir Thomas Browne, but by a maiden lady who was full of quiet fun. They had talked of omnibuses and also of barouche landaus. How far away her gentle voice seemed now! Yet it was scarcely three hours since he had left her up the alley.

His mother called through the door. "Dear, you are to come down and to bring your poetry with you."

He came down, and found that Mr. Bons was in the smoking-room with his father. It had been a dinner party.

"Here is the great traveller!" said his father grimly. "Here is the young gentleman who drives in an omnibus over rainbows, while young ladies sing to him." Pleased with his wit, he laughed.

"After all," said Mr. Bons, smiling, "there is something a little like it in Wagner. It is odd how, in quite illiterate minds, you will find glimmers of Artistic Truth. The case interests me. Let me plead for the culprit. We have all romanced in our time, haven't we?"

"Hear how kind Mr. Bons is," said his mother, while his father said, "Very well. Let him say his Poem, and that will do. He is going away to my sister on Tuesday, and *she* will cure him of this alley-slopering." (Laughter.) "Say your Poem."

The boy began. " 'Standing aloof in giant ignorance.' "

His father laughed again—roared. "One for you, my son! 'Standing aloof in giant ignorance!' I never knew these poets talked sense. Just describes you. Here, Bons, you go in for poetry. Put him through it, will you, while I fetch up the whisky?"

"Yes, give me the Keats," said Mr. Bons. "Let him say his Keats to me."

So for a few moments the wise man and the ignorant boy were left alone in the smoking-room.

" 'Standing aloof in giant ignorance, of thee I dream and of the Cyclades, as one who sits ashore and longs perchance to visit——' "

"Quite right. To visit what?"

" 'To visit dolphin coral in deep seas,' " said the boy, and burst into tears.

"Come, come! why do you cry?"

"Because—because all these words that only rhymed before, now that I've come back they're me."

Mr. Bons laid the Keats down. The case was more interesting than he had expected. *"You?"* he exclaimed. "This sonnet, *you?"*

"Yes—and look further on: 'Aye, on the shores of darkness there is light, and precipices show untrodden green.' It *is* so, sir. All these things are true."

"I never doubted it," said Mr. Bons, with closed eyes.

"You—then you believe me? You believe in the omnibus and the driver and the storm and that return ticket I got for nothing and——"

"Tut, tut! No more of your yarns, my boy. I meant that I never doubted the essential truth of Poetry. Some day, when you have read more, you will understand what I mean."

"But Mr. Bons, it *is* so. There *is* light upon the shores of darkness. I have seen it coming. Light and a wind."

"Nonsense," said Mr. Bons.

"If I had stopped! They tempted me. They told me to give up my ticket—for you cannot come back if you lose your ticket. They called from the river for it, and indeed I was tempted, for I have never been so happy as among those precipices. But I thought of my mother and father, and that I must fetch them. Yet they will not come, though the road starts opposite our house. It has all happened as the people up there warned me, and Mr. Bons has disbelieved me like every one else. I have been caned. I shall never see that mountain again."

"What's that about me?" said Mr. Bons, sitting up in his chair very suddenly.

"I told them about you, and how clever you were, and how many books you had, and they said, 'Mr. Bons will certainly disbelieve you.' "

"Stuff and nonsense, my young friend. You grow impertinent. I—well—I will settle the matter. Not a word to your father. I will cure you. To-morrow evening I will myself call here to take you for a walk, and at sunset we will go up this alley opposite and hunt for your omnibus, you silly little boy."

His face grew serious, for the boy was not disconcerted, but leapt about the room singing, "Joy! joy! I told them you would believe me. We will drive together over the rainbow. I told them that you would come." After all, could there be anything in the story? Wagner? Keats? Shelley? Sir Thomas Browne? Certainly the case was interesting.

And on the morrow evening, though it was pouring with rain, Mr. Bons did not omit to call at Agathox Lodge.

The boy was ready, bubbling with excitement, and skipping about in a way that rather vexed the President of the Literary Society. They took a turn down Buckingham Park Road, and then—having seen that no one was watching them—slipped up the alley. Naturally enough (for the sun was setting) they ran straight against the omnibus.

"Good heavens!" exclaimed Mr. Bons. "Good gracious heavens!"

It was not the omnibus in which the boy had driven first, nor yet that in which he had returned. There were three horses—black, gray, and white, the gray being the finest. The driver, who turned round at the mention of goodness and of heaven, was a sallow man with terrifying jaws and sunken eyes. Mr. Bons, on seeing him, gave a cry as if of recognition, and began to tremble violently.

The boy jumped in.

"Is it possible?" cried Mr. Bons. "Is the impossible possible?"

"Sir; come in, sir. It is such a fine omnibus. Oh, here is his name—Dan some one."

Mr. Bons sprang in too. A blast of wind immediately slammed the omnibus door, and the shock jerked down all the omnibus blinds, which were very weak on their springs.

"Dan . . . Show me. Good gracious heavens! we're moving."

"Hooray!" said the boy.

Mr. Bons became flustered. He had not intended to be kidnapped. He could not find the door-handle, nor push up the blinds. The omnibus was quite dark, and by the time he had struck a match, night had come on outside also. They were moving rapidly.

"A strange, a memorable adventure," he said, surveying the interior of the omnibus, which was large, roomy, and constructed with extreme regularity, every part exactly answering to every other part. Over the door (the handle of which was outside) was written, "Lasciate ogni baldanza voi che entrate"—at least, that was what was written, but Mr. Bons said that it was Lashy arty something, and that baldanza was a mistake for speranza. His voice sounded as if he was in church. Meanwhile, the boy called to the cadaverous driver for two return tickets. They were handed in without a word. Mr. Bons covered his face with his hand and again trembled. "Do you know who that is!" he whispered, when the little window had shut upon them. "It is the impossible."

"Well, I don't like him as much as Sir Thomas Browne, though I shouldn't be surprised if he had even more in him."

"More in him?" He stamped irritably. "By accident you have made the greatest discovery of the century, and all you can say is that there is more in this man. Do you remember those vellum books in my library, stamped with red lilies? This—sit still, I bring you stupendous news!—*this is the man who wrote them.*"

The boy sat quite still. "I wonder if we shall see Mrs. Gamp?" he asked, after a civil pause.

"Mrs.——?"

"Mrs. Gamp and Mrs. Harris. I like Mrs. Harris. I came upon them quite suddenly. Mrs. Gamp's bandboxes have moved over the rainbow so badly. All the bottoms have fallen out, and two of the pippins off her bedstead tumbled into the stream."

"Out there sits the man who wrote my vellum books!" thundered Mr. Bons, "and you talk to me of Dickens and of Mrs. Gamp?"

"I know Mrs. Gamp so well," he apologized. "I could not help being glad to see her. I recognized her voice. She was telling Mrs. Harris about Mrs. Prig."

"Did you spend the whole day in her elevating company?"

"Oh, no. I raced. I met a man who took me out beyond to a racecourse. You run, and there are dolphins out at sea."

"Indeed. Do you remember the man's name?"

"Achilles. No; he was later. Tom Jones."

Mr. Bons sighed heavily. "Well, my lad, you have made a miserable mess of it. Think of a cultured person with your opportunities! A cultured person would have known all these characters and known what to have said to each. He would not have wasted his time with a Mrs. Gamp or a Tom Jones. The creations of Homer, of Shakespeare, and of Him who drives us now, would alone have contented him. He would not have raced. He would have asked intelligent questions."

"But, Mr. Bons," said the boy humbly, "you will be a cultured person. I told them so."

"True, true, and I beg you not to disgrace me when we arrive. No gossiping. No running. Keep close to my side, and never speak to these Immortals unless they speak to you. Yes, and give me the return tickets. You will be losing them."

The boy surrendered the tickets, but felt a little sore. After all, he had found the way to this place. It was hard first to be disbelieved and then to be lectured. Meanwhile, the rain had stopped, and moonlight crept into the omnibus through the cracks in the blinds.

"But how is there to be a rainbow?" cried the boy.

"You distract me," snapped Mr. Bons. "I wish to meditate on beauty. I wish to goodness I was with a reverent and sympathetic person."

The lad bit his lip. He made a hundred good resolutions. He would imitate Mr. Bons all the visit. He would not laugh, or run, or sing, or do any of the vulgar things that must have disgusted his new friends last time. He would be very careful to pronounce their names properly, and to remember who knew whom. Achilles did not know Tom Jones—at least, so Mr. Bons said. The Duchess of Malfi was older than Mrs. Gamp—at least, so Mr. Bons said. He would be self-conscious, reticent, and prim. He would never say he liked any one. Yet, when the blind flew up at a chance touch of his head, all these good resolutions went to the winds, for the omnibus had reached the summit of a moonlit hill, and there was the chasm, and there, across it, stood the old precipices, dreaming, with their feet in the everlasting river. He exclaimed, "The mountain! Listen to the new tune in the water! Look at the camp fires in the ravines," and Mr. Bons, after a hasty glance, retorted, "Water? Camp fires? Ridiculous rubbish. Hold your tongue. There is nothing at all."

Yet, under his eyes, a rainbow formed, compounded not of sunlight and storm, but of moonlight and the spray of the river. The three horses put their feet upon it. He thought it the finest rainbow he had seen, but did not dare to say so, since Mr. Bons said that nothing was there. He leant out—the window had opened—and sang the tune that rose from the sleeping waters.

"The prelude to Rhinegold?" said Mr. Bons suddenly. "Who taught you these *leitmotifs?*" He, too, looked out of the window. Then he behaved very oddly. He gave a choking cry, and fell back on to the omnibus floor. He writhed and kicked. His face was green.

"Does the bridge make you dizzy?" the boy asked.

"Dizzy!" gasped Mr. Bons. "I want to go back. Tell the driver."

But the driver shook his head.

"We are nearly there," said the boy. "They are asleep. Shall I call? They will be so pleased to see you, for I have prepared them."

Mr. Bons moaned. They moved over the lunar rainbow, which ever and ever broke away behind their wheels. How still the night was! Who would be sentry at the Gate?

"I am coming," he shouted, again forgetting the hundred resolutions. "I am returning—I, the boy."

"The boy is returning," cried a voice to other voices, who repeated, "The boy is returning."

"I am bringing Mr. Bons with me."

Silence.

"I should have said Mr. Bons is bringing me with him."

Profound silence.

"Who stands sentry?"

"Achilles."

And on the rocky causeway, close to the springing of the rainbow bridge, he saw a young man who carried a wonderful shield.

"Mr. Bons, it is Achilles, armed."

"I want to go back," said Mr. Bons.

The last fragment of the rainbow melted, the wheels sang upon the living rock, the door of the omnibus burst open. Out leapt the boy—he could not resist—and sprang to meet the warrior, who, stooping suddenly, caught him on his shield.

"Achilles!" he cried, "let me get down, for I am ignorant and vulgar, and I must wait for that Mr. Bons of whom I told you yesterday."

But Achilles raised him aloft. He crouched on the wonderful shield, on heroes and burning cities, on vineyards graven in gold, on every dear passion, every joy, on the entire image of the Mountain that he had discovered, encircled, like it, with an everlasting stream. "No, no," he protested, "I am not worthy. It is Mr. Bons who must be up here."

But Mr. Bons was whimpering, and Achilles trumpeted and cried, "Stand upright upon my shield!"

"Sir, I did not mean to stand! something made me stand. Sir, why do you delay? Here is only the great Achilles, whom you knew."

Mr. Bons screamed, "I see no one. I see nothing. I want to go back." Then he cried to the driver, "Save me! Let me stop in your chariot. I have honoured you. I have quoted you. I have bound you in vellum. Take me back to my world."

The driver replied, "I am the means and not the end. I am the food and not the life. Stand by yourself, as that boy has stood. I cannot save you. For poetry is a spirit; and they that would worship it must worship in spirit and in truth."

Mr. Bons—he could not resist—crawled out of the beautiful omnibus. His face appeared, gaping horribly. His hands followed, one gripping the step, the other beating the air. Now his shoulders emerged, his chest, his stomach. With a shriek of "I see London," he fell—fell against the hard, moonlit rock, fell into it as if it were water, fell through it, vanished, and was seen by the boy no more.

"Where have you fallen to, Mr. Bons? Here is a procession arriving to honour you with music and torches. Here come the men and women whose names you know. The mountain is awake, the river is awake, over the race-course the sea is awaking those dolphins, and it is all for you. They want you——"

There was the touch of fresh leaves on his forehead. Some one had crowned him.

ΤΕΛΟΣ

. . . .

From the *Kingston Gazette, Surbiton Times,*
and *Raynes Park Observer.*

The body of Mr. Septimus Bons has been found in a shockingly mutilated condition in the vicinity of the Bermondsey gas-works. The deceased's pockets contained a sovereign-purse, a silver cigar-case, a bijou pronouncing dictionary, and a couple of omnibus tickets. The unfortunate gentleman had apparently been hurled from a considerable height. Foul play is suspected, and a thorough investigation is pending by the authorities.

The Sea-Cow

BY JOHN STEINBECK AND EDWARD F. RICKETTS

WE COME now to a piece of equipment which still brings anger to our hearts and, we hope, some venom to our pen. Perhaps in self-defense against suit, we should say, "The outboard motor mentioned in this book is purely fictitious and any resemblance to outboard motors living or dead is coincidental." We shall call this contraption, for the sake of secrecy, a Hansen Sea-Cow—a dazzling little piece of machinery, all aluminum paint and touched here and there with spots of red. The Sea-Cow was built to sell, to dazzle the eyes, to splutter its way into the unwary heart. We took it along for the skiff. It was intended that it should push us ashore and back, should drive our boat into estuaries and along the borders of little coves. But we had not reckoned with one thing. Recently, industrial civilization has reached its peak of reality and has lunged forward into something that approaches mysticism. In the Sea-Cow factory where steel fingers tighten screws, bend and mold, measure and divide, some curious mathematick has occurred. And that secret so long sought has accidentally been found. Life has been created. The machine is at last stirred. A soul and a malignant mind have been born. Our Hansen Sea-Cow was not only a living thing but a mean, irritable, contemptible, vengeful, mischievous, hateful living thing. In the six weeks of our association we observed it, at first mechanically and then, as its living reactions became more and more apparent, psychologically. And we determined one thing to our satisfaction. When and if these ghoulish little motors learn to reproduce themselves the human species is doomed. For their hatred of us is so great that they will wait and plan and organize and one night, in a roar of little exhausts, they will wipe us out. We do not think that Mr. Hansen, inventor of the Sea-Cow, father of the outboard motor, knew what he was doing. We think the monster he created was as accidental and arbitrary as the beginning of any other life. Only one thing differentiates the Sea-Cow from the life that we know. Whereas the forms that are familiar to us are the results of billions of years of mutation and complication, life and intelligence emerged simultaneously in the Sea-Cow. It is more than a species. It is a whole new redefinition of life. We observed the following traits in it and we were able to check them again and again:

1. Incredibly lazy, the Sea-Cow loved to ride on the back of a boat, trailing its propeller daintily in the water while we rowed.

2. It required the same amount of gasoline whether it ran or not, apparently being able to absorb this fluid through its body walls without recourse to explosion. It had always to be filled at the beginning of every trip.

3. It had apparently some clairvoyant powers, and was able to read our minds, particularly when they were inflamed with emotion. Thus, on every occasion when we were driven to the point of destroying it, it started and ran with a great noise and excitement. This served the double purpose of saving its life and of resurrecting in our minds a false confidence in it.

4. It had many cleavage points, and when attacked with a screwdriver, fell apart in simulated death, a trait it had in common with opossums, armadillos, and several members of the sloth family, which also fell apart in simulated death when attacked with a screwdriver.

5. It hated Tex, sensing perhaps that his knowledge of mechanics was capable of diagnosing its shortcomings.

6. It completely refused to run: (a) when the waves were high, (b) when the wind blew, (c) at night, early morning, and evening, (d) in rain, dew, or fog, (e) when the distance to be covered was more than two hundred yards. But on warm, sunny days when the weather was calm and the white beach close by—in a word, on days when it would have been a pleasure to row—the Sea-Cow started at a touch and would not stop.

7. It loved no one, trusted no one. It had no friends.

Perhaps toward the end, our observations were a little warped by emotion. Time and again as it sat on the stern with its pretty little propeller lying idly in the water, it was very close to death. And in the end, even we were infected with its malignancy and its dishonesty. We should have destroyed it, but we did not. Arriving home, we gave it a new coat of aluminum paint, spotted it at points with new red enamel, and sold it. And we might have rid the world of this mechanical cancer!

Rules for Judicial Conduct

Things Necessary to be Continually had in Remembrance

BY SIR MATTHEW HALE, KT.

Lord Chief Baron of the Exchequer, 1660–1671
Lord Chief Justice of England, 1671–1676

I. That in the Administration of Justice, I am entrusted for God, the King and Country; and therefore,

II. That it be done, 1. Uprightly, 2. Deliberately, 3. Resolutely.

III. That I rest not upon my own Understanding or Strength, but Implore and rest upon the Direction and Strength of God.

IV. That in the Execution of Justice I carefully lay aside my own Passions, and not give way to them, however provoked.

V. That I be wholly intent upon the Business I am about, remitting all other Cares and Thoughts, as unseasonable and Interruptions.

VI. That I suffer not myself to be prepossessed with any Judgment at all, till the whole Business and both Parties be heard.

VII. That I never engage myself in the beginning of any Cause, but reserve myself unprejudiced till the whole be heard.

VIII. That in Business Capital, though my Nature prompt me to Pity; yet to consider, that there is also a Pity due to the Country.

IX. That I be not too Rigid in matters Conscientious, where all the harm is Diversity of Judgment.

X. That I be not biassed with Compassion to the Poor, or favour to the Rich, in point of Justice.

XI. That Popular, or Court Applause, or Distaste, have no Influence into anything I do in point of Distribution of Justice.

XII. Not to be sollicitous what Men will say or think, so long as I keep myself exactly according to the Rule of Justice.

XIII. If in Criminals it be a measuring Cast, to incline to Mercy and Acquittal.

XIV. In Criminals that consist merely in words, where no more harm ensues, Moderation is no Injustice.

XV. In Criminals of Blood, if the Fact be Evident, Severity is Justice.

XVI. To abhor all private Sollicitations, of what kind soever, and by whom soever, in Matters depending.

XVII. To charge my Servants, 1. Not to interpose in any Business whatsoever, 2. Not to take more than their known Fees, 3. Not to give any undue precedence to Causes, 4. Not to recommend Councill.

XVIII. To be short and sparing at Meals, that I may be the fitter for Business.

THE THREE READERS

Section II: Selected by Sinclair Lewis

Introductory Remarks

OF THAT bright, hardy country which stands at the head of the Great Valley—Wisconsin, Iowa, Minnesota, the Dakotas, with slivers of Illinois and Michigan—one would be able to trace the whole history in a narrow shelf of fiction: Rölvaag's *Giants in the Earth,* Rose Wilder Lane's *Let the Hurricane Roar,* Hamlin Garland's *Main-Travelled Roads,* the books of Zona Gale and August Derleth, the city novels of Grace Flandrau and William McNally and Margaret Culkin Banning, and, as a spiritual accounting of the whole business, the two short novels reprinted in this book: Ruth Suckow's *Country People* and Eleanor Green's *The Hill.*

Since they all possess reality, these stories fit together, no matter how varied the moods. Harrit and Vinnie, the highly literate American girls of *The Hill,* might be the granddaughters of Miss Suckow's German August Kaetterhenry, or Rölvaag's Norwegian Per Hansa, or Rose Lane's Yankee Charles, or of Garland's Civil War soldier limping up a Wisconsin coolly.

The first three of these crossed the Mississippi into a shining desolate prairie at about the same time, between 1870 and 1880—only seventy years ago. These novels tell better than maps and figures how that hostile sun-land became human.

They indicate, too, how varied the prairie civilization became in less than three generations. Regarding any new society it is highly common and even more highly irritating for outsiders to speak of it as uncomplex and insular. In this goodly year of 1943, when the Russians say to the British—and the British say to the New Yorkers—and the New Yorkers say to all Middlewesterners, "When are you fellows going to wake up and hear about this war that's going on?" then the amount of heat kindled is about equal in all three cases.

The Midwestern mentality is at least as contradictory as that of New England. One or both of the grandfathers of Vinnie, in *The Hill,* may well have been a Dakota homesteader. He lived in a dark dugout, he was beset by blizzards, wolves, armies of grasshoppers; he sowed by hand and plowed with oxen; and his laborious and risky life was only a hand-turn different from that of the original American pioneers of 1620. It was, indeed, no fatter or more secure than a Saxon peasant's existence in the year 1000. From the pioneer's arrival on the plains to Vinnie contemplative on a hill is in chronicle time only fifty or sixty years, but in aspects of civilization it is a millennium.

Vinnie's friends are still of the farm, still of the country of La Follette, yet they would be just as much at ease if they were studying singing in Milan or physics in Upsala or frivolity in Cannes. They are international. They and their families have in sixty years covered three centuries of cultural history, from Wesleyanism to Freudianism, from witchcraft to hysteria. Possibly they have ripened too quickly, and grown soft, ready for the pessimistic eye of a Spengler.

In their preoccupation with the delicate flight of bird and cloud and fragile country sound, in their self-defeating demand for no less than perfection in love, their quivering consciousness that old people are frustrated and tragic because none of them has known an undiminishing passion, in all their sympathetic yet neurotic sensitivity, Eleanor Green's young people are, like the cultural refugees of the Left Bank, circa 1925, or like T. S. Eliot or Ezra Pound or Isadora, iridescent flies caught in the black web of an ancient and amoral European culture. They have in imagination returned to the Europe from which their grandfathers fled, but they have returned to the coffee houses, not to the hills.

They know and shiver to a beauty that their pioneer ancestors never conceived; if their prairie is more narrow in acres, it is ten times more crowded with exhausting wonder, and if they have shut out the blizzard, they have also shut it in.

To the grandparents, if they are still alive—and they easily may be, aged somewhere over eighty—these modern children must seem selfish, idle, weak, and terrified of ghosts; armored in luxuries of which the old folks never heard, yet whimpering because some finicky sweetheart does not like the length of their noses. And to the grandchildren, the pioneers seem as hard and narrow as the steel rails that, on a prairie track, stretch bleakly out till they meet.

And how wrong both generations are! If the characteristic American jump from potatoes straight to Proust is a little dismaying, it also indicates a lively and incalculable mind.

The young generation has, in the airplane cockpits of 1943, revealed that under its glib and glittering sloth, it has as much iron as anything on the frontier. On the other hand, the older generation once had, in the first sight of the young wheat, in sleep after toil, in visits to neighbors, in reading aloud from the Old Testament's poetry and tricky ethics, in annual pilgrimages to some vasty city of five hundred population, a course of pleasures that were not essentially different from the ecstasies of these young people over a dive bomber or over the Shostakovich *Seventh* conducted by Mitropoulos.

In the years outlined by Miss Suckow and Miss Green together, we have a flight through time dizzier than any fantasy of H. G. Wells.

II

The fiction of Eleanor Green is as shy and secluded as a marsh at sunset, with the coloring rich beyond the soft browns of the foreground, but it has none of the Celtic Twilight of earlier lady novelists because, though she loves mistiness, she also has a passion of tenderness and pity for ordinary human beings. As:

"She realized with exquisite clarity what living had meant to her father. These many years they had lived together, he and her mother, and these many years he had hungered for her love. Being a shy man, he thought that he annoyed her, and so had sought in every way to make himself as inconspicuous as possible. If it is my hands, Vinnie imagined him thinking, I will keep my hands from her sight. If it is my hair or the way my whiskers grow, I shall keep my hair cut and my face shaven. If it is my mouth, or the way I eat my food, I shall say little and chew carefully."

Miss Green has brought off a difficult technique in allowing for the whole time-extent of her story only four or five hours. The outward events are as simple as they are brief: a Wisconsin village family goes picknicking, and afterward, Vinnie meets her lover. But we know the whole family and their hidden hearts, and the little Wisconsin valley where "the shadows lay in a blanket over the sheep and the grass, the deer and the thrush, and the whole place was bewitched."

Eleanor Green is still very young, and as yet she has published only three brief novels: *The Hill* and *Pastoral* and *Ariadne Spinning*. She has seen enough of New York and of an Eastern college, but she has had the good sense to live mostly in the Wisconsin where she was born. That is very fortunate for Wisconsin, whether or no that lovely state is aware of the fact.

III

Where Miss Green skims through the trees, a bird at twilight, Miss Suckow tramps the road at hot noon. I don't know which will get the farther, nor whether loops and lineal rods can be compared.

Ruth Suckow, born in 1892 in Grant Wood's Iowa, where there is nothing to be seen but corn stalks and college towers and secretaries of agriculture, has stayed there except for aberrations into heathen California and Greenwich Village, and that is very fortunate for Iowa, which she has re-created in such genuinely native novels as *The Folks* and *The Bonney Family* and the recently published *New Hope,* with its beautiful memory of the magic that is in the mind of a growing boy.

No doubt it has been suggested to Miss Suckow as not being a virtue that she seems more pedestrian than such thunderous pietists as Rölvaag, whose Norske God rides every blizzard, or the more fanciful school of Zona Gale and Eleanor Green. This suggestion Miss Suckow has answered with spirit, in her own comments on her *Country People:*

"The book is not an attempt to sum up all of rural life. It is not 'a saga of the pioneers' nor yet 'an epic of the soil.' In certain respects, as a rural novel, it is not typical, but perhaps unique. There is no writer or artist concealed among its characters who is destined to come back . . . to write a book about, or paint a picture of, the farm of August Kaetterhenry. August himself never offers a soliloquy upon The Soil; he never seduces a hired girl; and he dies in bed, not overlooking his broad acres, nor clutching a handful of his own good earth. The author suggests that, if on no other grounds, she deserves credit for such abstentions. . . . The style has no particular beauty of its own. Yet it does fit the subject matter: in its careful country minutiae, its touch of dry country humor, even its hardness and tightness. It has a certain monotonous music, like the tuneless air of the windmill in the stillness of the country air."

If Miss Suckow and Miss Green are opposite in almost every mood—so much the better for the Great Valley which produced them and which in turn they are now producing.

IV

Aside from their regional kinship, *Country People* and *The Hill* have a tie in being excellent samples of a swift-winged and not too common form of fiction: the short novel, which conveys an impression of life without either the incompleteness of the short story or the often tiresome insistence of the long novel. It has been rather neglected, perhaps because magazine editors consider a tale of thirty or forty thousand words too long, and the book-publishers wail that it is too short.

Of this *genre* there have been only a few American masters, such as Willa Cather, Joseph Hergesheimer, Edith Wharton, Henry James, Hamlin Garland, Sarah Orne Jewett. To them may be added now Eleanor Green and, though most of her stories run longer, Ruth Suckow. They indicate that if a man has written twenty thousand excellent words, it is not always desirable to add to the pot some eighty thousand words of tediousness in order to call the resultant stew a Novel.

SINCLAIR LEWIS

The Hill

BY ELEANOR GREEN

I: THE MIDDLE OF A MOSS

THEY MOVED slowly, a human caravan laden with memories that weighed more heavily upon them than the baskets of food which they carried. It must have been so, for the young went ahead, eager to find a place to stop, while the old dragged behind, knowing how grotesque anticipation may be. A girl with vivid hair led them. The wind made sails of her hair and she was sent forward like a ship. Walking behind her it was hard to know when her feet touched the earth, and the bottoms of her feet, revealing themselves as she walked, were like the backwash of a boat,—constant, recurring. The motions of her body were not careful and quiet, as the others' were; she walked along the road, the road that lay between forest and cornfield, lightly, and so swiftly that the sand could not catch the imprint of her foot, nor move quickly enough to encircle it. She might well have been a figurehead upon a ship, but the vessel moved reluctantly behind her. She preceded it like a thought. The girl's name was Harrit.

It was Vinnie's thought that Harrit moved like a ship. But if Harrit were figurehead, she, Vinnie, was the stern of the ship, for she came last. After her there followed a wave of footprints, a foam of dust. Between the two sisters, between the prow and the stern of the boat, rode the rest of the family, spending a week cruising about together in the past, sailing into forgotten inlets, down sheltered streams. They had come together, making the home of Vinnie's parents their port. From it, from time to time, they would make short excursions, returning to their port at night, returning to the family in the midst of which to rest. They were making one of those excursions now. They were steering their craft toward a hill, and Harrit, her hair bellied out like a sail, cut the wind with her body, and her feet floated over the water.

Vinnie stopped suddenly at sight of Harrit standing on a projecting rock. Her body, sheathed in orange, alert and sharp, shone like a dagger held into the light of a fire. She was motionless, her eyes looking out over the marshes to the far hills, to the world that lay beyond the hills. The rest of the family,—cousins and aunts, parents and uncles,—moved on, drawing themselves nearer to Harrit as a tired man shins a rope,—slowly, laboriously. Harrit looked out past the limits of man's sight. She was not bounded by sky and earth, by hill and marsh, as the others were. She stood on the shore of womanhood sounding the depths of the water, knowing the beauties and the horrors of the deep sea, feeling herself to be ephemeral, and yet, by some inscrutable grace, important. To the family, moving laboriously on, she was a red-headed girl in an orange dress who stood waiting upon a rock. To Vinnie, who had the generosity to attribute to all men more good than she knew to exist, more grace than any saw, Harrit was figurehead and ship and the spray that follows the ship. She was motion in her most quiet moment, she suggested air and wind and flying things, she suggested gayety and joy, and to Vinnie, who was three years her elder, she was the essence of beauty.

Harrit turned, and Vinnie saw her draw her attention to one and then another of her relatives, until finally her eyes met Vinnie's. Between them, one standing on a rock looking down, the other standing in a road looking up, there hung a delicate web of thought. In the sunlight it sparkled and turned, like a spider's web; it changed color and then changed back again. Vinnie, standing tiptoe to the moment, felt this thing between them to be tangible. I wonder, she said to herself, how it is that such a thing exists?

The late afternoon was being lulled to sleep by crickets; dark shadows lay in strips across the meadows; the air was sweet and warm, like scented eiderdown. Above the high rocks dark birds dropped into the sunlight, and dove, calling, deep into the air. Cows, half-bored, half-philosophic, gave meaning to the meadows. Fences overgrown with wild grapes marked one man's acres or another's. Butterflies the color of blue china tantalized the flowers. As it had been for decades, so it was now. Nature fulfilled herself, gave beauty to her agents, mystery to her intent. The still afternoon tucked the hills in; a narrow stream of water glided like a snake among the marsh grass and the willows, and between Vinnie and Harrit, who were also Nature's agents, hung the rare web of understanding. It was pliable; the wind did not break it. So sure was Vinnie of the tangibility of it that she reached up to touch it. Harrit thought she was waving, and waved back, turned and jumped swiftly from rock to rock and disappeared into a clump of trees. Vinnie moved on.

When she caught up with the others they were already settling themselves. Juliette sat on a camp chair with a black umbrella over her head. Uncle John was watching an ant through a microscope. Her mother was spreading a cloth on the grass, setting pickles and olives, jelly and butter at the four corners to keep the wind from crowding under. Stewart was making a daisy chain. He sat in the midst of a field of high grasses and reached out with his thin arms to pick the yellow daisies. Only his head and shoulders could be seen. The grass closed in upon him like light, or water. Harrit lay in the shadow of a great pine tree, her hair falling against the dried needles like bright creepers from a plant. From the hill came the sound of children's voices. The small cousins, Jane, Mary, Sibyl, David and Joie, were racing to the top. Susan and Marie stood over the fire. Vinnie, like a shepherd counting his sheep, numbered them to herself. One, two, three, four, five children, five grownups, three in-betweens. No, that was wrong; fourteen of them had started.

Mr. Morison, his arms laden with dry wood, came through the trees.

Of course, said Vinnie. There's Father.

Working quietly with her mother, unwrapping silver, opening bottles, Vinnie considered the isolation of personality. Each one of them, she reflected, remains himself. Seeing them separately occupied, reviewing the picture of them as she straightened up, Vinnie felt that she had seen it all before. It was inevitable that each should do just as he was doing. Even Juliette under her black umbrella, with her hands folded in her lap. Even Stewart in the midst of the daisy field. And myself? she asked. Yes, and myself.

She was not doing what she wanted to do, but it was her nature to do what others expected of her. She was quick to sacrifice herself for the petty and limitless desires of those about her.

The children are like all children, she thought. Their voices floated like a cloud above her.

Suddenly Harrit burst into laughter. Like a waterfall her voice started high and in broken tones fell into a pool of glee. "Stewart!" she shrieked. "Stewart!" Again her voice tumbled from the precipice, again it lost itself in its own sound, was drowned in itself.

Vinnie, who was unable to turn quickly because of an ingenious feat of balancing which she was performing in transferring a cake from its box to a plate, heard Harrit's laughter, and before she had seen Stewart her voice joined Harrit's in the pool of sound. At last she was free to enjoy the spectacle. And such it was, for in the center of the daisy field stood Stewart, stripped of his clothes, with a crown of daisies upon his head, a chain of them around his neck, and a loincloth dexterously woven and fitted about his middle. In his hands he held a brown-eyed Susan, and very patiently waited to be admired. His long body, growing daisy-bedecked out of the field, frightened the birds, and they flew about scolding. From all the treetops they came, beating the air with horrified wings like a flock of wingéd Christians. Vinnie held her sides with her hands, lest laughter wrench her apart. Harrit, rolling under the pine tree, threw the needles over her head; she was showered with a sharp, sweet-smelling rain. Uncle John, his microscope forgotten, laughed silently, his mirth shaking him; he was unable to maintain his equilibrium under the strain of it. Marie and Susan, twins in position, stood, legs apart, arms akimbo, with roasting forks in their hands. Mrs. Morison, whose levity was seasonal and whose season at present was winter, busied herself with the cloth. Mr. Morison, picking up dry sticks in the woods, watched, fascinated, through a break in the foliage. He was laughing quietly, the tears rolling down his face, the leaves about him quivering. Juliette held her umbrella before her face. She sat frightened and eager before this strange thing that was a naked man. Hidden behind her shelter she was at liberty to look long and minutely at him. It never occurred to her that Stewart, standing naked in the daisy field, knew that she could see him as clearly through the umbrella as though it were not there. The umbrella allowed her a very careful study of the male anatomy.

While they still laughed, Stewart, being fundamentally theatrical, sank down into the grass as miraculously as he had risen. The frightened birds settled back into the sky, carrying their distress with them. Susan and Marie returned to the fire, Mr. Morison closed the opening in the foliage and scurried about like a squirrel. As he emerged some minutes later laden with firewood, Mrs. Morison was relieved to know that her husband had missed this latest folly. Juliette remained behind her umbrella, from time to time feeling of her forehead, which was very hot. Harrit and Vinnie floated upon the eddy of their amusement.

The voices of the children came nearer. Now they were bright and clear, and again the wind would carry the sound away. Marie drew a policeman's whistle from her bosom. She blew on it three times. The hills tossed the shrill sound from one to another. It scratched at the sky like the voices of women who sit long at their supper gossiping. Once again she blew thrice upon it, and the sound of the whistle lay over the marsh. The leaves on the willow trees trembled, and the grasses along the creek bent down into the water.

Standing in the midst of her family, Vinnie was isolated by a sudden awareness of eternity. Reality hung like a ragged garment about her. Once she may have been clothed by the sense of time and the sequence of things, but the metallic note of the whistle had cut like small blades through the cloth of her mind, and it hung in shreds about her. She shivered, chilled by her new perception. Across miles of feeling came her mother's voice. "No, I am not cold," she answered, and slowly drew her mind back to these people. The echo of the whistle rolled over the hills. The strange calm lay even now upon every bush. Juliette was hidden behind her umbrella; she had not come out from behind it to see this miracle. Susan and Marie bent witchlike over the fire. Uncle John had returned to his minute study. Mrs. Morison was strengthening the tethers of the tablecloth. Mr. Morison stood wary beside her. Harrit alone had heard it. She sat motionless; she too was breathless before it. Vinnie, who was filigree, could not know that Harrit, who was fire, was thinking of her lover.

The children came down from the hill. Sibyl had found two pheasant feathers. They waved above her helmet of hair. Mary and Jane carried pine cones and wild flowers, David, an armful of dry sticks, and Joie, occupied with a bulge in his blouse, came last, stepping carefully. Vinnie alone welcomed their return.

"What is it, Joie?" she asked.

Joie whispered his answer. "It's a rabbit. A little rabbit."

"A rabbit, Joie? Where did you find it?" Vinnie also was whispering.

"It came to me. I was sitting in the middle of a moss, and all of a sudden he was there, just like that."

Joie winked at Vinnie to show how the rabbit was there, just like that. There was pride, in bright splotches, among his freckles; his brown eyes were serious. Vinnie knew that if the rabbit were taken from him tears would wash away the dark, intent look, and his eyes would be hurt and frightened, as though life centered in the soft warm body. As indeed it did. For Vinnie, possibly because of her quite recent perception of eternity, possibly because she remembered her own childhood, realized that children alone live in the present. Live now, this moment, with no thought of the future, of tomorrow and the day after, and next week and a million years hence. She felt that the cycle of human experience finds its axis in children, that the moment at hand is for a child fragile and everlasting.

"Just like that," Joie said again, and turning away from his mother, he opened his blouse so that Vinnie might peek. Against his stomach lay the young rabbit, his eyes closed, his nose pressed into Joie's navel. "Isn't he a nice one?" Joie's face grew hot with pleasure. "Did you ever see anything so cute? Did you? Did you, Vinnie? Did you ever?"

"Never," said Vinnie.

"But what'll I do with it? I mean so's Mother won't see? She won't let me keep it, you know she won't. I gotta hide it someplace. What'll I do, Vinnie?" He laid his free hand on Vinnie's arm, fright robbing his eyes of their pleasure. "You help me, Vinnie, will you?"

Vinnie pressed her finger to her lips. "Sh," she said. "Don't let them hear."

But it was too late. Marie, straightening up from the fire, saw them whispering and guessed a conspiracy. "Joie!" she called in a round, deep-echoing voice. She had resumed her watchful position, with legs apart, arms akimbo. The heat of the fire lent no kindness to her face, and the roasting fork was a menacing weapon.

"Vinnie," cried Joie. He closed his blouse front and folded his arms across the lump the rabbit made. Vinnie smiled at him, pledging her loyalty.

"What have you got in your blouse, Joie?"

Joie made no answer.

"Tell Mother. What is it?"

Still he said nothing.

"Joie!"

"A little rabbit." He spoke as though he were betraying the little animal. Tears hovered in a cloud over the sunlit meadow of his eyes. Pride had fled from his face, and in its place fear, pale and inarticulate, made startling contrast with his freckles. "It's just a little one," he pleaded.

"I don't care how little it is, or how big. If it's little, it'll be big some day, and if it's big it'll be having little ones all over the place. Take it right back where you found it. And hurry. Supper's all but ready."

Joie made no move. The battle had just begun.

"Joie, do you hear me?"

"It's my rabbit."

"Joie, how can you say that? You take a little rabbit out of its nest and then say it's yours."

"I didn't take it out of its nest. I was sitting in the middle of a moss, and all of a sudden he was there right next to me. Just like that." He winked to show, once more, how it was there, but his eyelids pressed the tears from his eyes, and they rolled down his cheeks. "I was sitting in the middle of a moss," he repeated, "and all of a sudden——"

"I don't care where you were sitting, Joie Carter, I won't have a rabbit cluttering up my house. You might as well make up your mind to it now. Sooner or later you will have to take the thing back up the hill, and you might as well do it now, and have done with it. And hurry, before your supper gets cold."

Stewart, walking up from the daisy field, fully clad but carrying the daisy chain in his hand, called out to Marie to let him keep the rabbit. "It might be a male," he suggested. Mrs. Morison gave her attention to cutting the bread. Susan stood at the fire, encouraging Marie. Juliette took refuge behind her umbrella.

"After all," said Stewart, "if women will have children they should remember that children will have rabbits."

His words fell limp. Only Harrit heard. Stifling her laughter, she rolled in the pine needles.

"Joie, go this minute. Don't let Mother have to speak again."

Joie turned to Vinnie. The warm thing was moving against him. Its cold nose poked at his navel, and its whiskers tickled the delicate surface of his stomach. "It's moving against me," he said, the tears streaming down his cheeks. "I can't let him go, Vinnie. He's moving against me.

"He came to me," he added. "I was sitting in the middle of a moss and all of a sudden he was there, just like that."

Vinnie knelt down beside him, covering him over with the mantle of her affection. Between Joie and her lay the young rabbit moving slightly and making a frightened sound. She held Joie carefully lest she hurt the animal between them, but she could feel the motion and the design of its body. Together they protected it. Vinnie thought that the thing moving against her might have been a baby.

"Let him keep it, Marie." She hardly knew that she spoke. "He loves it so. It will make only a little bother, and it must be worth it to see him so pleased with a thing. I'm sure Joie will clean up after it. Won't you, Joie?"

Hearing Vinnie's comforting voice, Joie took heart, and running to his mother he opened his blouse. "See, Mum, he's such a nice one. He's so soft. He feels good against me. And he likes me; he's got his nose right in my button."

Vinnie marveled that any woman could stand up under such entreaty. For a long moment in which mother and son gazed at each other, the parent punishing the child with a cold smile, the child pleading through his tears, Vinnie pressed her hands against her cheek. Don't say no, she said to herself. Don't do it. He'll remember it, and when you're old he'll tell you and you will cry at night. When your son is grown and when he has gone away, the memory of today will be stark company. Don't do it, Marie. Don't do it.

Upon whatever gods there might be, though Vinnie found it impossible to believe in any, she called. Upon the saints of men and the saints of animals; upon the gods of love and the gods of mercy; upon nature; upon the Virgin Mary. Such things, thought Vinnie, such little things as this, make children hate, make rebels out of men. Of such little things comes sorrow. Of such trivial substance, joy. These little things, she thought, make life or mar it. Don't mar Joie, Marie. You wouldn't crush his head, you wouldn't deform his body. Keep your hands away from him, keep your hands from his heart. Let him have his rabbit.

"Go now, young man."

Joie ran to Vinnie. Once again she took him in her arms.

"Joie, darling, don't cry," she said. He trembled against her. It is worse than death, thought Vinnie, to see a child like this. "Don't cry, Joie, don't cry."

"My dear Vinnie," said Marie. "If you don't mind!"

"But I do mind, Marie. I mind very much."

"Come," said Mrs. Morison. "Supper is all ready."

"You may take the rabbit back after supper, Joie. Come now and eat, and stop your crying."

"I'll take the rabbit, Marie. I couldn't eat under the same tree with you. And don't wait for me to come back. I'll walk home alone."

Joie gave the rabbit to Vinnie without hesitating. They had more in common than their love for the little thing. After she had taken it in her arms Joie ran toward the thicket in which Mr. Morison had taken refuge, but just as he reached it, he stopped and ran back. He laid his head close to the rabbit, smelled of its fur, touched noses with it. Then he kissed it, his tears falling like warm rain into its ears, and ran back to the thicket where Mr. Morison waited with his arms outstretched.

Vinnie turned from them. She walked carefully, bending the branches gently lest she break them. To Stewart, who watched her, spellbound, she was like a saint, like a madonna with the rabbit in her arms. Her dark hair, braided about her head, reaching out with fine feelers to catch at the sunlight, was like a halo, and the blue of her dress was lost in the shadows of the bushes; she became a part of the woods. She walked away from them up the hill, picking her way carefully, her head bent, her body lending protection to the frail animal. She looks as though she were saying a prayer, thought Stewart.

And he was right.

II: THE BELLOWS OF AN ACCORDION

IT WAS very still, the delicate songs of birds and crickets lost in the folds of the afternoon. On the hill no leaf stirred, but in the valley a soft wind rustled the leaves of the willow trees, and glimmering silver in the sunlight, they were like silent bells. It was one of those fragile and immeasurably beautiful afternoons when living, alone, is important; one of those days when the volume of the soul seems infinite, when every sound that falls upon the ear, every sight which the eye beholds, is a thing imperishable and secure. The sun, shorn of its heat, and lying naked behind a cloud, sent out long shafts of light, tight and even, like the warp threads of a loom, and far below, in the valley, farmers, riding thoughtless behind their teams, were covered with a thin layer of gold, like gilded human toys.

Vinnie looked down into the valley. Below her sat the family. She could see that they were talking, though no sound of their voices could be heard. Seeing them from above, they were squat little people, grotesque and pitiable. She felt, as she lay upon the rock, the rabbit cradled in her back, as though she were a gargoyle hewn for some medieval cathedral. My family, and they know so little of living. She felt saddened and hurried. Time passed too rapidly. Life would very soon be finished, and she would have learned so little. My family, she said again. They know so little of living. The stream of her pity fell heavily upon them, like rain emptied swiftly from a spout.

She looked down upon them and with the blade of her imagination made deep incisions into their lives. "It was strange," she said aloud, "how little I wanted them to come. But now that they're here, I love them all." Her mental fingers moved swiftly through their task.

They sat below her in the valley, unaware of the operation being performed upon them. Paralyzed by the mechanical motions of life, they were unable to react to the delicate instruments of sympathetic thought. They ignored beauty in one another and shut themselves in so that no faintest perfume of delicacy could escape. Like butterflies, once beautiful, who wind themselves into a second cocoon, thought Vinnie. Her blade cut carefully.

How did it happen that Uncle John told me about Grace? How

do I come to know my own mother so much better than before? How can it be that people stay hidden for years, and then suddenly stand naked before you?

Filled with the tragedy of each of them, feeling herself to be not only Vinnie but the shell for these others as well, like a pregnant woman who loses her identity and becomes something more than she knows herself to be, Vinnie's mind was weighed down with too many sorrows. She felt that her body was deformed by the size of the pity within her, as the woman Dorothea must have felt before being delivered of nine children at one birth. And as Dorothea might have regretted her conception, so Vinnie rebelled against the tragedy grown great within her. Don't they know that there is no time for weeping? Don't they know that they have given half of themselves to me, that now I also am responsible? But no abortive measures were successful. She was impregnated with the fierce fluid of individual failure. To Vinnie it was not tragic that each should have had a very unhappy experience; tragedy lay in the fact that no one of them had grown beyond it. And now here am I, deformed by their deformity.

The fine needle of memory drew the poison from Vinnie's mind, as a doctor, to relieve pain, draws fluid from the spinal cord. She heard again Harrit's voice: "Don't let it come. I don't want it to come. Don't let it, Vinnie, please." She will grow beyond it, thought Vinnie. She will not be deformed, nor paralyzed. She surely will grow beyond her tragedy. But how can it be that she didn't tell me sooner? How could she have waited so long to reveal it?

The days folded back upon themselves like plaits in the bellows of an accordion. It was no longer today, no longer Friday. It was Wednesday, day before yesterday, at daybreak.

"Don't let it come. I don't want it to come. Don't let it, Vinnie, please!"

Vinnie, to whom each day offered a miracle, wakened suddenly, and discovered her sister kneeling before the window. She watched Harrit kneeling there, her bare feet arched against the floor, her elbows on the window sill; she noticed the straight back and the delicate curves of her thighs. Seeing her there, kneeling like a child at his mother's knee, Vinnie thought how like a mother to Harrit the earth, the day, the sunrise were. A cricket, making plaintive song in the wide daybreak, as though the world were too beautiful, even for crickets, caused Harrit to throw back her head in delight, and Vinnie marveled at this first morning miracle. Such beauty was seldom felt, such beauty as the cricket's song and Harrit's body that veritably leaned against the day and added beauty to it. To watch Harrit move was beauty, and to watch her when her body was still was prayer. Grace, strength, spirit. How can one person have so much? thought Vinnie. She loved her own life for allowing her a part in Harrit's.

"Don't let it come, Vinnie," whispered Harrit again.

"Don't let what come, Harrit?" Vinnie turned over in the bed that she might give her whole attention. With this serene generosity Vinnie gave herself to everyone, bestowing not only a sort of compliment thereby, but an understanding that made speaking simple. So now she gave herself completely to Harrit's delicate world.

"The fall! Don't let it come." Harrit turned from the window, and Vinnie thought how shamed the beauty of the daylight lay before Harrit's beauty.

"Why not, Harrit?"

"It's too lovely. It comes all of a sudden and then it's all over, and there's not time enough to enjoy it as much as I want. Only yesterday it was spring and the robins came, and now today I heard a cricket and the air smells of forest fires, and before I know it winter'll be here, and everything will be thin and cold, like an old woman sleeping alone. I like the fall best of any season of the year, anyway."

"You say that about every season, Goosie. You said it about spring and summer, and you're saying it about fall, and when winter comes you'll say it about winter."

"Oh, I know, but I do love the fall. Don't you, Vinnie?"

"Love it," said Vinnie, which allowed Harrit to return to her own world of listening and beholding. Vinnie bade Harrit get back into bed or put something warm around her, for though the morning was bright, the air was cold and penetrating.

"In a minute I will, Vinnie. In a minute," she said. Vinnie, knowing she would, recalled herself from Harrit's world, and again turning in the bed, lay separate, no threads of thought binding Harrit and herself together.

Far out in the valley below her a lean spire pricked through the threads of sunlight, but Vinnie, being transported to day before yesterday, did not see it.

Vinnie followed the pattern of her imaginings through the rooms of the house. She thought of Juliette whose bedroom was downstairs. She imagined her in bed.

Juliette wore a gown that buttoned high at her neck, and a nightcap that was starched and ruffled. She would lie straight in her bed, the sheet turned carefully back over the blankets and her arms close to her sides. She made only the faintest mound under the bedclothes, except where her feet stood up straight like two sentinels on guard. The most unbending feet, they were, thought Vinnie, and wondered if they ached from holding them so stiff. She was so immaculate, so precise; her motions were measured, her step never varied; she always walked with her left hand laid carefully over her chest. You always said chest of Juliette. Remembering Harrit's body, at once alert and peaceful, pure and suggestive, Vinnie pitied Juliette. She understood her queer little steps and her immaculate hands that traced the edges of the pleats in her skirt, or lay palm down upon her lap, like two nuns absolving themselves before some stern and superperfect god. How it must feel to look at yourself at night when your clothes were off and see a body so barren, so sterile! Loving life and her own body because it was a symbol of life, an instrument with which she could measure all living, Vinnie understood Juliette's life, though only momentarily. How could anyone love life without first loving himself? she asked. How could you love all men if for yourself you had no love? If you were not beauty, how could you know beauty; if you were not song, how could you sing? But everyone was beautiful, everyone was song, all history lay within you; there was knowledge and love, conquest and hate all pulsing under your skin. But Juliette didn't pulse; her blood trickled through her veins. And thinking this, Vinnie loved her aunt for the things she had missed, and pitied her for the thing she was.

How strange, how good to see her in this way, she thought, and wondered why she had never seen her so before. She was afraid to think lest she lose this new ecstasy. She felt that she stood on a high place, with all the world lying below her. The sun shone, and the earth was exquisitely divided into seas and lakes, forests and fields. She was about to comprehend all things; she lay breathless beside her sister, trying to preserve this new thing for the future. Her head was cleared of all doubt and fear, and she felt herself to be everlasting and infinite. Remembering Juliette who was garden without flowers, body without beauty, the sensation of discovery disappeared: a miracle had just escaped fulfillment.

Juliette with wings on her head, Dad who was sorry, she knew not for what, Mother who comforted her body with her hands, shifting her gown as she walked and breathing a fierceness into the air. Vinnie who was filigree, Harrit who was fire and lay like a prayer beside her.

So Vinnie considered them, drawing them closely together, pulling the threads of her mind tight, as one draws the shirring string in a bag or a chemise.

What do they mean, these people? asked Vinnie of herself. Juliette who is barren, Mother and Dad who lie apart at night, Harrit and Vinnie who are filled with anticipation of the future? What does it mean that I should lie this way beside my sister? she asked. What does it mean that so beautiful a person should be my sister, that we should be born of the same parents? Seeing herself blessed beyond all other men, in having a sister who was life and prayer and child of the earth, Vinnie turned to Harrit, whose hands had used Vinnie's back for a muff, and whispered, "What does it mean that we should be different from Juliette? What is it that makes us beautiful?"

III: FIRE AND FILIGREE

A FLOCK of pigeons, flying high, looked like scraps of paper as their wings caught the light and lost it, and as they dropped slowly to the earth it was as though the sun had burned them, for without the sunlight white upon their wings they became dark spots and settled down carelessly among the trees like charred paper. The rabbit, lying asleep in the curve of Vinnie's back, waked suddenly and forsook his shallow cradle for her arm, but she gave no ounce of her attention to him, although she stroked his ears and laid her nose into his fur. She was oblivious of herself; she had forgotten the rabbit and Marie and Joie and his child's grief. A late-singing mourning dove linked her even more closely with the day before yesterday. The eerie sound was like a ghost making music upon a reed.

They had lain, she and Harrit, for some time, silent, unmoving. Remembering now, it seemed strange that she should have had no premonition. She had been thinking of Juliette and the way her hands lay upon her lap, and while she thought of how her family slept in their beds, and how her parents slept apart at night, Harrit had been waiting to talk to her.

"Don't let it come. I don't want it to come. Don't let it, Vinnie, please."

A hurricane of emotion beat in upon Vinnie as she began to comprehend her sister's meaning. She was unable to evade its force and lay weak beside Harrit, waiting for her to continue. Neither of them betrayed the feeling within her. They lay motionless, as self-contained as Spartan women, as fair as Helen.

"It will be born in February."

Vinnie, standing on the brink of tragedy, lost her foothold and fell leaden, the breath beaten out of her by Harrit's words, her wingéd protection of reason proving worthless. She was sucked deep into sorrow. Pregnant, pregnant; my sister; pregnant. The words filled her mouth and her ears, and her eyes smarted with them and she breathed them down into her lungs. Pregnant. My Harrit. Harrit! O God, no. Not Harrit. Me, rather. Make it me.

"Are you sure?"

"I have been to the doctor."

"But is there nothing you can do?"

"I waited too long."

"What did George say?"

"He doesn't know."

"But Harrit, you must tell him. You must tell him at once and get married."

"Marry him? But I don't love him!"

"You don't love him? But how could you—— Oh, Harrit!"

"Vinnie, you don't know anything about that sort of thing. You don't know what it is to be persuaded by a man's body. You may have wanted Peter; I am sure you have, but not because he was a man. You wanted him because he was Peter."

It is easy for me to be good, Vinnie said to herself, because I am never tempted.

"Do you think I am awful, Vinnie?"

Awful? Harrit awful? How can I tell her what I think? How can I tell her how admirable she is?

Harrit turned suddenly, and Vinnie, holding her in her arms, comforted her. They clung together, Vinnie's lips covering Harrit's hair with kisses, and Harrit's tears hot against Vinnie's skin.

The body lost its identity; it was not Vinnie and Harrit who clung together, washing each other with their tears, their bodies intertwined like the roots of trees, their hair lying in a careless, two-colored pattern. It was not Harrit who was fire and Vinnie who was filigree. It was a pregnant woman, frightened and sorry, and another woman who was kind.

A seagull, far inland, cut into the light. Its pointed wings, opening and closing with miraculous precision, were like the blades of a knife. Vinnie watched, hypnotized by its beauty, but her mind's attention was in memory.

"Tell me about it," she said to Harrit after a little, and Harrit, her face in the pillow, whispered with Vinnie.

She told how he praised her, her body, the touch of her hand. How he smoked in the firelight, his eyes half-closed, his toe tapping the floor. How he stood behind her, whistling, and laid his hands on her throat, slipped his hand into her dress. She remembered the little fires in her belly, the sweat on her hands. She remembered her back. She whispered it all to Vinnie, shaking. And laughing a little. She had laughed that night.

Harrit had laughed and leaned back against the wall. When she moved her head the rough surface of the stone caught at her hair. It was late in May, but they welcomed the fire on the hearth, for the stone hut was still damp and the earth about it cold from the winter. In the woods owls called out, and occasional birds, wakened by a twig's falling or by the electric shock of a shooting star, sang out in ecstasy or fear. A single candle set on a shelf of stone that jutted out from the wall burned slowly, the wax enlarging upon itself and joining the candle and the wall. Other than that there was no light except that of the fire that blazed, fell back and blazed again, like lust. In their laps they held wooden plates, carved thin and polished to a rare finish. About the rims words were carven: "Forgive us our trespasses." The words encircled Harrit's plate in a cylindrical prayer.

Vinnie knew the hut to which they had gone. She and Harrit, walking in the autumn, had come upon it, and had met George. Knowing the place, and understanding her sister, it was not difficult for Vinnie to reconstruct the evening. Harrit spoke little. Between her sporadic words breathless pauses allowed Vinnie to imagine what had happened between that moment and the next of which Harrit would speak. It was evident that Harrit was recalling it all, step by step. Vinnie chose to accompany her; and if in her imagination she occasionally side-stepped, if she walked through mire where Harrit trod upon dry ground, or if she mistook a weed for a flower, a cloud for an ominous shadow, it must be forgiven. The paths of the imagination are more varied and more illusive than the cryptic paths of dreams, and filigree and fire are not molded in twin crucibles. Whatever the design of their travel, they arrived together, having seen the same landmarks, having smelled the same fragrance, now sweet and again pungent. Had a psychologist been able to look simultaneously into their minds, had he been able to cut into their lives, as Vinnie had done, lying face down upon a rock, the rabbit asleep in the crook of her arm, he would have been astonished at the likeness of their thoughts. But being a psychologist he might not have known what sweetness and understanding do sometimes exist between sisters. It was not sagacity on Vinnie's part. It was nothing more nor less than devotion which allowed her to move and feel oblivious of herself. So, as they lay childlike in the bed, Vinnie rebuilt all that had taken place, and with occasional hints from Harrit learned how it had happened.

The night pressed down around the hut like snow falling, quiet and heavy, and the wind fretting about like a nervous woman sent the smoke down the chimney. The air in the room was laden with the smell of it, and their eyes, smarting with it, were bright and red, like the eyes of lovers.

"His eyes were so bright," Harrit said. "And I didn't want that." And George, beholding in her the likeness to that strange forerunner of passion, thought: My God, she wants it too.

So quick are lovers to misunderstand, thought Vinnie.

He threw more wood onto the fire, and the flames, jumping out from the logs, made a crown of fire about his head as he knelt at the hearth. His mind matched the fiery crown. It licked out at things, and quickly satisfied, retreated, leaving only ashes to show where it had been. Like fire it never retraced itself, but waited until a new growth had sprung up to offer a more hearty meal. The fire, burning bright and swift, lighted Harrit's face and cast it in shadow, so that without changing the expression of her features she appeared now to smile and again to fall into a sort of elegiac reverie. Her eyes were shut not only to the smoke but to this man who vexed her mind and excited her body. When he moved across the room to bolt the door it was as though some anodyne had relieved a great pain, for his presence near her was a weight, and she found it difficult to breathe.

He stood watching her, filling his pipe slowly and carefully. She leaned back with her eyes shut, her hair following the cracks between the stones. She seemed not to breathe. Wave upon wave of beauty broke about her; it was as though she were a rock in the sea, upon which the little birds would stop to rest, and over which the water would glide, reverent and still. About her feet bright fishes would tangle the threads of their color, their soft tails waving like chiffon scarfs, their sharp noses encircled with wreaths of minute bubbles. Seaweed would grow about her ankles in green lace pantaloons, and upon her breast the sea would weep. Hearing the sound at night, sailors would wonder. When the wind, in a fury of jealousy, beat at the sea, she would stand adamant, betraying in no smallest way her inner torture.

If, indeed, such there were. George was unable to decide.

He moved back across the room to Harrit. She might have been a deaf-mute, and blind besides, for she showed no sign of knowing he had come. He was unaware that his moving towards her held her as in a vise.

Once I loved a man, she said to herself. Once I loved a man, but it wasn't like this. I didn't wait for him to have done with his words. Whatever he said I listened to, and he spoke of curious things. Of mathematics and women. And he spoke of music. If he had talked of microbes and hunting I might have liked it better, because then I could have talked with him. As it was, I only listened. But I never sat with my eyes shut, no matter how much they burned. What is it this man is talking about? Heredity? Environment? But I'm not going to marry him; I don't want children. Once I loved a man, but it wasn't like this.

A wide desert lay between them. They walked forever towards each other and never met. Once, possibly, in their whole existence, the sun and the moon would be at such a point in the heavens as to cast two shadows from one to the other. And so in their own shadows they would meet, and shadow being like shadow in substance, they would mistake the shadow for the reality and exchange some intimate folly. But when the sun sank deeper into the night and the moon rose higher into the sky, the shadows would retreat, like tidal waters from the shore, and by the time the zenith had been reached they would again be two creatures separated by a wide desert, an illusory oasis marking the spot where they had met.

"He told me of something that happened in New York," said Harrit. "He was standing in the window, and he saw two men and a woman supported between them. He thought she was ill. She was very handsome and well dressed. The janitor of the building across the street was sweeping the sidewalk; his shirt hung out over his trousers, and he had long hair. He wore a large black hat; he was colored. George said he was pretty terrible-looking. The men turned in at the house. The woman regained consciousness just in time to see this ominous-looking negro. George could only see her back, but he said that never in his life had he seen the terror that the woman betrayed. One of the men got behind her and shoved her in, like a cow into the slaughter pen."

This is what the hundred generations of humanity have won for us, thought Vinnie. To such heights have we ascended. Christ and the Virgin Mary have lost their meaning. They are no longer symbols of the spirit and of the flesh. They have no denominator in common with the human mind.

"What did he do?" asked Vinnie.

When Harrit answered, her voice sounded as though she had spent the night in a grave. "Nothing," she whispered.

George, watching Harrit as he talked, had seen her eyes open wide and tears gather in them. The tears rolled slowly down her cheeks, and reflecting the light of the fire they were like drops of blood. What kind of woman is this? he said. I talk to her all evening of marriage, of our life together, and all evening she sits with her eyes closed, still as death. She sits without saying a word, like a deaf-mute, or someone stricken with sudden and utter sorrow. And when I speak half in jest of something I saw, she opens her eyes and weeps. What kind of woman is this that sits by my fire and refuses to answer me? What does she think? What does she feel? What is it like to weep? And he fell to speculating about the mysteries of her body, wagering with himself that she was thus, or so. He could not know that she wept for him.

Harrit cried into her hands. How can he sit there and tell me about it? Doesn't he know how I hate him? He tells me he did nothing, and expects me to love him. Why don't I go? Why don't I tell him I hate him and go? Oh, because he's going away. For two years he'll be gone and I won't have to see him at all. I won't have to think of him. I'm here tonight because tomorrow he's going away. Anything can happen in two years. God, how I hate him! What if I had been that woman? What if he had stood there watching me be shoved into the doorway, and done nothing about it? God, God how I hate him!

"Tell me, Harrit, were you ever in love?" George's voice rapped like a fine hammer upon her hate.

Once I loved a man, but it wasn't like this. The words crowded into her mind. No, that's not what you say when someone who loves you is going away. Once I loved a man. But it isn't true. I still love him. You don't stop loving people when they die. It's as though they were spending a month in the country, a long month, where there is no mail service, and no telephone. Once I loved a man, but God, it wasn't like this!

She raised her head and turned her face to the fire.

She was unutterably weary. No exercise tires the body with a rapidity comparable to the speed of hate. Like a leech it sucks vitality from the mind, and although in a spurt of anger the body may acquire incredible strength, the fury ended, the body is weak and as feeble as that of an old man. She had no respect whatever, and certainly no love, for this man who saw a woman forced into slavery, and did nothing about it. What good would a man like George be in time of crisis? What support in childbirth, what comfort in death? A man, however wise, needs great compassion.

What would it be like to live with him? Every day and every day he would be patient and kind, and every day he would continue, argumentatively, his pursuit of peace of mind. He would allow me no tears, no change of mood. He would even smile sparingly to save his energy for more important things. He would walk around my mind as though it were a curio under glass. No, I could never live with him, thought Harrit.

A young owl screeched. It sounded like a baby, and Harrit caught her breath. George watched her. Her eyes were suddenly alive, her whole body listening. She was no deaf-mute now. Every sense of her being was awakened and waiting. Fear makes any body strangely articulate, but with natural beauty like Harrit's, it can transform a person into a symbol, and Harrit became a cornered animal, sure prey to the pursuer. She was a bird poised for flight, but four stone walls and a roof surrounded her. She was a fish encircled with speed, but a mesh of net ensnared her. To George she was a woman of surpassing beauty with a body as fine as silk and as stern as steel. What would it be like to love her? What if she wept? My God, how I want her!

His passion was fanned to a great flame by the breeze of his imagination. He was eager to know her body with his hands in the way that a hungry man longs to possess the food behind the glass. One can break the glass. One can risk it. Better to wait.

The owl screeched again, and Harrit, the shadows hanging from her in tatters, ran to the door. George was quick to follow.

"It's a child," she said, her eyes in the half-light gleaming like the eyes of a coyote. George stood laughing at her, his back against the door.

"Silly girl. Don't you know that's an owl?"

She moved from him, her body aching with his nearness. She sat once again by the fire.

"Open the window," she said.

"Never. You might fly out. You might really, you know. For all I know you may be a vampire."

"Please open it," she said. It seemed to her that she would die if no breath stirred in the room. The room grew small around her. Storm clouds came up from every corner of the sky, a round range of mountains grew and grew together. When they met above her there would be complete darkness; no air would stir. The room came closer and closer about her.

"Please open it," she said again. She was suffocating with fear. "I can't breathe," she said. The pulse of her blood was like hammers in her ears, her whole body moved as her heart beat. George stood in the dark watching her. Prey and pursuer, bird and four walls and a roof. The owl screeched close by the hut. "George," she said, covering her ears with her hands, "I can't stand that noise!" Let me out of here, she said to herself. Let me out. I can't breathe. Oh, please let me out! Let me out!

To hold off the inquisitional walls she thrust out her arms.

She wants me, thought George, and he moved slowly towards her. As he touched her she withered in his arms, like a frail flower. He mistook her despair for consent.

So quick are lovers to misunderstand, said Vinnie to herself again. She withdrew her memory and her imagination. The moment at which the sun and the moon would cast two shadows, one to the other, had come, and shadow being like shadow in substance, each mistook the shadow of the other for reality, and exchanged folly.

A single cloud sailed lazily over. From the valley a man's voice, calling the cows home for the night, rose like a spire. The wind ruffled the water of the creek, and the path of sunlight shining upon it was broken up into bright pennies of light. The rabbit lay asleep in Vinnie's arm, and the late-afternoon air was pure and transparent, like the skin of little children.

IV: THE BURROWS OF GRIEF

And then there is Mother, thought Vinnie. The man in the valley who was calling the cows home for the night began to whistle. It was a mournful tune, a sort of doleful pleasure, like charity. There is Mother, she said, and examined her own knowledge of her so that she might behold its structure. There is something malignant in each man's life, thought Vinnie. But she herself seemed immune.

As she recalled that she had discovered her mother's tragedy on the same day that she had wept with Harrit, it appeared to her that there was a special omen attending that day; this whole reunion. So far it had been a series of discoveries. Every morning she wakened half-frightened by what the day might reveal, half-thrilled by the anticipation of it. She was like an artist whose work is about to be brought before the public; an artist who, beset with dread and ecstasy, wishes he might sleep for a year, but would not, if some kind fairy were to offer it, accept a potion that would make him drowsy for an hour. Waking, Vinnie would close her eyes quickly to coax herself back into oblivion, but with her eyes shut her senses would be filed to a keen edge, like the teeth of a saw. One day she had discovered Harrit and her mother. Another had offered only the sunlight shining in a cup of tea. Another day their being bound by blood seemed incredible. So it had gone, but it had started with Harrit and her mother.

Harrit, her hair spread out on the pillow like a copper fern, fell asleep, but Vinnie was wide awake, unable to sleep. They were two earthen jugs, one full, the other empty. The contents of the full jug had been poured into the empty one. It was no longer Harrit's tragedy; it seemed to have lent itself to Vinnie, to her body, as though the fetus had been transferred from the one woman to the other. There is nothing to be done, Vinnie said to herself. Nothing to be done. She got noiselessly out of bed and dressed hurriedly. Her mind ached with its new knowledge,—a grab bag from which countless ribbons emerge. Each ribbon of thought was pulled tight; only the slightest increase in tension and the bag would break.

Vinnie went out into the hall, climbed the stairs to the attic, and in the corner, behind boxes and barrels, and cushioned in thought, she settled herself.

While Vinnie, burrowing in her grief, hid herself in the attic, her mother lay in bed waiting for the clock to strike. She awoke at ten minutes to five and lay there, waiting for the curtain of the day to be lifted with the five strokes of the clock. When they had struck she would get up, obeying some inner summons. She would turn down the covers and move cautiously, sliding her body slowly to the edge of the bed so that she would not waken Henry, who slept apologetically beside her. If she wakened him he would ask what she was doing at that hour of the day. Not that she would have told him in so many words. She couldn't very well tell her husband, at five in the morning, that she was getting ready to die. Besides, she was a woman who refrained from airing her intimacies, and dying, to Mrs. Morison, was a most intimate affair. More so than being born, than giving birth herself.

The clock struck five, and Mrs. Morison fell into the routine of living. The movements of her body were like consonants in speech, and like the consonants had some natural grace, some sense of beauty. Mr. Morison turned over on his side of the bed just as Mrs. Morison got out on her side. He turned over with a magnificent gesture, taking possession of the bed finally, triumphantly. It was altogether admirable, and Mrs. Morison admired fully as she stood looking down at him. Standing this way she was more like a child with a toy than a woman near fifty who was up at five getting ready to die.

The years of her life hung heavily upon her. They were like delicate veils, one hung upon the other, making a tapestry of infinite layers and varying shades of color. Standing beside the bed, looking down at her husband, Mrs. Morison began lifting the veils of her life, one by one. Last year and the year before, and the year before that, and before that and before that. She wondered, as she stood there in the bedroom, what made a life go on, what started a life in the first place. She wondered how she had come to marry Henry. She lifted the veil of the year of their marriage. The brightness of it hurt her eyes, the beauty of life, recalled momentarily, sucked at her heart like a leech. Drained of her strength, she let fall the veils of her thought, and she set her mind to dressing, and combing her hair.

Up in the attic, hidden behind boxes, Vinnie could not know what her mother was doing. She was not concerned with thought of her; she thought only of Harrit, of her firm body; of her integrity. But as she sat thinking of her sister, and her mother, downstairs, let fall the veils of her mind, they were joined inevitably, like two points of land by the water that lies between them, by Vinnie's wondering what her mother would say to Harrit when she learned that she was pregnant. She must be very kind to her, Vinnie said aloud, and suddenly started to weep, fearing the cruelty that women may reveal when confronted with the delicacy of their children's love. Mother and daughter joined by fear. No union at all, thought Vinnie, and propped up behind the boxes, she fell asleep.

Downstairs her mother walked quietly through the room, through the hall, down the stairs. Tiptoed through the living room to stand in the door open into Juliette's room. Juliette slept religiously, a sort of piety invading the place and an air of circumspection hanging like dew from the objects about her. As on other mornings Mrs. Morison wondered what it was that drew her to this sight of her husband's sister, what it was that made the room so definitely virginal. Perhaps it was the underclothes folded neatly on the chair. Or the shoes placed exactly, side by side. Or the umbrella hanging on the foot of the bed. Or was it the shades drawn down? Or the sheet folded back over the blanket?

Mrs. Morison asked these things of herself every morning. It was not from habit that she questioned, but from a deep and very real wonder that the sight aroused in her. Every morning she stood there, asking herself what it was, what it felt like to be Juliette. She went noiselessly up the stairs again, past Mr. Morison sleeping triumphantly on the bed, past the closed door behind which Harrit lay sleeping. Poor Juliette, she said to herself, and opened the door that led to the attic.

As the smell of old things greeted her, Mrs. Morison ceased wondering, ceased caring. This other thing, this strange and greater thing, filled her. She was thrilled and excited, like a runner at the start of a race. She closed the door after her, and very quietly, not to avoid disturbing the others, but to keep them out from that world of excitement which she found each morning upon opening the attic door. As she climbed the stairs, breathless, her excitement increased. Coming to the top she whispered, with a gayety that would shame the whispers of lovers, I'm getting ready to die. She surveyed her world.

Shelves built from the floor to the ceiling lined the north end of the attic. Cupboards took up the west wall. Against the east one were trunks and boxes, weirdly shaped bundles, countless magazines. In the center of the room stood a long table with scrapbooks, pencils, labels and paper clips. Mrs. Morison summoned the attic together as she sat down at the table. It was no longer a gabled room with shelves and cupboards, boxes and barrels. It was something important, something ordained; it was the paradise of a woman lonely in the midst of things.

Letters. Today it would be letters. Monday, with one week of letters before me. I must work hard and rapidly, to get on to recipes and poems, colored silks and old lace, hats and white cottons. Letters. She began sorting them out.

The rhythm of laying them down, of picking them up and laying them down, of reaching and placing, placing and reaching, swayed her body. One, two; one, two; and one and two and one and two and. The letters rose in a wall around her. Mother, Father, Ida, Jane. A few from Harrit, many from Vinnie. She sorted them out, put them in order, labeled them. There were letters which her own mother had received, letters that had grown yellow and brittle with age, and crumbled like dry leaves when her fingers touched them. The handwriting on them was so fine as to be unbelievable; it was like the lines of etchings. Mrs. Morison wrapped the letters in paper and labeled them, printing the words on the label with care, loving each line that she made.

Reaching and placing, placing and reaching, her body swayed with the rhythm. Her body swayed, and the years of her life, hanging in layers about her, took the same tempo, and the memories of a woman with a body fulfilled and living complete grew taut within her mind, and she was like an instrument well tuned and surely strung. Touching now this letter and now that was like playing first upon one string and then another. One, two, one, two; and one and two and one and two and. The years of her life followed the beat of the metronome, the memories marched by impersonally, like an army or a herd of sheep. One, two, one, two; and one and two and one and——

"God," said Mrs. Morison.

Vinnie waked suddenly. The room pressed down about her. The windows offered no breath of air, the shelves and cupboards no surety. The table became a maze, the stacks of letters, with their old tales told, a labyrinth. What is she doing here? she thought. What is my mother doing here?

"God," said Mrs. Morison again, and laid her head down on the table.

Vinnie waited.

After some time her mother looked at the letter in her hand, looked past it, out over the trees, out to the hills. She was afraid to go on, knowing that she would be sorry, but one does not discover, twenty-odd years after it has been written, a letter whose seal has never been broken, and leave it unread. She sat in the attic of the house in which she had borne four children and lost two, and looked out of the window, holding in her hands the letter she had long awaited when she was twenty. And here it was in her hands, her life lived, her body fulfilled. Here in her hands she held her life, as she had dreamed it. She sat in the attic, her memories piled carelessly about her, her husband lending distinction to the bed by the way in which he lay full upon it, his arms outstretched, his legs straight.

She, Mary Morison, waiting for her courage to return, sat in the attic above him, while Vinnie, her daughter, waited for the room to enlarge, for the walls to fall back, the ceiling to lift, the air to move about. These things happened, one by one, and Mrs. Morison read on. She read slowly, as one reads a foreign language, for it was a tongue strange and wonderful to her.

Vinnie, like a mole in the darkness of his burrow, scuttled about through the network of her mind. Her mother sat before her reading a letter, and as she read the tears rolled down her cheeks. Her grief was inexhaustible. This woman who sat before her, this woman who sat in the midst of the attic, and by the movements of her body summoned the room together, making something important of it, something ordained and beautiful,—this woman was her mother. Why should she sit here in the attic weeping? What is there that could make my mother weep? Vinnie was besieged with a great curiosity, and then at once was smitten with a sense of shame, for, for the first time in her life, she thought of her mother as a woman like herself,—a woman who has choices to make, children to bear, sorrows to endure. She was ashamed that she had never thought to question her mother's happiness, had never considered her as anything other than a woman whose most distinguishing experience had been in bearing her children, in bearing Vinnie and Harrit. Up one burrow of thought and down another she ran, digging at the soil about her with the claws of her anguish. My mother who sits in the attic and weeps. My mother who has the same feelings as I. It was as though she had always looked upon the likeness of her mother, upon her statue, or a painting of her, and only now, for the first time, beheld the living, breathing woman. And emerging into the light of her mother's experience, Vinnie was blinded by the brilliance of it, and hidden behind the boxes and barrels, she wept silently, and through her tears beheld a strange beauty descend upon her mother.

That beauty mingled with her hair, like so many jewels, losing itself and becoming a part of her. Her mother sat like a statue, and Vinnie's comprehension of her as a person, instead of one mainly, if not solely, her mother, shed its light upon her until she was covered with glory. It was shed over her whole body, even to her hands. They were no longer old hands. They had bathed babies, they had nursed men in their illness, women in childbirth. They had assisted in death. And as people sometimes defend themselves, or others, knowing they are in the wrong, so now Vinnie sought to persuade herself that her mother's life had been full, that it had been complete, that no more could be asked of any life than she had had in hers. But as she assured herself of these things, the voice within her cried out. You are lying, it said. You are lying.

Yes, said Vinnie, I'm lying. She understood what it was that sent her mother bareheaded into the rain, what it was that made her comfort her body with her hands, promising it respite, and shifting her gown as she walked with a fierce gesture.

She has had a home and a husband and children, she has had enough to eat, enough to keep her warm. What more could any woman want? What more is there? But Vinnie knew that there was something more that a woman could have, something more her mother had wanted. She did not give it a name, she did not label it as her mother did the letters about her, the bits of silk, the scraps of lace. She did not call it happiness, nor joy, nor peace. But it was all of these, and something more. It was that other thing that gave meaning to life; that other thing was illusive, nameless, but it gave joy and beauty to the smallest moment. It is a sort of enchantment, Vinnie said to herself.

Perhaps she loved another, thought Vinnie, and if so, what has it been for her to live with my father? What can it be like to sleep with a man in whose body you find no delight? What must it be to eat breakfast every day for twenty years with a man who holds no pleasure for you, whose hands confer no blessing? What, indeed, can life mean with no magic whatever in its bosom?

And now she pitied not only her mother, but her father as well, for his devotion to her was evident in the gifts he brought her—a blue jay's feather that he found in the path, or a single flower with a single leaf. What is it that life does to people? asked Vinnie.

Thought of those years of her mother's conceiving and bearing, nursing and burying her children, sheared Vinnie of her comprehension of existence. She saw her mother as a quiet woman in whose heart no ecstasy could flicker, in whose mind no joy could ever be. It is a rare world, the world of enchantment, and those who dwell there are particularly blessed, no day too dreary for delight, and no delight too frail for great enjoyment. But the land of the enchanted is not a world ruled by Bacchus in which the inhabitants make merry from day's end to day's end. It is a land, rather, whose inhabitants walk now over roses and now over thorns. Their pleasure is minute, and their grief, exquisite. As their joy may be in gentle things, so also may their sorrow. So it happened that Vinnie contributed to her mother more sorrow than actually existed. She was not tragic; she was only very lonely.

While Vinnie thought of her mother, her mother allowed her

mind to take whatever course it chose, loosing the reins with which she had held it, with which she had guided herself to this forty-sixth year of her life. What she had read meant little now. It was like reading a book, like hearing a story. She did not identify herself with the woman to whom the letter was written; she did not even remember the shape of the hands that had written it. But she realized that if she had read this letter twenty years ago, she might now possess that more-than-something; she might, though less well fed and colder at night, have held her life to be something precious, instead of sitting in her attic preparing for death as a bride prepares for her marriage.

But where has it been, this letter? she asked. Between two letters that had belonged to her mother she found it. That meant——

Mary folded the letter and laid it inside her dress. Leave the weak unharmed, leave the dead buried. When a hero is defamed, leave the laurel wreath upon his grave, leave the song sung. But I loved him, she said to herself. I loved him. And this my life, fulfilled, complete. Her hands moved in a tired gesture, and the attic lost its dignity and became a gabled room cluttered with boxes and barrels, magazines and bundles.

As Vinnie watched, the veils of her mother's life separated and fell apart, leaving her naked, leaving her shorn of experience, of living, of identity with any man, or any child, or any dwelling. The jewels fell away from her, and she was left stripped and shivering.

She is very lonely, thought Vinnie, and wept behind the barrels. Her despair for her mother was like a flurry of snow. It lashed her cheeks and blinded her eyes and everything that she beheld became a part of the storm. When it had passed, when the wind of despair no longer blew against her, when her eyes were no longer blinded, her mother had gone. Only a wide stillness lay over everything, as after snow; even the peaks of her ecstasy were snowcapped, and wisdom bore down upon her in a glacier.

V: NO ANODYNE

"You are ridiculously lovely, Vinnie."

Vinnie, who considered herself ridiculously plain, turned to her cousin, but seeing his eyes upon her, turned from him again, preferring to ignore his adoration. While she had sat on the hilltop, looking down into the minds of her family, Stewart sat below, thinking of her, his thoughts rising with extreme delicacy to encircle her.

"Tell me," she said, "why you came up here."

"To talk to you. To ask you about Uncle John. About the microscope, really; he's never without it. It's a positive mania with him."

Vinnie forgave the interruption of Stewart's appearance. Only the catastrophe of John's life filled her mind. She wondered what she could tell Stewart. It would not be easy to satisfy his curiosity. One thing she knew for certain, however. She would not tell him all that she knew. She would not lay Uncle John open to his scrutiny, nor betray his trust in her. Stewart lay back in the grass, watching the rare, elfin beauty of Vinnie's face as she sorted over the details of John's story, choosing carefully the words she would use. This I will tell and that I will not. This is betrayal, but that is not. So Vinnie combed the threads that had spun a firm cord for her uncle's heart. She recalled each point minutely, from the beginning of his revelation to the end of it. It had begun quite simply.

"Tell me, my dear," he said to her. "Can it be that at your age and with such gentle hands, you are not in love?"

They sat together in the garden, hidden from sight by a hedge of little trees. The other members of the family were resting: Mrs. Morison in her room with the windows wide and her clothes off, a tall pitcher of grape juice next to her bed; Stewart in his room with a book of Spanish painters propped up before him; Marie sleeping heavily, and Susan soaking her feet; the children in the back yard, each with a book and a pillow, and Juliette in her room with the curtains drawn and a black stocking laid over her eyes. Vinnie forgot to take account of her father, but he was in the workshop, whittling beads of finest wood for Mrs. Morison's birthday, and Harrit, driven to despair, exercised madly in her room, the tears streaking her lovely cheeks. Vinnie, going out into the afternoon to escape the sight of Harrit's face, came unexpectedly upon her uncle hidden behind the little trees. It was a sanctuary to which she retreated unnumbered times, and coming now to it and finding it occupied by another, she was like a priest without a sacristy, a hermit without a cell. She stopped to talk to him, thinking he must find ants through a microscope intolerably dull.

While Mrs. Morison rested with her eyes open and a glass of grape juice in her hand; while Mr. Morison puttered about in the shop, devout and awkward; while Harrit, fearful of bearing a child whose father she did not love, strove to dislodge the root of its being with heat and cold, stretching and compressing; while Stewart fled from himself to the gaunt figures of El Greco,—Vinnie and her uncle, thoughtless of the others, discoursed behind the hedge of little trees.

The flowers, like fragile fruit, grew close about them, and one hummingbird, illusive and secure, treaded air around a bush of ageratum. It was an afternoon sinister in its silence. The quiet lay like a poultice, drawing the sliver of tragedy to a fevered head. Vinnie, as she sat looking into the center of a morning-glory, wondered what antiseptic of the mind she could apply. When the sliver is out, how shall I disinfect the wound? Seeing thunderheads unroll along the margin of the sky, she prayed for a storm.

"Tell me, my dear. Can it be that at your age you are not in love?"

"But who said I wasn't in love, Uncle?"

"Nobody said you were. That is the thing. If you were to be married, we would all be talking about it."

"Can't one be in love without expecting to be married?"

"Oh. Forgive me."

How strange, thought Vinnie, to be drawn into this partial confession. She had never before revealed to anyone but Harrit her love for Peter, and finding him now a common thought between her uncle and herself, she was frightened to have spoken so easily of him, and delighted with her uncle's quick perception. "He is like you, Uncle John. He, also, is a doctor."

"Poor devil." If he had been comforting a child he could not have spoken more gently.

"Don't you like being a doctor?"

"I don't like being responsible for so many lives."

"No, I shouldn't like that, either."

The body and its infinite detail, with its immutable miracle of creation, was to Vinnie cause for everlasting wonder. The study of human anatomy delighted her—the application of science to the shell of the spirit. She thought first of the beauty of the body, with its unlimited variations and its intrinsic poise. A group of people sitting together about a fire, or walking heedless of one another down a street, were to her like a Bach chorale, while boys playing ball, catching and throwing, throwing and catching, were like men antiphonally singing. Dancers with their reedlike grace; athletes with their certain feet and sinuous thighs; these alone, resolved prismatically by beauty into a spectrum of human light and shade, endeared the body to Vinnie. But it was not only symmetry of form, certainty of rhythm, clarity of meaning that she thought of. The spiritual thing that evolved physical perfection; the incomputable variances of spirit, the misshapen bodies and the deformed minds of imbeciles, the dearth of grace in the lives of miners and all impoverished laborers; these, also, she thought of. Sitting in the garden it was to ugliness and disaster that she turned her mind. It was as though she knew what manner of revelation her uncle would make, and thought prelusorily in the vein of catastrophe.

"I would like to talk to you, Vinnie, if you have time." He begged for her attention. He told her in few words of the operation which had been fatal to his wife. Vinnie supplied the details, remembering operations she had witnessed. Like an actor who identifies his part with his own life, Vinnie imagined one patient she had seen to be her aunt, and one surgeon, her uncle. She recalled the hospital with its aloof air and its impersonal furniture; the rooms with their deadly stillness, and the sound of feet muted by rubber heels and constant tiptoeing; the currents of deftness and silent motion; the breathless suspense of a port that harbors transient, human cargo; the relentless bearing and dying of humanity.

Grace, with her hair tied back and her eyes hard in fright, being rolled down the hall noiselessly. The elevator door, with its rubber buttons, closing certainly upon her; the nurses smiling with eyes that had wept themselves dry. The elevator stopping, the noiseless wheels rolling in minute and eternal circles, the tension of the mind when faced with the possibility of death. The torrent of emotion that breaks through the dam of reason; the utter futility of all living, untimely death in the balance.

In one room Grace, a woman who loved life, who was devoted to her husband, waiting for the moment to come which would solve the mystery of her illness. In another room John, her husband, his heart torn between hope and fear, standing before an open window, breathing deeply to calm his nerves. In one room a woman praying that she might not die; in the other room her husband, with no prayers. In one room Grace, remembering their early and exquisite love; in the other room John, remembering another woman. Grace who was faithful, John who was not. Man and woman. Life and death. The moment was at hand.

Careful hands assisted her, lifting her gently onto the table. Great lights, their glare diffused, filled the room with an unearthly brightness. Instruments of infinitesimal variation lay spread upon a table. Eyes smiled above masks, heads bent in concentration. The room filled with silent people moving meaningfully about. Then John and the two surgeons who would perform the operation coming into the room, their presence charging the air with the imminent task, their voices strong and vibrant, nerves balanced, their hands unbelievably beautiful in their rubber gloves. Grace smiling up at John, saying simply: "I love you, John." The room coming suddenly to life. Grace willing her body, in a last flicker of consciousness, to the powers of love. Then the rapid breathing and the hot forehead; the incision clean as lightning; skilled hands working deftly. Layer of flesh, layer of muscle; veins, arteries, peritoneum, and finally the malignant secret of the woman's ill. Sponges, needles. The woman wrapped in blankets, tucked around with hot-water bags, wheeled away down silent corridors, visitors in the hall standing silent as she passed, wondering what it felt like. The woman laid into bed, the room darkened with shades, the dull tread of feet going on unceasingly in the hall. John in the shower, not believing. Downstairs a woman who wouldn't live long; upstairs a man who detested his life. Then to her room swiftly, regret for the past putting quicksilver in his shoes. In the room with him two nurses rubbed the woman's hands, consulted their watches. The eyelids pulled back. The eyeballs revealed.

John walked to the window.

From the deep wells of remorse he sought to pull his attention from the wide future. He was striving to bring himself up with the present. Beyond the window lay the hills and the river. Beyond them, hills and more hills, rivers and more rivers, he said to himself. And they last and are infinite, but we are finite and perishable. We are fragile and delicate, but the hills are everlasting. But what has our life together been? It is a joke, because I loved Leila. It is a lie, because I don't love Grace. And realizing suddenly that soon this woman whom he once had cherished, whose body had yielded him pleasure, whose mind had done him no harm, would die, he discovered that he had not ceased to love her.

"John," she said. "John."

Hills and more hills. Rivers and more rivers. They last and are infinite. And the soil within the hill, the current within the river, they are everlasting. But what shall become of our life together? The fulfillment of our bodies, where has it gone? And the sense of reality and the sense of time, wherever again shall I find them? In the hills and more hills. In the rivers and more rivers. But she has spoken to me and I have not answered. She will die before I can speak. Let me speak, let me go to her. But he had not the strength to turn.

The door opened and closed, and dull steps went softly down the hall. "Yes, darling," he said, and exerting every atom of energy, turned slowly from the window. But the cycle of her existence was complete. He was not John, surgeon and husband, beholding his dead wife. She was not Grace, whose husband gazed upon her. They were merged in death.

"When I turned she was dead."

The word swelled and enlarged, taking added meaning as it grew. The hummingbird ceased treading air and sank out of sight into the bushes. It seemed that the whole earth would be covered with the sound of it, that it would lie upon the earth like snow. Vinnie held the morning-glory in her teeth. The stem was soft and sweet. She was aware of the roundness of it.

"People do frightful things, don't they, Vinnie?"

"Hideous."

Her uncle turned from her and, removing his microscope from its case, sought the stamen of a heavy flower. Vinnie watched carefully as he bent over it. He was a moderate man in height, in build, in humor. She knew vividly what Grace's life with him had been. Comfort, boredom. A man who shaved slowly, who read the paper at breakfast, returned late in the afternoon to dress slowly for dinner, eat, and settle himself for a careful perusal of his medical papers; or spend the evening making his calls. At eleven, if he was not out on a case, he suggested they go to bed, and with formality they did so, he lying in his bed comfortably, glad that passion no longer cut short the hours of sleep; Grace lying in hers, lonely in that way peculiar to women who love their lords unreciprocally. John dropping swiftly off to sleep, Grace, hearing his heavy breathing, stealing downstairs to sit before the fire which they had left dying on the hearth. She would recall their first passion and wonder what leech of fate sucked the vitality from people's lives. She had been honest, she had been kind, she knew not why she had failed. Superbly loyal herself, she never thought to question John's loyalty. What she must have felt, thought Vinnie, as she lay on the operating table saying simply, I love you, John. How she must have rebelled against the hypnotic powers of gas, and sought to retain consciousness long enough to hear her husband say: "I love you, Grace." But John was silent, and the anesthetist swift. There was no accounting for what people might do.

"But that is not all," said John.

"No," said Vinnie. And she then grew suddenly indignant at the endless adolescence of her family. Their lack of wisdom, their lack of humor, their ignorance of integrity. Their lack of maturity, without which relationships become a farce.

"No, that is not all."

"Tell me the rest."

"Afterwards I married Leila. I didn't love her. She died. It's strange, Vinnie, the things people do. I thought I loved Leila. Grace died. I married Leila, but not because I loved her. You can never wholly love a person for whom you have committed some grave transgression. It is a strange thing that integrity is more important than love. People do frightful things, don't they, Vinnie?"

"Everyone does." Her words were unmeaning, remote for him.

In the house Mrs. Morison lay staring up at the ceiling. Stewart nodded over his El Greco, and Marie and Susan clipped their toenails. Juliette stood before her mirror resenting her sparse image, while above her, sleeping on the bed, lay Harrit, exhausted by her very fertility.

"He blames himself for failing Grace." She gave her attention now to the valley, to Stewart who watched her with devotion, to the sky and its infinite quiet. She looked down upon the heads of her family. They were oblivious of her.

VI: AN ENCHANTED PLACE

"There is an island," said Stewart, "off the coast. A very beautiful island, but a secret place. I never tell anyone about it because I want to keep it to myself. It's like a girl—it is like that with any man—I do not want another to possess her, nor even to see her beauty. I cannot talk about her body, nor praise her hands. To love her takes all my strength. I cannot even tell her very well how I feel. She must know it by my eyes or my voice. Even my back may betray me. And this island, you know, is very beautiful; I would like you to love it. I should like to share it with you. It is a very beautiful island."

Vinnie listened. The stillness of the evening had descended upon her. "Tell me about it," she said.

"There are about a hundred miles of shore. The island itself is long and narrow. It is connected to the mainland by a slender bridge that looks like the skeleton of some prehistoric animal. Nobody lives there, except at one end there's a little town built up of driftwood and pieces of tin. The inhabitants make their living by fishing. It is a very strange little town. There are lots of dogs, but they are all very small, and they do a great deal of barking. They stay among the shanties and never go into the island. And there are lots of children, and they're nice children. They're shy when you come upon them.

The water is warm at the shore, and the children dig holes in the sand and build castles of sea shells. They're very dirty; the grown people seem to be a race of their own. They have dark skin and pale eyes and black hair. The wind dries their skin and blows sand into their faces and they are old before they are thirty."

Stewart spoke slowly. He looked out across the marsh and the meadows, loving each thought, caressing each memory. He was silent for a little, and Vinnie shut her eyes to keep the vision of the island.

"They are silent people. The women smoke pipes and watch the sea gulls for hours without moving. Once I sat among them in the evening, and they were so still I thought I was dreaming and that they were statues. They go barefoot, and their toes are long, and they pick up clams with their feet. When a storm comes, and they come quite often, they all flee into the island with the children and the dogs, and after the storm is past they go back to the place where the town stood, pick up the driftwood and start building new shanties."

"And the rest of the island?" said Vinnie.

"The rest of the island is what I would share with you. It is nothing but sand dunes. Great hills of sand that is as white as snow. One dune dissolves itself in another, and that one in yet another. It is like the waves of the sea."

It is like people, thought Vinnie. They are all combinations of other people. People are dissolved in one another as the dunes are dissolved. One seldom meets a person complete within himself. One dune lends beauty to another, one person adds beauty to the next. And still one does not love a mass. One loves individually. One loves Stewart, for instance, but not necessarily the people who have made Stewart what he is. Or one loves Peter. Certainly one loves Peter.

And there is not long to wait. A couple of hours and I shall see him. And she began to wonder what it was about Peter that she loved. If she had not happened to love him she would have taken little notice of him.

"Nothing grows but one creeping vine," Stewart was saying to her. "It has blue flowers, like a morning-glory. You stand at the top of a dune, and all you see is rolling white sand and blue creeping flowers growing on a dark stem, and sea gulls that dip down almost to the earth and shoot up again. It is very still. Only the birds circling about and calling, and little dogs barking in the distance. You can go naked in the sunlight, and it is warm and comforting, and you discover that you are quite as beautiful as the island. At night you roll down the sandy hills, and the sand gets into the crevices of your body, and you feel very clean. And then you bathe in the cool water and run along the beach to get dry. And you talk quietly. The island is the most exciting place I know."

"But doesn't anyone else know about it?"

"Apparently not. Few people ever go there."

"How long do you stay when you go?"

Stewart's smile was like a window thrown open. "As long as I like. There's no one to tell me to go, and the people in the village don't mind. They sell me fish for a few pennies and seem to have no curiosity at all. The island takes care of you. You sleep in the cradle of a dune. You eat fish that swarm the place. You wash in the sea. There is fresh water in green pools. If the night grows cool, you cover yourself with sand, and in the morning shake yourself free of your bed. There are no covers to straighten, no floors to sweep. I took my paints with me once when I went to stay for a month, but everything was so beautiful that I couldn't take my eyes away long enough to paint what I saw."

Tears hung in Vinnie's eyes. Stewart watched her, enchanted. He knew why she was weeping. For that alone I could love her, he thought.

Below them the family bubbled about, like vegetables in a kettle. Seated on their rock, Stewart and Vinnie courted silence. It is good to get away from people, Vinnie was thinking, while Stewart said to himself, How do I come to have so charming a cousin? They smiled at each other.

"What are you going to do with the rabbit, Vinnie?"

"I'm taking it home to Joie."

"Marie will despise you."

"I despise Marie. Of course I don't, really. But I'd like to. But you know, she has such big feet, and she walks like a peasant, so I can't despise her, because I like peasants."

"Vinnie, you're a fool."

The notes of their laughter, like links in a chain, were welded together. Their laughter hung in festoons from the hill; the air sparkled with the sound of it, and the leaves shook. The hill became a chandelier of sound. The whole valley was covered with a canopy of joy. Even the family, who had seemed so insensitive, looked up at their rock. Mr. Morison shaded his eyes with his hand. John deserted his microscope. Marie and Susan saluted them with the roasting forks, and Juliette waved her umbrella. The children scampered away into the bushes.

"Those vixens are coming up here," said Stewart. "Can't we hide?"

"If we hurry." And while the children raced up one side of the hill, Stewart and Vinnie fled along the ridge.

They came suddenly upon a deep ravine. Sheep grazed there, lifting their small heads quickly as they heard the intruders, and then turning their attention again to the grass that grew luxuriously on either side. Shadows possessed the place. There was a small log house whose doors and windows were boarded up. The roof was thatched, and a rain barrel, long empty, stood beneath a broken waterspout. Dead apple trees surrounded the house, and their exquisite bare branches twined and intertwined like the words of lovers. Save for the tinkling of the sheep's bell there was no sound. Shadows and silence were the owners. The serenity held them spellbound.

They sat down under one of the trees and leaned back against a tombstone that was covered with moss and creeping vines. "Is the island lovelier than this?" asked Vinnie.

"This is an enchanted place," said Stewart.

The sheep moved slowly over the grass. At the bottom of the ravine a little stream meandered towards the valley. In the cool bright water stood a crane, one leg tucked up out of sight. Flies, like teasing children, dashed at the water and retreated, their wings making emerald music. It seemed as though no human creature had ever before been there. Thrushes, copper birds with fluted throats, sang in the bushes, darting out occasionally to prove their reality. It was a cloister, with pine trees for pillars and bird songs for bells. A doe came skillfully out through the trees, her pointed ears quivering like the petals of a flower. She bent down to the stream, and her little legs with their pale fur were like slim poplars growing at the water's edge. A buck followed her, and together they drank at the stream. A song sparrow fluttered down between them and drank of the cool water, tilting his head as though he would burst into song. The sheep's bell called all furred and feathered things to worship, but the sheep himself ignored the summons and nibbled at the grass. The shadows lay in a blanket over the sheep and the grass, the deer and the thrush, and the whole place was bewitched.

"The island is beautiful in a different way," said Stewart. "And I was there with someone I loved. That makes a very great difference."

For a long time Vinnie waited, and waiting, wondered what it would be like to love Stewart, to be loved by him. His lean body, his long fingers, his cadaverous face, with the high cheekbones and the great dark eyes. He would either be very exciting to love, or he would fill you with disgust. Either he would love you with unbearable passion, or weakly, in a frightened way.

"She was a strange person. I never could tell what she would do. Once she disappeared for a whole day. I thought she had drowned. But she was in the village playing with the children. When I found her she was angry. Once she threw sand in my eyes and I groped about like a blind man for hours. When I got the sand out she was laughing at me."

"Are there really people like that?" said Vinnie.

"Quite like that. She was very beautiful."

"Where is she now?"

"I don't know, and somehow it doesn't seem to matter. I loved her a great deal, but she never loved me. I think she hated me sometimes. I used to say to myself that she must love me a little, or she wouldn't have gone to the island with me. But now I know she didn't love me at all. She was fond of me. She liked my mind and the way I paint, but my body irritated her. I would walk towards her across the sand, and she would shriek out and laugh at my legs. She pretended it was in fun, but I know she never would have made a game of it if it hadn't bothered her. Sometimes she said I looked like a skeleton. But there were times when she would let me love her, and then she was most extraordinarily kind. But suddenly she would leave me, as though she had just remembered how unlovely my body was. Once when I tried to caress her she hissed at me, and ran to the village and hid."

People are dissolved in one another. People are not wholly themselves.

"Tell me, Vinnie, am I serpentine?"

"Look!" she said. Twin lambs suckled their mother.

They sat close, she and Stewart, leaning against one headstone, covering the graven name with their bodies, covering the memory of the grave with their thinking. The quiet was now and again heightened by the long call of an owl; the stillness, by the passing of a bird. There was a sense of intimacy with death; only a thin frosting of grass separated them from layer upon layer of soil and silence. Where the grass began and her body ended, Vinnie could not tell. She was all one with the grass, and the grass with the grave, and in a rare abandon of reason she found herself to be a part of the earth; she could not tell where the wind touched her body. She tried to feel herself as a thing in space, a moving substance with form that was defined, but she could find no outline of herself in the air about her, and looking at herself in the shadows, she could not distinguish between her dress and the grass. And then there was this person beside her for whom she could feel nothing. The marble slab had frozen her heart.

She knew that Stewart was turning and turning a thought about in his mind. She grew dispassionate. She was glad that her heart was frozen, that it had been taken from her, like the core of an apple. Stewart spoke.

"I do adore you, Vinnie."

Slowly the name rewrote itself on the headstone, the little mound of earth beneath her meant something, but from the unreality out of which she had come, she ran headlong into this new emptiness. The effort of hearing what he said wearied her. They were surrounded by pines whose branches made music. Below them the sheep grazed lazily and the shadows of hawks circling above them fretted the little valley. He cannot mean what he says, she thought.

"But I am your cousin, Stewart."

"That doesn't make you any less a woman. You know, Vinnie, you are very lovely. Your hair and your somber eyes. And the way you move. And all the things you say, but more particularly the things you don't say. Like Uncle John, for instance. It isn't true, what you told me about him, but you won't tell, and I love you for it. And for Joie and the rabbit."

"The rabbit! Where did I leave it?" Her eyes filled with fear, and she was like a child.

"You left him on the rock when we ran to hide."

Already she had disappeared among the trees.

Stewart followed her. Occasionally he caught sight of her between the pines, and now and again he saw her bend to pass beneath a branch. They went separately, Vinnie moving easily, like one who is used to the woods, Stewart following her, the motions of his body making him grotesque. Vinnie thought only of the rabbit. She thought of the frightened rabbit and Joie's eyes puckered with grief; of Marie and her big feet and her adamantine discipline. Of the joy Joie would have had at finding the rabbit asleep on his bed. I must find it, she said over and over to herself. I must find it. She ran into branches that caught at her hair and scratched her face. I must find it, she said again. Stewart lost sight of her.

When he finally came to the rock, he found her lying on her back with the rabbit asleep on her chest. For a long while they were quiet, Stewart sticking pine needles into the braid of her hair. She lay with her eyes shut, the lashes lying like fine embroidery against her cheeks.

Stewart thought that she was asleep, but she was thinking of him. He is serpentine, she said to herself, and thought again of his love-making. His hands would seek hers in a frightened manner; he would not know well how to love a woman. Poor Stewart with sand in his eyes, she said, but she understood how the girl with the pale hair had done it. Stewart with a body like a snake. Does he really love me? She shuddered at thought of his caressing her.

"Are you cold?"

Vinnie did not answer.

"Tell me," she said after a bit, "what you are painting."

"Nothing. I stopped painting for a year. I was afraid of becoming a trickster, because I was working on a theory that design and color are disassociated. It is very hard to explain, and there are lots of difficulties. I don't mean to be a trickster; I would rather not paint at all than be dishonest about it. I can't put it very well in words."

"I know what you mean by tricks. It's like an actor who plays stock. He makes a grand show, but it's not the real thing."

"Yes, it's something like that."

"And yet not like it."

"Not exactly like it."

The wind edged in about them. Below them houses turned to homes as women lighted lamps, and cows gathered magic as they trod slowly through cool pastures, silent dogs bouncing gayly beside them. Owls, like beggars, flew from tree to tree and disappeared in shadows; night hawks piqued the stillness that held the valley.

"Couldn't you love me, Vinnie?"

"Not that way, Stewart. Not as you want me to love you; but if I were someone other than your cousin I might love you very much. But I am not someone else. I am Vinnie Morison, and I am sitting on a hill hiding from my family."

As she spoke there was the sound of someone moving in the bushes. They turned to see Juliette's umbrella appear in the midst of the foliage.

"My God," said Stewart, "I can't stand that woman. She's a fright." He disappeared over the edge of the rock. Vinnie saw him bumping down the steep hillside. As he stopped, finally, in the midst of a prickly bush, he waved merrily at her and vanished among the trees.

She turned her attention to Juliette, who stood at the summit of the hill looking out over the valley. The umbrella was forgotten and lay open at her feet; it yawned at her. Her body gained beauty from the sunset. She was no longer haggard, but rather a woman taut and fine. In her hands she held a paper bag, but she had forgotten it. She was spellbound by the beauty before her.

At last Juliette turned to her. Tears seamed her cheeks. This is not Juliette, thought Vinnie. This is some virgin saint.

Juliette came towards her, holding the paper bag as though it were a bouquet. "I thought you might be hungry," she said.

Far down in the valley a solitary loon called out. Only its echo answered.

VII: BEAUTY ON STILTS

THEY SAT for a long while together, the peace of isolated places hanging over them. Vinnie held the rabbit in her lap and ate slowly of the sandwiches Juliette had brought her. She beheld the design of the valley, the colors of the twilight. She listened to the familiar sound of crickets drumming with their tiny wings; all that she beheld and heard filled her with delight. The world enchanted Vinnie.

But while she reveled in the beauty about her, Juliette was filled with grief, and her face was like that of one who suffers extreme pain. I had forgotten the world was so fair, she said to herself. She did not, like Vinnie, behold the design of the valley, nor the colors of the twilight, but she saw that many people lived regardless of one another in little houses where lilacs grew in clusters at the doors. She saw that one might walk for miles across the marsh and never meet a soul. She saw that the world was wide beyond her comprehension, that there could be generosity in all living, and the beauty that she saw frightened her.

And so they sat, two women upon a hill, one who was young, the other wishing herself younger. For time had taken a deep draught of Juliette's life. There was little but the dregs left, and realizing this suddenly, Juliette was like a drunkard who, waking, finds his glass empty. Like a drunkard she staggered against reality, fell back and struck at it. Her senses reeled as she looked out over the valley and considered the immensity of existence, of the earth and stars and the stars beyond sight. The world seemed very gay with its meadows and pastures crisscrossed with bright streams and dark woods. She had no extraordinarily clear vision of herself. Her thoughts reeled to the future, to death and the disintegration of the body, but she was drunk with the desire for life. Strong liquor warmed her throat and quickened her mind. To Vinnie, who was watching her, she was no longer Juliette; she was beauty on stilts, giddy with life.

Juliette lay back in the grass and ran the pine needles through her fingers as though she were combing wool. Vinnie watched her inarticulate hands.

"See!" cried Juliette. "That lovely bird!"

"He looks as though he were ice skating."

Having lived like a turtle beneath her umbrella Juliette had not often seen birds flying miraculously high. The birds she remembered were robins and sparrows that fluttered close to the ground. She had not lain in the grass, nor climbed to high places. A turtle moves slowly and with effort, the very shape of his shell keeping him from expanding, from turning over on his back to gaze at the heavens. Life to a turtle must be a most laborious affair. Such it was, at least, and certainly, to Juliette. Or so it had been.

"I feel like a different person up here." The words sauntered out of her mouth.

And then shortly they started to talk about Joie and the rabbit, Marie and Susan, Stewart and Mrs. Morison.

"I sometimes think they are all dead inside," said Juliette. "But I suppose they're not, really."

"No," answered Vinnie, "they're not, really." She lay flat upon the rock and looked down onto the family.

"You know," said Juliette, "I feel so funny. I feel as though I had never known anything before. I feel as though I were just being born. You know, maybe I came full-grown, like Minerva from the head of Jupiter. Only I'm being born out of the head of the valley." She was delighted with the idiocy with which she teased herself.

"Only it's my pain. The child is not supposed to suffer at birth, but I do." She looked about to see if the hill was in labor. "You see," she said, "there isn't a quiver in the valley."

That she suffered, Vinnie was sure. Her eyes were bright, as they are when one has a fever, and her cheeks were crimson. Her voice had a sharpness to it that sounded like blades in her throat. A sudden twist of wind showered her with leaves and fragrance. "I'm dizzy," she said. "There's so much wind and so much space. It's like being God." She caught the rabbit up in her hands and pressed him to her cheek. "Isn't he soft?" she said. Her laughter was small and crisp.

"If I were to open my arms, I could fly," she said.

"Don't do it," said Vinnie. "I want you to stay."

Vinnie saw that life had suddenly become a living thing to Juliette. It was all glitter and bright sound. It was like a woman with little feet who clips across a hard floor in high-heeled slippers. It sparkled like a dress of sequins (and the dress fitted her well), like bright fish in water, like silver in the hands of the needy. It was as though

Juliette had been a beggar all her life and had come suddenly into great wealth. Her mind was like a Christmas tree hung with tinsel and silver baubles. The mere passing of a bird caused the baubles to quiver, the glowing candles to bend down their flames, the little white angels to flutter from their sweet-scented branches. Little birds of cotton nested in the tree, and bells of thinnest metal made harebell music. Her hands that had always been so immaculate, her hands that were like two nuns absolving themselves, had learned a new beauty. They held the little rabbit as though it were an offering.

"My dear Vinnie, I am so happy."

Vinnie wondered if Juliette were not also just a little holy, happiness being a miracle for the layman. She imagined Juliette sanctified, a statue made in her likeness and placed in a niche in a long cathedral. Saint Juliette Morison: because she was happy.

"Saint Juliette," said Vinnie. They laughed together, vying with each other in the clarity of their tones. Juliette's joy was evenly distributed, like sunlight shining through a lattice. This I shall never forget, thought Vinnie. I must remember everything. She laughed at her own greed. What do I know of sorrow, she thought, since I am never lonely? What do I know of life at all? What thing do I know in the world, save that the earth is beautiful, and that I love Peter?

The children were singing. They sat around the fire, and Harrit and Stewart lay in the grass, smoking. Marie and Susan stood guard at the fire. Mrs. Morison and John, both expert putterers, fitted the picnic things into the baskets, while Mr. Morison sat in the shadows. Sibyl's pheasant feathers drooped over her face, Mary and Jane threw pine cones onto the fire. Joie sat cross-legged, his chin cupped in his hands. He was not singing with the others.

"Poor Joie," said Juliette. "He'll never forgive his mother, not even when you bring him the rabbit."

Vinnie turned to her, and Juliette mistook her wonder for interrogation.

"He won't, you know. Children never forget. And it's funny, the things you remember. At least I remember funny things."

"What do you remember?" asked Vinnie.

"I remember that my mother gave away my first patent-leather slippers, and I begged her to let me keep them. I thought they were very grand. I used to take them to bed with me, and I tried to share my candy with them. They were human to me. When I wore them I stepped lightly to keep from hurting them, and I forgot about my underwear in lumps at my ankles and my teeth set too far apart. Joie will remember about the rabbit. But the things you remember when you're older. They're strange, too. Just words, for instance. And people's hands. Their hands and their mouths."

"Their hands and their mouths?" It was a long time since Juliette had talked intimately with anyone. That she wanted to say more, Vinnie was certain, and so she provided steppingstones in her questions, and Juliette, placing her feet carefully at first, walked swiftly through memory to the past.

Candles burned steadily on the table. The faces of the family were immobile, the shadows as certain as paint. In the kitchen Cook tiptoed from sink to stove, from stove to sink; tiptoed into the room, moving from one to the other silently. The smell of flowers gave a strange flavor to the food. Stale smoke squeezed into the folds of the curtains. The candles burned with a demoniac precision; the eyelids of the flames never drooped. Cook labored into the room. Her body was stagnant: through it no beauty had run. Her breasts lay heavily in her dress, and her hands, like twisted cord, encircled the bowl of rice. Her large body frustrated Juliette.

Juliette looked from one to the other. Frances, with her glasses pinched onto the bridge of her nose, who stirred her tea with vigor, scraping at the bottom of the cup. Henry leaning back, blowing smoke rings into the air. They did not quickly dissolve, but hung about his head in clusters. Blue curls, thought Juliette. Mamie, who ran her fingers over her endless chain, and ate of her rice one kernel at a time. Dode, whose soft hair and red cheeks enhanced the grief of her eyes. Myself, thought Juliette, and tried to see herself as though she were a stranger. Juliette. Very plain. Very thin.

We are like birds, she thought. Juliette, Frances, Henry, Mamie, Dode. Juliette is a sparrow, careless of her food, picking at the dung of horses. Sleek body, unpleasant voice. Void of beauty. Frances scrapes at her cup like a dark grackle, and holds her head as though she saw with the end of her nose. Her hair grows grim about her face; there is no intimacy between hair and cheek. Henry is a mocking bird. No stability to him. Mamie. My God, why doesn't she leave her chain alone? Your fingers are not beautiful, Mamie. Neither is your neck. Stop playing with your beads. Mamie is a jay. She mistakes sound for tone.

Cook trundled into the room. Cook is a pelican. Her neck is too big.

"I suppose," said Mamie, "you won't mind if I pack up the things right away? The old bureau I'd like. And the piano. And the bookcase that stands in the hall."

Henry drew hard upon his cigarette. Like butterflies ring upon ring of smoke fluttered out from his mouth. They encircled his head in a helmet of smoke. He was indiscernible within it. His voice pierced the helmet like a fine steel blade. "It seems a little premature, somehow. Let's wait till tomorrow."

The room grew breathless. The air was absorbed by the walls, and the walls became a sort of spongy matter. The design on the wallpaper grew heavy, like damp moss about the room. The door squeaked shut behind Cook, and the slight breeze made by the closing door shook the tatters of Juliette's mind. If I sit very still, thought Juliette, the pieces will fit themselves together. She dared not breathe. She looked from one to another, shifting her eyes but not moving her head.

Under the table their feet pressed into the carpet like lifeless things. They seemed not to be a part of the body. Juliette's feet entwined the legs of her chair. They were crude and ugly. These feet, they never knew passion. Dull legs sheathed in silk. Without beauty, without purpose. These ugly bodies. My sisters and my brother. Myself. God, we're an ugly lot. The deceitfulness of our legs under the table. Our smiling eyes.

"Mamie, let me see your beads."

She reached across the table for them. A woman reaching across the table for her sister's beads. Relentless candles. A man with a helmet of smoke. I must sit quiet, thought Juliette, and drew her hand back slowly. The beads lay in her lap in a glittering pool.

There is no sense to it all. I am not even alive. I must sit quite still.

We are all birds. Juliette is a sparrow, Frances is a grackle. Juliette's thoughts swung back and forth like a pendulum. Henry is a mocking bird and Mamie is a jay.

Juliette is a sparrow,
Frances is a grackle,
Henry is a mocking bird
And Mamie is a jay.

The moment was endless; towards it all living pointed. Nothing existed beyond the walls of the room, save Cook whose shoes squeaked in the kitchen. Maybe she's sitting on the table and her shoes are walking around empty from stove to cupboard and cupboard to stove. Juliette rang the bell. The sound of it was like a trumpet call. Cook rumbled down from her heaven.

"Your feet, please," said Juliette.

Cook protested.

"You must get some new shoes." No one seemed to have heard. Juliette was not sure it had happened.

"Have a peppermint, Frances."

It seemed now that Frances listened with the end of her nose. Next she will drink with it, thought Juliette. Frances's poor husband.

"Poor Walter."

They all looked at her.

"Because of Frances's nose," she explained. The beads slipped from her lap like a thin child. They made a brittle sound as they came together under the table, and Dode, frightened, spilled her water. She sat, watching the wet spot increase. The tablecloth absorbed it. It spread like the sound of laughter.

"Ring for Cook," said Mamie. The room absorbed the sound of her voice as the tablecloth absorbed the water. Juliette sat motionless. A swaying snake would have fascinated her less. The walls of the room edged in to see; the moss hung close about them. It breathed upon their necks like an animal. The candles stared at the wet spot. The spongy matter of the walls sighed audibly. Dode's hair hid her face from Juliette; it was pale and soft. Sin is a gaudy thing, she thought.

A sharp noise in the kitchen, and they turned their heads to the door; the walls breathed upon their necks. Cook pushed open the door with her head. Pelican, thought Juliette. Her neck's too big.

"They buried her with her head downhill!"

The eyelids of the candles drooped. The walls were sucked back into place.

"Juliette, you look like a rat when you chew." Mamie's voice ate the stillness.

"I always remembered that," said Juliette.

"She must have been very tired," said Vinnie.

"No, but it's true. I chewed before a mirror, and I did look like a rat. I thought how everyone must hate to sit at the table with me, how they had hated it ever since I was born. I got to wondering if my mother thought I looked like a rat when she nursed me. Every time I sat down to eat I thought of it. And I thought of it between meals. Finally I was thinking about it all the time. I'd waken in the night and remember it. I'd think of it while I was reading. One night I dreamed that I fell and hurt myself so that I couldn't get up. As I lay there, rats gnawed at me until I was devoured, and each rat looked like me.

"And now?" said Vinnie.

"Now I eat behind my umbrella."

"I used to have a game of finding what animals people looked like. And I found something for everyone. Even for myself."

"For yourself?"

"Yes. I look like a sheep."

They smiled at each other, Vinnie offering a limp sandwich from the bag, Juliette accepting it.

Squirrels played about in the trees. An acorn, piercing the leaves as it fell, dropped with a soft muffled sound. A thrush sang, hidden deep in the woods, while foxes moved slowly in the shadows, their fine noses quivering with the sense of adventure.

They were no longer one who was young, the other wishing she were younger. One was not beautiful and the other plain, one was not eager and the other grieving. They were two women whose minds were tingling with anticipation, two women for either one of whom the future might hold as much adventure as the foxes courted in the shadows. The mind of one was like a Christmas tree hung with fluttering angels and fragile, doll-like bells. The mind of the other was like a glockenspiel. Any note was clear and vibrant, and anyone might play upon it with the hammers of his integrity.

"Juliette!" Marie called from the valley. Her voice was like a sieve; the fine things had gone through it. Juliette waved.

"Will you go with me, Vinnie?" She was shy in asking.

"I can't, Juliette. I'm going to meet Peter."

"Who's Peter?"

"Peter? Oh, Peter is a friend of mine." But her eyes and her voice betrayed her. Juliette heard only the sound of her voice. The words fell about her, leaving her bright and cool. In the valley the foxes quivered.

"Tell me," she said. "Tell me about it. What is it, Vinnie? What is it like, a man's love?"

I cannot tell her how it is, thought Vinnie. I cannot tell her how a man loves with his hands, with his voice, with his eyes. I cannot tell her about these things, for she will never know any of them. "It is quite like being up here," she said.

"I shall come often." Juliette started down the path.

"Don't tell Joie that I have the rabbit, Juliette."

"Of course not. You want to surprise him." She picked her umbrella from the bush. "In case it rains," she said. The umbrella vanished; Juliette descended with her parachute.

VIII: HELOISE TO ABELARD

HARRIT, JULIETTE, Stewart, Mother, John. Vinnie fitted the edges of their personalities together, made of them that which they had been before: a family, a unified design. I shall not break the puzzle again, she said. She felt that if she were to look into the mirror she would find that her very eyes had lost their own color and had acquired an ambiguous shade, a combination of her sister's, her mother's, her aunt's and her uncle's. She would discover a composite face instead of her own. Her heart and her mind had lost their identity. She had been raped of her personality; she was no longer Vinnie Morison, daughter of Mary and Henry, but a sort of mental harlot who had been seduced by pity.

The sun, floating like a scarlet bobber on the calm surface of the horizon, disappeared suddenly. The valley grew miraculously still. In the cool waters of the creek herons, like etched birds, stood silent, and their long bills tilted to the sky were like high notes in music. Quail, those shy and proper birds with wind under their wings, stopped mincing through the leaves and allowed the evening to come into the valley with dignity. Late larks, flying high, rested their flight upon the wind, and as they turned their bodies to the earth their songs trailed after them like smoke, or the tails of kites. Deer in sheltered places raised their antlers from the ground, and turning their faces to the sky, closed their eyes. The beauty of the evening was akin to pain. No creature stirred. Even the little fishes kept in the shadow of the overhanging marsh grass, and turtles hung like lockets from the surface of the water.

The family was quiet. Joie lay face down in the leaves, at some distance from the others. Marie and Susan stood side by side at the fire, waiting to throw water on it. Harrit sat under the pine tree, her knees drawn up, her face hidden in them. John looked at his watch; Mrs. Morison, after folding the tablecloth, sat with it in her lap, her fingernails making sharp ridges of the folds. The children made castles of acorns, and Juliette watched a hawk bank and glide. Mr. Morison, a handkerchief to his face, kept his eye on Joie.

It isn't real, thought Vinnie, and wondered how the moment would ever cease to be, how it would be the next moment, and the family would move carelessly down the road through the valley, how the night would encompass the evening; how the night would dissolve into morning, and day into night. She wondered how death consumed the body. Did it work from the outside in, or from the core of the body out? How did fish know when to spawn; trees, to bud? What would become of Joie's heart? Is love one with the flesh, or one with the spirit? Is it infinite and everlasting, or temporal and transient?

The voices of the children brought the moment to a close. Eternity was once again fluid, the frost that held it immobile tempered by a child's warm voice. The valley grew suddenly restless. The blue herons flew up from the creek, the turtles snapped at flies. If the children had not laughed, thought Vinnie, the moment would never have ended.

She watched the family as they moved about. She felt as though she were a puppeteer, and they, her dolls. She knew so well the threads of their minds that she felt confident of her control of them. Harrit will go first, she said, and Harrit, as though in response to her thought, got up from the ground, and catching up the heaviest basket ran down the road. Poor frightened child, said Vinnie aloud. Let my love protect her. Let my love help her in childbirth, my devotion insure her well-being. She felt comforted, as though she had laid the robe of God upon Harrit's shoulders. She has a fine body; she will do well in childbirth. Vinnie spoke aloud to persuade herself.

Harrit went first, moving from them in haste. Once again Vinnie thought of the figurehead upon the ship. Erect, her body bent into the light, she moved forward more like the thought of motion than the motion itself. The ease of her body and the grace with which she moved were a surety of life. She moved swiftly, a bright spot that disappeared and came into view, and again disappeared. Moving farther down into the valley she was lost from sight. The trees had devoured her.

After Harrit went Joie kicking a stone down the path and throwing twigs up into the trees. His mother, calling to him to come back to carry a basket, went unheeded, and when she called a second time, he dove into the thicket. Vinnie, holding the rabbit close to her, whispered into its long ears that that was the little boy they were going to surprise. After Joie went the other children, and Marie and Susan, well-laden with baskets, trudged after them. Vinnie, in spite of herself, was moved to pity for them. Because they are so content, she said. And so unlovely. Then Stewart, balancing Juliette's umbrella on his chin, pranced down the road on his toes, while Juliette, who was giddy with life, staggered after him, Stewart's wreath of daisies tilted over one eye like a bacchanal. Mrs. Morison and John, their secrets hidden from each other, walked solemnly into the valley. After they had disappeared, Mr. Morison came out from the thicket. He walked down into the meadow and picked a daisy, pulling the petals from it one by one. She loves me, she loves me not. She loves me, she loves me not. The last petal said that she loved him. He looked at the center of the shorn flower for some time, and then, shaking his head, let it drop from his hand, and turned to the road. Joie in hiding in the bushes had been waiting for him, and surprising him with a growl, dashed out, laughing. They talked together for a little, Mr. Morison taking from his pocket something for the little boy. Though Vinnie could not see what it was, she was sure that it was a carved rabbit. They vanished among the trees, walking hand in hand, the child's bright laughter mingling with the man's mild voice.

That is my father. A man of fifty pulling petals from a daisy. But how well he knows. How well he knows that my mother doesn't love him. She realized with exquisite clarity what living had meant to her father. These many years they had lived together, he and her mother, and these many years he had hungered for her love. Being a shy man he thought that he annoyed her, and so had sought in every way to make himself as inconspicuous as possible. If it is my hands, Vinnie imagined him thinking, I will keep my hands from her sight. If it is my hair, or the way my whiskers grow, I shall keep my hair cut and my face shaven. If it is my mouth, or the way I eat my food, I shall say little and chew carefully. And so he had grown to be apologetic, and Vinnie, remembering how he slept in the bed, understood his body, his manner of coming into a room, his way of looking up from under his grey eyelashes. And being, though shy, a man eager for love, and for the comfort of a woman's nearness, his life, as she now understood it, seemed to Vinnie to have been unutterably bleak and desolate, as, indeed, it had been. She knew nothing of her father, except that he was a little man with grey eyes who was kind and quiet, who held his hands behind his back and came into a room as softly as a shadow. That was all she had known of him until that moment when he stood in the daisy field pulling petals from a flower. Like a bee, she opened the bud of his life, and perceiving the sweetness therein, drank deep of his goodness and sorrow.

As they had disappeared into the trees, lost in the intricacies of nature's abundance, she allowed thought of them to drop from her. She was like a swimmer emerging from the water glittering and immaculate. Bathed in the chilling perception of their lives, she stood now cool with tolerance, brilliant with understanding. How delicate a thing living is, she said to herself. Harrit with her baby, Juliette and fear, John and his conscience; these people who walked down into the valley, exiles from their native happiness, were no longer sister and parents, uncle and aunt to Vinnie. They were humanity. They were a part of her life, a part of her body. They moved farther and farther from her, moved through the trees towards her home where they would go to bed and sleep, and wake again in the morning to rise and eat, and complete another day. Their voices became fainter, and Vinnie was no longer sure that she heard them at all. They moved from her, league upon league of wooded land lying between them, but the essence of each of them stayed with her.

After the sun had set, the air grew cool. The end of summer was at hand, and soon the leaves would turn and the earth would grow hard and the wind, crisp. There would be a brittleness to living. In the morning the hoar frost would weave the marsh to the hills and the hills to the sky in a subtle pattern, and the trees would emerge like skeletons. The bittersweet berries would crack open, and growing against the grey wall of the house they would look like drops of blood. Ducks would fly desperately over the marshes, the labored beating of their wings betraying their fear, their rigid throats pressed against space, while deer, loving life, would desert the deep woods, and proud of their antlers, play target for men, their soft-eared does trembling, grieving, in the forest. All these things would happen, and the late summer would bleed itself away in brilliant splashes. A meadow and a hill, dull at sunset, would be crimson in the morning. Squirrels, in the midst of the infected land, would dash about through the trees with madness in their little minds, and lean birds would fly south in terror. All this will happen, and more, thought Vinnie. Like the fall which consumes the summer, and the summer the spring, my youth will be surrendered to life, my life, to living, and my living, like all living, to the generations to come. The things that I love and the things that I know will be forgotten, like this day, this splendid summer day that is even now darkened with twilight.

But there is Peter, she remembered, and the moment which had been barren bloomed like a flower with the thought of him. Peter to Vinnie was like the North Star to the sailor or to the man lost in the maze of a forest. Like the needle in the compass infallibly turning north, Vinnie's mind sped to Peter, were she in the depths of the wood or on the pavements of the town. Waking suddenly in the night at the sound of an acorn's falling, she thought of him; or when she talked to her family she would be ever conscious of his person, were he near at hand or a hundred miles away. She regretted this, for she longed to keep the thought of him secret, hidden. But she carried him in her mind as a woman carries a handkerchief—casually, tucked down into her bossom, or stuffed up into her sleeve. But jewel-like the thought of him sparkled in her mind, and no hour of any day was dull, nor any day quite long enough for thought of him.

Yes, there is Peter, she said, and laughed aloud, and the sound, in the still twilight, was like a silver thread woven through dark cloth. There is Peter, she said, and bent down, like a reed in the wind, to pick up the rabbit. There is Peter, and we are going to meet him.

She looked out across the valley: dark hills that encircled the neck of the valley like a fur; thin threads of smoke rising from doll-like farmhouses; cows standing thoughtful at the fence; these things and the sound of a woman's clear voice rising like a slow mist from the valley, and the fragrance of hay and pine needles and sweet marsh grass, she sought to remember. And when she had beheld them, one by one, and loved them over again, she turned from the valley into the woods. We must get down before it is dark, she said, and parted the branches of the trees and bushes to make a path for herself. She put the rabbit inside her dress, and it was warm and soft against her, and she was free to use both hands. She was conscious of the outline of her body; the cool air encircled her, and moving among the leaves one would have thought she was a Druid as she made her way along the ridge of the hill.

Vinnie, harlot of compassion, descended into the valley, leaving only a broken twig, or leaves falling. She passed among the bushes easily, a woman of beauty and grace. A Druid she might have been, or an Indian woman. But she was Héloïse walking through the woods to Abélard. The evening was heavy with anticipation, and like a woman who, eager for her lover, sits motionless at his approach, the dusk halted. It drew no nearer to night, and even the birds in the sky seemed to fold up their flight and lie still like leaves upon a motionless pool. But though Vinnie was quiet and beheld the silence and the dusk that lingered like a spoiled child, although she herself was still in the midst of the woods, her eagerness to see Peter preceded her. Her mind was already with him; the hours before their meeting seemed endless, and as she made her way towards the marshes, descending to them like a stream that finds its source in the hills but its comfort in the valley, she wondered what common magic certain things possess, that they should fill the heart with an eternal beauty, and how the mind manages to seek out the things that it will cherish: a child's first patent-leather slippers; flowers growing by a deserted house; church bells rung at twilight in a little town; birds who build their nests in furrows and fly out stricken at man's approach; a dog sitting by a closed door, and a hungry man who looks at flowers.

She came, finally, into the valley, and the moon like a child's bent toy toppled over the hill, while the earth, scarcely dark from the sunlight, was bright again, for the earth can be a most inconstant lover. She was like a piece of metal attracted by a magnet. She tried to harden her desire for Peter, to keep it firm in her mind, but it ran through her body as the veins from her heart, and no part of her was free from it. Her fingers, extraordinary miracles of gesture, grew strange to her, and looking down at her body she could not identify it as her own. To hear his voice, to see him walk towards her with his peculiar, halting steps; for this she waited. And waiting, it was as though quicksilver ran through her body, as though a thousand little bells rang in her veins. As she walked in the valley, stepping carefully and bending the sharp bushes aside, she was not aware of moving. She had walked out to the middle of the stream before she realized that she was near the water. Standing there, her face and throat as white as alabaster in the moonlight, her wet dress clinging to her thighs and legs as though wind beat against her, she herself was like a blue heron. The stars reflected in the water were like bright shells floating with the current which swept about her legs, and the sandy bottom sent up necklaces of bubbles.

IX: OLD MAN DYING

"If I were never to see you again, I wonder what thing about you I would best remember. Would it be your lips and the shape of your kiss, or would it be your voice? Would it be the way you run, or would I remember your hair?"

Vinnie felt that she would stop breathing if Peter said more words. She tried to keep him from going on. She needed time to remember these words. For the future she must have them, when there would be no words, no Peter, no night with a moon and the smell of the soil, and a sick Indian giving an excuse for the two of them to be together. He lay there dying, the old man, not two hundred yards away. There in that hut with the windows shut tight and three squaws sitting around, their heavy thighs pressing into the dirt floor, their breasts resting against their bodies like tired children, lay an old man dying. He was very old. Some said he was over a hundred. The room was hot and the air foul, like the breath of very old people, and in the corner, on a fruit box, stood a lamp that burned in a ragged flame. The light threw shadows on the walls and along the ceiling, and the heat and the swaying bodies of the women closed in upon the old man.

"And the old man lies there dying, and here we are, loving each other," she said.

"What of that?" said Peter, and laid his hand over hers.

"It doesn't seem right to me."

"But it is right; it's life, and we can't deny life."

"No, but what does dying have to do with loving?" asked Vinnie.

"Everything," Peter answered.

The word fell heavily into Vinnie's mind, sending out ripples of fear, as a stone does, or a pebble, dropped into a pool. The word moved as in an eddy, touching now with this current of thought and now with that one. She could feel the dark places beneath the water, she could feel the undertow. Everything. Everything. But it doesn't. It has nothing to do with love. That old man with his grey curls and his brown body broken with age has nothing to do with Vinnie and Peter, sitting here in the night. It has nothing to do with us, this old man's dying.

"No, Peter, not everything," she said. But Peter, instead of answering, put his head in her lap and blew smoke into her face.

"Tell me a fairy story," she said.

"Once there was a little girl and her name was Vinnie and she loved a little boy and his name was Peter, and when they grew up they were married, and lived happily ever after."

Vinnie laid her hand upon Peter's face. Gently, as one who has reverence for the human body, she passed her hand along his forehead. She stroked the lids of his eyes and followed the line of his brows with her fingertips. In her two hands she held his face, looking down into his eyes as though they were something she had never seen. He was not Peter, whom she loved, but a symbol of life. She sat looking down into his face, searching for some miracle of knowledge. How strange a thing a face is, that in the nighttime lies like a dead thing upon a pillow and in the daytime becomes alert and beautiful. She loved the feel of his skin, the mass of bone beneath his hair, the long thin nose. She loved the feel of the pulse in his veins. It was maddening; it beat like tom-toms against her hands. That moment, as she sat there in the night, waiting for the old man to die, each beat of Peter's heart was an arrow in her flesh. She was afraid of tomorrow and the next day and next year and the year after and the long years in the grave. She wanted to preserve his life, to stop the progress of living, to arrest his aging day by day. She wanted to keep it forever tonight, forever this moment, with Peter's head in her lap and the earth cool beneath her. She wanted to keep the old man from dying; with his death life would speed up to another death, and she and Peter would be waiting for someone else to die, or perhaps she would be waiting alone, with no head in her lap, no deep, eternal mystery throbbing between her hands.

"I know what I would remember. It would be your hands. They make me feel very young; I want to cry when you touch me. I would surely remember your hands."

A girl awakened suddenly to womanhood is a terrifying and beautiful thing, and Vinnie loved herself and this moment, sought to remember so that later, when she was a woman without beauty, without love, without Peter, she might love him and herself over again, as she did now. She felt that she had reached the summit of the spirit, and feeling so, she bent her head to kiss him.

The door of the hut opened, and a faint blur of light framed a man who stood dumbly in the doorway. This was the moment for them to go, for them to move apart and return to the bedside of a dying man. The moment having come, they did as was demanded of them, separated their thoughts and passed into the hut where the three squaws swayed back and forth. Three men had come in after them, crowding the doorway. The old man lay on his pile of rags and moaned. "Girl," he whispered. "Girl." Very slowly he moved his hand from under the blanket. Quickly Vinnie knelt down beside him and took his hand in hers. It was the name he always called her. "Girl," he said again. Vinnie thought he smiled. Such a brown skin, she thought. Such a tired, thin hand. It was like the shadow of a hand. Too fragile, too beautiful for life. But it isn't for life, she said to herself. It's for death.

Peter asked her for water, and she poured it over his hands. He took from his bag, which in this light and with these people became a witch's kit instead of a medical bag, his needle and serum. He prepared everything deliberately, slowly, and Vinnie, watching him bending over the old man, felt that it was something she had seen before, something infinitely good, infinitely just. The beads of perspiration stood out like embroidery on the faces of the women, and they pressed their thighs into the ground. When the old man opened his eyes suddenly, Peter said quietly to him, "See. You feel better after this. This will make you feel good. See." He thrust the needle into the delicate skin. "That didn't hurt, did it?" he said, as though he were talking to a child, and the old man smiled up at him; the women ceased swaying.

"It's easy, isn't it?" asked Peter, as they walked away from the hut, down through the woods.

"Too easy," Vinnie answered, and Peter, hearing tears in her voice, set his bag down in the grass and held her to him. His body pressed to hers restored her courage, and laughing softly she turned her face to his.

They walked on, stepping carefully through the underbrush, and speaking softly, as though they were afraid of disturbing the small animals that must indeed be very tired by nighttime. They stopped for a moment; about them no leaf stirred, but Joie's rabbit listened to the quiet as though it were filled with shouting.

Coming out of the wooded place they walked down the road without speaking, having found in each other's presence a certainty that needed no words. Vinnie felt the earth now hard, now soft about her feet. The rain had packed the sand tight and fitted the loose grains together, so that their feet coming down upon the ground made a sharp sound, like laughter. Occasionally when she found the imprint of a horse's hoof the sand would hurry to encircle her foot. Owls called in the woods, and birds cried out. But feeling the earth now hard, now soft under her tread, and hearing the owls and the birds, she still thought of other things, and gave no more of her attention to the earth and the sounds in the air than was necessary for recording them. She could not recall herself from the hut and the squaws, the foul smell and the meager light, from the pile of ragged blankets that made the deathbed for the old man. She thought of Peter bending over, the embroidered faces of the women. She thought of herself kneeling on the dirt floor, of the old man's hand lying in hers. He would soon be dead, he whose hand had lain in hers a little while ago. Where would the feel of her hand be then? Where would be the image of her that lay long enough in his mind to make him smile? What would become of his knowledge?

"Do you know," said Peter, "how much I love you?"

"How much?" she answered, knowing well what he would say. And he was saying what she expected him to. More than anything in the world, more than life itself, he was saying. But he went beyond her expectation; told her that he never had loved anyone as he did her. Even your wife? she asked, and he answered that people marry for strange reasons. They walked together down the road with their love for each other between them, like a child, or a plate-glass window, seeing each other through it, each understanding the other because of it. As parents feel occasionally, exquisitely and with agony, that their child will grow beyond them; that somehow their fulfillment in each other will be taken from them and lost; that the grown body of the child will steal the germ of creation which once was theirs, so now they felt as their hands came together in the night, as their fingers touched for a fine second, like thin streaks of lightning or separate songs simultaneously sung. And for the second time that night Vinnie sought to engrave upon her senses the touch of Peter's hand, the sound of feet, of birds frightened by two lovers passing, the sight of the marsh laden with moonlight, the heart within her.

They came finally to the fork in the road. He held her hard to him, pressing her body against his so that his hipbones bruised her flesh. She listened to him tell how he would devour her, like a beast his prey, so that he might carry her inside of him and possess her completely and forever. She laughed, her breath bitten off by the pressure of his body. God, she thought, I can't hold any more love. Then he left her and walked a little way down the road that turned to the right. She saw him get into his car that stood in the shadows; she watched him drive away in darkness.

For a long time she stood there, the rabbit secure and warm against her. There is no time for weeping, she whispered, and knowing, as women do at birth, that identity lies within oneself alone, and that all lives run separately, she turned towards home.

The night, like a weighted shawl, hung down about her.

Country People

BY RUTH SUCKOW

PART ONE

I: AUGUST KAETTERHENRY'S PLACE

SOME OF the best land in the country, people said, was right here in Richland Township. The soil in Wapsipinicon County was a little inclined to be sandy, didn't bring quite the price of the very best Iowa farming-land; but this stretch in here between Richland and "Wapsie" didn't give the farmers much chance for complaint.

This was the road that was later made a highway. It had a slight jog about a mile out of Richland. Tall cottonwoods grew on one side, on the other a tangle of bushes. There was always a kind of mud-hole here, sifted over with leaves and little fluffs from the cottonwoods; a bad place in the road, closed in and shaded.

Beyond this it was all straight going to "Wapsie." The land spread out rich and rolling, in smooth, tilted vistas of square fields, green, yellow, and earth-brown, trees growing in full-leaved clusters down about the banks of the little caved-in creeks in the pastures or standing lone, and slanting, on the crests of the low, rounded hills. In the distance the groves of farms were softened, blurred together; the far-off rising land was swathed in blue, a faint milky tint in which dim figures of trees were swimming.

A pink frame school-house stood on one side of the road. The long grass was trampled this way and that by the children's feet. Over beyond Ed Angell's place lay the Grove, where Sunday-school picnics and Fourth of July celebrations were held—a rich, thick cluster of trees, oaks and hickories, spreading over the hill and down the depressions of the slope, dark green upon the paler green of the short-cropped grass on the hill-side. The road went high and straight until it dipped down into "Wapsie," which lay deep in trees, the red stone tower of the court-house rising out of thick tufts of elms.

The farms were good along this road. A good class of people had settled here, German and English most of them. Men who kept an eye out for land deals noted shrewdly how well the buildings and barbed-wire fences were kept up, the red barns and silos, the prim white houses, square or with an ell, some of them with front yards enclosed in fences, and rose or snowball bushes growing. Most of these farmers—except the LaRues, who lived in a dingy, unpainted house with a bare farm-yard and a hog-pen of trampled, sloughy mud—drove into town in neat "two-seated rigs" with good teams. The cattle feeding in the pastures that sloped down, emerald-green, turfy, almost mossy, to the edges of the creeks were sleek and brown.

Over on the cross-roads there were more woods, and it was hillier. The farm-buildings were poorer, the fences slacker. These were the farms where people from "Wapsie" drove out to buy cheap a chicken, a goose, or a few crates of berries.

The place on the north of the road, beyond LaRue's, was August Kaetterhenry's.

It was a neat, plain farm, two hundred and fifty acres, virtually all under cultivation. The house was set back at what was termed "a nice distance" from the road—a white house with pink trimmings and a narrow porch. The front yard was not fenced in, but August made the boys keep the grass mowed, and it presented a neat appearance. Tall summer lilies, orange with dark spots, grew near the front porch in a spreading patch. On the west of the house stood the wind-break—two rows of elms that were lofty now, rather thin, and close together. The lawn ended at their trunks in a ridge of high grass and feathery weeds that the boys could not keep cut. A barbed-wire fence, caught together in one place by a wooden staple, separated them from the cornfield. The lofty upper branches rustled and moved slightly against the blue sky. In the evening their outlines were blurred and there was a sadness in their dark leafiness, high and motionless.

The wide yard sloped east to the barns and sheds across "the drive." It was worn bare of grass about the buildings and scattered with chicken fluff and droppings. The geese ran squawking across it when teams drove in. The great barn stood at the end of the slope, raised on a high foundation, with an inclined platform of heavy planks that thundered and shook under the horses' hoofs. Everyone about here remembered when August Kaetterhenry had put up this barn. It was painted white, as was the silo, and on the peak of the roof were two cupolas with slatted sides, and lightning-rods that glittered intermittently upon the blueness of the sky. On the side toward the road was painted in large black letters slowly getting weather-dimmed:

AUGUST KAETTERHENRY
1907

It was one of the best barns in the country there when it was put up. All of Kaetterhenry's buildings were good. The old barn had been made over by his brother-in-law, Hans Stille, into a granary and milk-house, painted white, too, the ground always slippery and muddy about the milk-house, a dribble of yellow ears leaking out from the corn-crib, kernels scattered in front of it, where the chickens were pecking. On the slope nearer the house the windmill stood, with the tank beside it, a bare steel skeleton giving off sudden flashes, the grey-painted wheel turning now fast, now slow, up there in the sky.

"Yes," people said when they drove past, "Kaetterhenry's done pretty good here. Well, he's a worker all right."

They admired the neat, square fields of oats and corn, the high, rolling pasture dotted with white clover, a few wild plum-trees set slanting, delicate and lonely, here and there.

"Yes, sir, he's got a nice farm."

II: THE KAETTERHENRYS

AUGUST KAETTERHENRY had not always had a farm like this. He had had to work for what he had got, like most of the people in that country. He hadn't got prosperous by wishing. There were plenty of people who could remember when he first came into the Richland neighbourhood. Along about the early eighties or late seventies it must have been, because he had worked for Henry Baumgartner, and it was in 1884 or "somewheres around" that the Baumgartners had moved into town. He came from Turkey Creek, where there were still "a whole raft of those Kaetterhenrys." August was one of old Casper Kaetterhenry's boys.

Turkey Creek was a little backwoods town about fifteen miles north of Richland, up in the timber. It still had no railroad and was "years behind the times," but some of the farmers around there had money, if they only cared to spend it. It was a good trading-centre. There was a large German settlement around Turkey Creek, more Germans than in the country near Richland, which had a good many settlers from Somerset, in England. Turkey Creek had had Scotch and Yankee settlers in the first place, trappers and woodsmen; but the Germans coming in to farm had crowded these people out. They were a slow, hard-headed set, those Turkey Creek Germans, but they were better than the timbermen, who had had, as old men who knew that country liked to tell, "some pretty rough characters among them." The Germans were hard-working, money-savers, and they had come to make homes for themselves.

It was Henry Baumgartner who had brought them there in the first place—old Henry Baumgartner. He was gone now, but he had been "quite a character" in his day. He was a Prussian who had come to this country when he was only a boy. He was said to have worked at one of the forges in Pennsylvania. There was a story of how, when he had been working there, he had been converted to German Methodism. He had come out to Iowa in a very early day and had bought up large tracts of timber-land when it was selling for almost nothing. Later, in the interests of both riches and religion, which the old man had always shrewdly worked together, he had sent back to Prussia and got a dozen families to come and settle on his land, promising them help in getting started on the condition that they should all become German Methodists. He had been afraid that the German Catholics, who had a settlement over in the hills at Holy Cross, would "get a hold" in the Turkey timber. That was the way that large German Methodist community had first started. Other Germans had begun coming in until the region was full of them. Most of them had been Lutherans in the old country, but Henry Baumgartner had been careful to see that there was no Lutheran church started here.

It was a hilly region, timber- and bottom-land. The people had lived primitively there; many of them did still. There were still a few of the old log cabins to be seen in isolated places, down on the Turkey Bottom. In those early days they had all lived in log cabins. The old-timers could remember well when the first frame-house in the country had gone up on old Herman Klaus's farm. Turkey Creek had been a wild little timber town with a few wooden stores and houses, after the first old log buildings had gone down, and the town hall, of the native yellow limestone, that was standing yet at the end of the business street, and where now the community held the harvest-home supper and the young people had dances.

The Kaetterhenrys had lived in one of those log houses on the same land where one of them, a half-brother of August's, was living now—the farm about three miles straight north of Turkey Creek, the one with the small white house and the patch of timber. It had all been timber in those days.

The Kaetterhenrys had not been among those whom Henry Baumgartner had brought to this region—they came a few years later—but their history was not very different from that of many families in the community. They came to this country from Germany in about 1849 or 1850, Casper and his wife and two children, and his brother Adolph and his wife. Casper's wife's brother, Johann Rausch, had preceded them. He was one of those who had drifted over into Iowa from Ohio or New York, coming because others were coming, because everyone was talking about the West. He had written back to his relatives in the old country, full of enthusiasm, praising the country and telling how fine the land was, until he had got Casper and Adolph persuaded to come.

They landed at New Orleans after a voyage of eight weeks and three days in a sailing-vessel, and from there took boat up the Mississippi to St. Louis. They spent the winter there, waiting for spring. The older child, Joseph, died of cholera while they were there. Early the next March, as soon as the river was open, they again took boat, and went up as far as north-eastern Iowa. They bought oxen and farm implements at Guttenberg, the little river town where they landed, and from there went straight over to Turkey Creek to join Johann. He soon after pulled out again and went on West, but Casper and Adolph took up land near each other. Casper started right in clearing his land and putting up the log cabin in which the family lived until the children were good-sized.

The cabin had one room at first; later, two more were added. They did their cooking, eating, sleeping all in there. There the children were born, one after another—Mina, Kurt, Mary, August, Sophie, Heinie, Ferdinand. They had had only Lena when they came there, since little Joseph had died on the way. They lived all crowded into that little cabin, four children sleeping packed into a dusty feather-bed over which the covers were hastily drawn in the day-time. Feather-beds and pillows and a little black tea-pot with raised blue flowers were all that the Kaetterhenrys had brought with them from the old country. They had had none of the "comforts of life" to begin with. They had saved up just money enough to pay for the journey and their first crude farming-necessities. They went through all the hardships of pioneer life, the clearing of the land, storms that killed their cattle and flooded their fields, the terrible blizzards of those days. Another child—Mary—died, and was buried in a little grave that Casper himself dug in a corner of their land. They had to work, all of them, father, mother, girls, and boys, just as soon as they could get into the field.

But they were a sturdy tribe: they could stand things. Casper Kaetterhenry had been a farm-labourer in the old country. He had always worked hard, and so had his wife. But now that he was working for himself instead of for some wealthy Pomeranian landowner who would get all the profits, he was willing to work. Now he was going to make a landowner of himself.

He brought up his children to know very little but work. The mother had little time for them. In the intervals of bearing them she had to work in the field. So did Lena, the oldest girl. Mina gave them all the care that was given. They always cared more for this sister, in a way, than for any other human being—Mina, a thick-faced, heavy, "Dutchy"-looking girl, slow and melancholy and conscientious and kind. She afterwards married Rudy Nisson, and had a hard time of it.

The older children had no chance for any schooling, but a schoolhouse was built on the outskirts of Turkey Creek to which the younger ones went off and on, as they could be spared, in the winter. That Turkey Creek school! It had wooden benches and a great stove on which one of the teachers—"Old Man Bartlett" they called him—kept hickory switches drying. Teachers were as irregular as pupils. Old Man Bartlett stayed only one week. He had already "licked" all the boys once or twice over, and he celebrated his last day by whipping every one of the girls. The next Monday he did not appear. He had "skipped the country." He had come to Turkey Creek from no one knew where, with only the clothes on his back, and no one ever learned what had become of him. There were a few attempts made to hold a German school, but they did not come to much. But it seemed to Casper Kaetterhenry that his children were in clover. He himself could do little more than write his own name. Even some of the other farmers about there said that Casper wasn't easy on his children. He expected them to work and that he should get all the benefit of their work. As soon as they were old enough to do anything, they had to help on the farm. That was the way to save up money. Casper kept them at it every minute.

As soon as August was eleven he began "hiring out" to some of the neighbouring farmers. He was a good worker. All of the Kaetterhenrys were. *"Ach,* those Kaetterhenrys!" people would sometimes say, meaning that they were stubborn and silent and *dumm.* And of Kurt or August or Heinie, *"Ja,* he's a Kaetterhenry all right." They were Pomeranians. "Pummers" people called them, making fun of some of their ways and the queer Low Dutch expressions that old Casper used. But August was good help. He could do nearly everything about a farm that a man could.

He worked for all kinds of people. For Schumacher once, and for Grobaty, a fat, black-bearded old German who beat his wife and his horses and was converted regularly at every camp-meeting. Grobaty's father lived with him. He had an immense white beard that reached below his waist. Usually he kept it buttoned inside his coat, but sometimes August would see him lift it out and fondly stroke and caress it. August tried blacksmithing for a while, too, but he liked farming better. He would go back to school in the wintertime, but when he was fourteen he quit for good.

By the time that he was fifteen he was virtually on his own resources. He did not get on well with his father. August had a temper and he didn't stand the old man's tyranny. August was the pick of the family, most people thought. He was not so slow as the rest of them, although he had all of the Kaetterhenry stubbornness. There was more of the mother in him. There was a different strain in the Rausches. They were more restless, more ambitious. People said that Mrs. Kaetterhenry might have liked to have things a little different from what they were at home if it hadn't been for "him." She was not a "Pummer." August was more like her. He looked like her, too, with a fresh-coloured skin and blue eyes showing temper in the way that they were set. Sophie, too, was "a Rausch."

It was mostly work in those days, but there were other things. Weddings were made much of in that community. Sometimes the celebration lasted three days, like Hans Nisson's wedding, at the end of which most of the men were laid out on the straw in the barn, dead drunk. There was still more intoxication at the camp-meetings which were held in the timber by travelling evangelists. People drove to them from miles around, camping out in the woods and attending the meetings. They were times of religious debauch. The shouting and singing and weeping, the general wallow of emotionalism, gave an outlet after all the hard, grinding work. August "went forward" at one of these meetings, along with the other young men, stirred and yet shamefaced at the same time. He believed that he was "converted."

Most of the life of the community centred about the German Methodist church out in the country, which Henry Baumgartner helped them to build. It was a plain white frame-building, bleak and small, a long hitching-board in front of it, and behind it the sheds for the teams and the two tiny outhouses all standing stark on a great clearing. Church was held in the afternoon. The farmers drove there in lumber-wagons, tying their horses to the long hitching-board, or in bad weather putting them in the sheds. They stood about on the church-steps, talking, the men together and the women in another group, until the preacher drove up. Then they all marched solemnly into the church. The congregation sat, the men and boys on one side, the women and girls on the other, facing the pulpit—a silent, stolid congregation, moving slowly and heavily in dark garments, creaking awkwardly as they turned to kneel on the hard wooden floor, some of the men poised precariously on their haunches, muttering the Lord's Prayer together in a guttural German that was loud in the silent country church, the women's voices a husky murmur above the deep, shamed rumble of the men's.

They had no regular pastor. Sometimes Wilhelm Stille, a farmer from over near Richland who "did some preaching," came. He was a thin, fervent man, with a greyish beard and long hair, who leaned over the pulpit and spoke in a high, thin voice, his deep-set brown eyes burning with a kind of mystic ardour. Sometimes they had one of the travelling preachers, old exhorters, who wept and paced the platform as they prayed for sinners, and pounded the Bible.

After the service the people went outside and talked a little before they drove home. It was for this that the young men came. They stood about in abashed Sunday-constrained groups, pretending to talk to one another, but aware of the girls, whose eyes were aware of them; in their thick, dark best clothes that made their skin look leather-brown, their brown and black felt hats, their feet clumping awkwardly in stiff Sunday shoes. This group of boys and young men was the last to disperse. The older people talked in German, about the weather and the crops. Then the men went out to get the teams hitched up to drive home.

August stayed around Turkey Creek until his mother died. She had been ailing for years, had bought "herb" medicine and liver pills and tonics from the medicine-man who drove around to the different farms with a horse and wagon selling remedies. No one had known what it was except stomach trouble, or had thought much about it. She had kept on working all the time. But finally, when she was almost confined to her bed, could digest virtually nothing, and could hardly drag herself into the kitchen to see how Mina, whom they had called in, was doing the work, Casper thought it might be time to drive into town and have the doctor come out with him. Of course it was too late then. Otherwise it would have been foolish for the doctor to be called. He too muttered something about stomach trouble, but the neighbour women who came in whispered "cancer" to each other. The children were sent for, and stood in awkward panic about the old walnut bed where their mother lay "wasted to a shadow," as the neighbour women said. The children had not actually realized that there was anything the matter with her until now. She died, and was buried in the little Turkey Creek cemetery near the German church.

"*Ach*, that old Kaetterhenry!" the women said. "He worked her to death, and then what did she have!" She had not lived to enjoy anything from all her toil. They had been for a few years in the new frame-house, but she had had to do things as she had always done them before.

It was expected that Mina would stay on at home and keep house for the old man, at least until Heinie, who worked on the home place, brought home a wife; Rudy Nisson was drinking and could not be counted upon to support Mina. But this was not at all what old Casper had in mind. A few weeks after his wife had died, he offered ten dollars to anyone who could find him a new wife; and astonishingly, gross and hard-fisted and stingy as he was, a fat old man with a rough beard who went around in his bare feet, a tolerably fair-looking young woman was found for him. He had never spent anything and he owned a good farm now. Poor Mina knew nothing of all this until he brought the new wife home; then she had to leave. Rudy was off in the next town, supposed to be working, and she had nowhere to go and no money to keep her. She had to stay at Sophie's until Sophie's husband could get Rudy to come back and find some sort of home for her. The new mistress proved to be very different from the old one: she made the old man Kaetterhenry stand around—build an addition to the house, get her some decent furniture. You never caught her working in the fields!

The children were furious. They talked about the insult to their mother and the injustice to Mina, but greed was at the bottom of it. This woman was a schemer; they could see that. Sophie declared that she looked like the kind of woman who would go about having children right away and beat the rest of them out of what was theirs by rights. What she had wanted was to get the farm left to her. It made them all angry to see how much she got from the old man while they, who had had to work like dogs for him from the time they were babies, got nothing. What had he ever done for them? It broke up the family and started a feud that still lasted after the old man Kaetterhenry had died and one of his sons by the second wife had the farm. But she did not get everything. Schemer that she was, she could never get old Casper to make a will, and the children came in for some of his property.

Most of the Kaetterhenry children married young and settled down to farming right where they were. August was the only one who did not. Sophie had married a Klaus, and her brother-in-law, young Herman Klaus, had gone up to Richland to work. August liked what he heard of the Richland neighbourhood. He wanted to get into a better community; he thought he could earn more up there. He went there and got a job with a wood-choppers' gang in the winter, and the next spring he hired out to Henry Baumgartner.

This old Henry Baumgartner was harder to work for than any man in that part of the country. August found that out soon enough. It was not for nothing that he was as rich as he was. He was worth at this time about a hundred thousand dollars in land and money, considered rich for a farmer in those days, but no one would ever have guessed it from the way that the family lived. The old lady Baumgartner hoarded the bread until it was mouldy. It was said that she was still wearing the same clothes in which she had come over from Germany. It was not until they moved into town and the children got hold of some of the money that it began to show. Old Baumgartner was inconceivably mean in petty things. August remembered about Mrs. Hooper, a widow in Richland who supported her family by doing washing. She wanted a little straw to pack about her house in the wintertime, and Henry Baumgartner promised that he would bring her some when he next came into town. Then he charged her not only more than the price of the straw, but for his time and for the hauling, although he had been bringing in other things at the same time. Plenty of farmers, as he knew very well, would have been glad to give the poor woman that little bit of straw for nothing.

Yet he had his big, effusive side. August had seen him at the camp-meetings groaning and praying and exhorting, tears running down the side of his fat nose and soaking into his beard. He was about sixty at this time, short, bulky, with a thick, square-cut beard, a broad smooth German under lip that showed his emotionalism, and mean little eyes. Afterwards, when he moved into Richland and joined the Methodist church there, he ran the church. The preachers looked upon him with fear as he sat short, heavy, belligerent in the front pew—he was getting deaf—giving little grunts of disapproval or breaking out into sonorous "Amens!" following the emotional parts of the sermon with a running comment of groans, head-shakings, tears. A terrible figure, with his big head and square-cut, bushy beard showing that wet, shining lower lip, the ominous glare of his small eyes. He was sincere, more than sincere, in all this. It was life to him. Plenty of people hated him, but they spoke of him as the most religious man around there.

If August managed to stick at the Baumgartners', he would be the first hired man who had ever done so. But August was a sticker. People soon found that out. He had no intention of leaving until he was ready to go. He went stolidly about his work from four o'clock in the morning until nine at night. He knew what he was after. All the time he was saving part of his wages, putting some away. He did not intend to let old Henry Baumgartner's meanness drive him out until he had saved enough to start in farming for himself. It was that for which he was working.

III: EMMA STILLE

August liked the new community. He saw that in some respects it was ahead of Turkey Creek. For one thing, there was a railroad, a main line of the Illinois Central that connected Richland directly with Chicago. It would be easier to market crops here. There would not be so much hauling to do. It was only eleven miles from "Wapsie," the county seat, and that was an advantage. And, then, he liked the looks of the country. There was not so much timber, more prairieland; and after all the clearing that he had had to do about Turkey Creek, August was not fond of timber. He said little, but he made up his mind before very long that he wanted to get hold of some land about here and settle down. Someone would be wanting to sell and move out. He had been saving ever since he started working for other people and was putting away some all the time. When he saw a good piece of land he was going to try to get it, paying for it gradually as he could. And he had his eyes open for some girl who looked as if she would make him a good wife.

There were not so many Germans here as around Turkey Creek, and there were some Lutherans among them, so that they had no German Methodist church. Those who were close enough drove over to the Turkey Creek church when the weather was good. Most of them began "going in town." They drove to the Richland church, four of them together, two girls and two boys, in a two-seated buggy. The old people did not care to go there because the services were in English. They thought that it meant, too, that the young people were getting away from them.

There were more good times not connected with the church than there had been at Turkey Creek. Socials at the country schools, bob-rides, and big country parties where they played the old country games and kissing-games until the whole thing ended in a general "spooning," with the lights out. August was bashful. Herman Klaus urged him to get a girl and come on. But he did not go to these parties very much until he began keeping company with Emma Stille.

That was in the first summer after he came to Richland. Henry Baumgartner let him go over to help the Stilles at threshing-time. The Stille boys had come over to help the Baumgartners. The Stille farm was about two miles from where August was working.

Old Wilhelm Stille was the one who used to preach in the Turkey Creek church. He was a gentle, dreamy kind of man. His threshing was always left until near the last. But old lady Stille saw to it that he did not get too far behind. People spoke of her as "someone to watch out for." She was short, squat, heavy. She had a round, wrinkled, crafty face with narrow, suspicious eyes. She looked as if she might just have come from the old country. She parted her hair smoothly in the middle and wore round ear-rings. When they drove into town, she never wore a hat, but a dark scarf tied over her head. Her dark, thick, shapeless clothes, her shawls, her scarf, her soft felt slippers, all added to the feeling of craft, of slyness, that she gave. People were afraid of her. She was stingy, too, as stingy as the Baumgartners; but the girls saw to it that the threshers were well fed.

There were two of the Stille girls at home, Emma and Mollie. Herman Klaus liked Mollie Stille pretty well. Everyone liked the Stille girls. They said that they were just nice girls, not so queer as their father and without their mother's meanness. They waited on the table when the threshers came. The men all knew them and joked with them. August had nothing to say, but he knew every move that Emma Stille made as she hurried around the long table bringing in more stewed chicken and coffee. She was not very large, but she looked like a good worker. Her black hair curled a little from the heat, and her face was flushed. Her lips, full German lips, curved, dark red, were slightly parted. The men teased her. "Hurry up there, Emma! Emma, you're too slow!" August sat eating industriously, without looking up; but when Emma came near him and put out her hand to take his coffee-cup, he caught the faint scent of heat that came from her, saw the little beads of perspiration about the roots of her shiny black hair.

He liked her. He wondered if she was pretty strong. She seemed to be able to get through with a lot of work. She did not look in the least like her mother. She was a giggler; she and Mollie both could seem to giggle by the hour, but just the same she was pretty sensible. She taught country school in the Benning Township school-house, but she knew how to wait on threshers.

The old man Stille was not badly off despite his preaching. He had come out in an early day and had managed—he and the boys together—to get hold of a good deal of land. He had helped the boys, and he ought to be able to help the girls a little, too. The Stille girls would have had more beaus if the young men had not been afraid to get mixed up with that old lady. She was down on all her daughters-in-law. That would not stop August. He'd like to see any old woman that could bother him very much.

The threshers were at the Stilles' two days. It was in early September, dry, burning weather, when the bright new evergreens in the grove at the north of the house stood motionless and pointed against the blue sky. The men worked with their old horse-power thresher out in the fields, where the stubble was bright and harsh under their feet and the sun blazed on the yellow-gold straw-stacks that piled up behind the machine. Emma and Mollie came out once to see them work. Some of the men stopped for a moment and "joshed" with them, offered to let them run the machine, told them they ought to be out here helping thresh instead of sitting around the house doing nothing.

"*Ja,* doing nothing!" the girls scoffed. "I guess we'd see what would happen if you didn't get any supper to-night."

"Oh, do *you* get supper?" Herman Klaus said. "I thought your ma did that, and you girls set around looking nice." They struck out at him until he backed off from them, holding up his hands and shouting, "Hey! Hey! I gotta work! Owgust, come here once and help!"

August was too bashful yet to join in. He pretended not to notice, but he saw the girls, standing there leaning against each other, half closing their eyes against the sun, which was bright on their black hair and flushed cheeks, the blue dresses against the blazing gold of the straw-stacks and the stubble out under the blue prairie-sky. The chaff filled the air, and the men turned to grin with a flash of white teeth in their blackened faces. That night August "cleaned up" very carefully, although usually he didn't think it was much use until threshing was over.

After that, Herman began to tease him about Emma Stille. August sat next to her at a bob-ride one night. Either she managed it, or he did, or Herman and Mollie, he didn't know just who. She had come with Herman and Mollie and didn't have any fellow of her own that night. The moon was not up yet. It was dark except for the dim, ghostly white glare of the snow. The fur of the buffalo robes was cold to the touch, but underneath them it was all warm, dark, secret, and intimate. He could feel Emma beside him, her arm against his, her feet close to his down in the warm straw in the bottom of the bob, her frosty breath. When the bob-runners struck a rut, Emma fell over against August. He steadied her and said, "Whoa, there!" Then he kept his arm around her the rest of the way until they stopped at the Stille farm, and she struggled out of the warm nest of straw under the robes. "Hey, August, ain't you cold? Lost your girl?" the rest all shouted.

He had never gone to the box socials, always grunting shamefacedly, *"Ach,* I don't want to go there; I ain't got no girl to take," when Herman urged him to go. But he went to one that winter, out in the Benning Township school-house where Emma taught. Mollie told Herman which was Emma's box, and Herman told August—a big shoe-box covered with ruffled red crêpe-paper and a huge green bow. When it was put up for auction, August turned as red as the box. Martin Graettinger, a young fellow from Benning Township, was bidding for it. Now that he had started, August was doggedly determined to let no one get ahead of him, and although he had no idea of paying so much, and it made him squirm, he got the box for three dollars and sixty cents. He and Emma and Mollie and Herman ate together in a corner of the room, which they barricaded with chairs, the girls giggling and Herman teasing them, August sitting red and silent, but happy. People thought that he and Emma would "go together" now.

But August was slow to get started. He did not take Emma anywhere until the next summer. He was cautious, and, besides, he had to save his money. Then he and Herman decided to ask the two Stille girls to go to the Fourth of July celebration at Richland Grove.

They started early and called at the Stille place for the girls. They had hired a team. They wore their best dark, thick suits, which made their hands and necks look browner. The girls wore striped summer dresses with tight basques, and Mollie had fastened a row of "spit-curls" across her forehead. August did the driving. Emma sat on the front seat beside him, and Herman and Mollie were "cutting up" in the back seat, Herman shouting, "Now, Emma, you make that Owgust act decent up there in front, where I can't look after him."

"You better act decent yourself," Emma retorted. August blushed furiously.

The big wooden gate of the grove was propped open. "This way, boys!" a man shouted jovially. They drove in slowly over the fresh wheel-marks that had smoothed down the long green grass and looked around for a place to tie. The buggy-wheels scraped over a stump half hidden in the grass, lifting up the buggy on one side and making the girls squeal. They stopped. No one seemed to know just what to do.

"Well, might as well get out," Herman said. "What you girls sitting in here for?" The girls stood aside while the boys staked out the horses. Then they all wandered off together, not knowing just what to do now that they were here. There were bunches of girls going around together, children darting off and being hauled back, women shrieking, "Come here, Mister! You don't get away yet. Come back here and fix this swing."

The grove had been well cleared of underbrush, and there were open spaces through which the sun shone golden-green. There were bur-oaks in clumps, larger oaks standing apart, full-leaved, casting a gracious shade. The ground lay in smooth, rounded slopes with long fine green grass that was full of little whirring things. It was sprinkled with wild gooseberry bushes, bitter-smelling white yarrow, clumps of catnip filled with black-bodied wild bees. The creek was dry, a narrow stream bed filled with hot white sand. Some children were running along it with bare feet.

There were swings put up, games going on. Rigs were standing all about: wagons, buggies of all descriptions, a carryall. Horses, big farm horses, were staked out with ropes. They would begin to eat the bark off the trees, and then the men would have to run up and tie them somewhere else. There were family groups, old ladies sitting on cushions or in buggies, unattached boys going about hoping to find girls, men pitching horseshoes. The four young people were glad when it was time for the program.

The speaker's stand was built of fresh new planks, with a resiny scent, bound around with red-white-and-blue bunting. There was an amphitheatre of planks laid across low saw-horses. August and Herman and the two girls stood at the edge of the crowd. There was a smell of perspiring people, cloth, starched dresses, planks. Babies cried. The chorus sang patriotic songs. A strong, fierce-looking girl went pounding to the front of the platform and declaimed "Barbara Frietchie" in a loud, coarse voice. When she came to "Dame Barbara *snatched* the silken scarf," she caught up the flag and waved it wildly. Some people clapped, others looked half gratified and half foolish. The chorus sang again, "We're tenting to-night on the old camp ground." Despite harsh untrained voices, there was something touching about the sad cadences, sung there in the open, breezy grove. State Representative Calkins, from "Wapsie," spoke. There was a scraping and moving-about when he first came forward, and then a long silence before he began. He spoke loudly, but it was hard to hear him. The breeze seemed to carry his voice away from all except the people directly in front of him. The children were still playing in the swings. Young people who did not care about speeches, the oak leaves rustling, the horses, the whispering on the outskirts of the audience, drowned the speech. Herman and Mollie got tired of it and slipped away. August and Emma felt foolish when they saw that the others had gone. Emma's brother, Willie Stille, was in the chorus, and he sat up there grinning at them.

They sat near the buggy to eat their lunch. Emma and Mollie had brought a huge lunch in a big red pasteboard box. The table-cloth was hunched up in places by little spears and bunches of grass. But eating seemed to dispel their awkwardness.

After dinner the boys went away for a while and pitched horseshoes. The girls went to sleep, and awoke with hot, shiny faces. They took down their hair, and were just putting it up again when the boys came back. They squealed. The boys teased Mollie about her spit-curls until she got angry and threw them away. Herman put them on and pranced around, and then he had to go after Mollie and make peace. August and Emma sat down on the buggy-robe on the grass. August took off his heavy felt hat. There was a white band of flesh that shaded into red-brown below the golden roots of his hair. The oak leaves rustled dreamily.

August and Emma wandered off together. They crossed the hot white stream bed and climbed the hill, sat down in the shade between some trees and gooseberry bushes. Emma picked some of the gooseberries to take home, and August helped her pull off the woody little hulls. He put his hand over hers in the grass. The hand quivered, and he held it closer, his hard brown fingers grasping a little higher on the wrist. There was an exciting incongruity between their halting self-conscious talk and the warm, thrilling animal intimacy of their hot, moist palms in the long fine grass. The shouting from the races down on the level ground came to them long-drawn-out and dreamily distant. They were aware of the little green things that jumped about in the grass and of the heat of their two hands on the cool earth near the grass roots.

When they went back, Mollie and Herman were sitting in the buggy "spooning."

August made Herman drive home. He and Emma sat in the back

seat. Herman kept saying, "Why are you two so quiet back there?"

"*Ach*, you shut up, and tend to your driving." August put his arm around Emma. She took off her hat and put her head against his shoulder. The weeds along the roadside were damp, and wet night odours and mists came up from the fields. There was nothing but riding, jolting on through the dusk, the horses' hoofs pounding on the hard road, the buggy-wheels scraping.

After that August and Emma "kept company right along." The old lady Stille made little trouble, for she wanted her girls to be married. Wilhelm Stille promised to let them go on one of his farms, the one between Richland and "Wapsie," with the privilege of paying for it gradually. Emma did not teach country school the next year, but stayed at home getting ready to be married. The wedding would be as soon as August had enough saved to start them out on the farm.

The first day that August could get away they drove into "Wapsie." The four of them again, in the Stilles' two-seated buggy, August and Emma and Herman and Mollie. It was late February, just before the last thaw. The road to "Wapsie" was a winter study in dull black and white. The snow, which had an opaque, thick look under the colourless winter sky, drifted down the black earth of the slopes; the plum-trees in interlaced masses along the creek, low, spreading, done in smoky black, purple tinging the massed farther trees and the bushes; the creek half under thin greyish ice cracked and broken down in places; the road dead black, sifted over with fine snow. The buggy looked small on that great expanse of land, the hoofs of the horses on the hard wintry road made a lonesome sound.

The town had a closed-up winter look. The girls did not speak as they drove along the wintry street. They sat small and subdued in their heavy country wraps and dark knitted hoods. They drove to the court-house. The two boys tramped solemnly into the old brick building, with its dusty wooden floors and brown spittoons and glimpses of littered rooms, with shelves stuck full of records. August got the licence of the county clerk, a little crippled man with one shoulder higher than the other.

Then they drove to the minister's house.

The girls got out of the buggy and stood stiffly on the board sidewalk while the boys tied the team to a wooden hitching-post. All four went solemnly up the walk to the house. They did not know whether to knock or to open the storm-door. No one heard them at first, and they went into the chilly, bare little entry, where overshoes and a fibre mat were piled, until August finally rang the bell.

"Ring again once," Emma whispered.

The minister's wife came, tall, gaunt, with spectacles. She said in a businesslike way:

"Did you wish to see Mr. Taylor? Step inside."

They filed silently into the parlour. They sat waiting, the girls clasping their hands nervously, staring at the hard-coal burner, the lounge, the pink sea-shell on the stand.

The minister came in with hastily brushed hair. They sat in frozen embarrassment.

"Is there anything I can do for you?"

August cleared his throat resolutely. He and Herman had been turning their caps on their knees, with hands red from the cold.

"We came to get married. If you——"

"Oh, certainly, certainly," Mr. Taylor assured them hastily.

Mrs. Taylor had thought "wedding" when they first came in, and had come back into the room. Now she asked the girls if they would not like to take off their wraps. She offered to let them go into the bedroom "if they wanted to fix up any," but they shyly refused. August asked her where the kitchen was, and after he had washed his hands at the granite basin, he came back and murmured, "Do you want to wash up, Emma?"

After many backings and exchanging of places, with a nervous determination on Mr. Taylor's part to mistake Mollie for the bride, which made Herman blush, the wedding party was arranged. August and Emma stood between the two windows, with Herman and Mollie in frozen attitudes on each side of them, and Mr. Taylor facing them.

"Dearly beloved, we are gathered together in the presence of God and these witnesses to join this man and this woman in the holy bonds of matrimony."

The voice sounded sonorous in the small, bleak room. Emma stood in trembling quietness. August had to clear his throat, and then his voice came out gruffly. Herman breathed hard and eased his weight. Some coal dropped in the stove.

They felt shy and happy under the congratulations of Mr. and Mrs. Taylor. They signed the certificate, and August fished in his pocket and brought out two dollars for the minister. Emma said that they would bring his wife a chicken in the summer.

They drove back to the farm down the dim, chilly road, the bare bushes thin and small, the fields spreading out black and sprinkled with snow. There was a wintry red in the Western sky.

They had supper at the Stilles', where the old lady had got up a big meal for them, inviting in all the married children. Emma was to stay there until August "got things fixed" at the farm and could come after her. But he had to go straight over to the farm in the morning. One of the Stille boys was staying there now, looking after things, but the next day August was to take possession.

PART TWO

I: THE FARM AND THE CHILDREN

THE FARM, when August and Emma first went there, didn't look much as it did later. It was one that Wilhelm Stille had got hold of almost by accident through a mortgage. It had had a poor owner, and then renters on it, so that it was in bad shape. Willie Stille had been "batching it" there during the winter months, but of course he knew that he wasn't going to stay, and had done no more than keep things going. But it was a piece of land that would pay the man who really took hold of it.

Few of the present improvements were there. The buildings were flimsily built affairs, some of them unpainted. There was a little one-story house with old-fashioned small-paned windows, dismal and dark and ugly. No yard, no bushes or flowers, and over on the west a tangled, half-grown wilderness of all kinds of trees and bushes planted together. August cut all those down later, except the double row of elms that he left for a wind-break. One thing there was, a good well. Otherwise it was like building a place up from the beginning.

The old lady Stille would have liked to keep the farm in her own hands, to have had August and Emma stay there merely as renters. She liked to keep a hold on the children. But August would not go there under any such conditions. He meant to work without stopping until he had paid for the farm. He had a genuine Kaetterhenry obstinacy and a desire to do things for himself. He would not stand interference; his mother-in-law soon found that out.

The Kaetterhenrys started in with almost nothing, as most young couples did in those days. August had something saved from all his years of work; Emma did not know exactly how much. He spent this very thriftily. At first they would have to get along with as little as they could, "until they got the farm paid for." He paid for part of his stock and implements and went in debt for the rest. To have a farm free from encumbrances; to own "clear" the stock, the machinery, and the land, was what he was working for. All that he had or could make went into the farm.

The house—*ach,* that didn't matter so much. It was a gloomy, bare little house. Emma brought along what she could from home: comforters that she and her sisters had been making through the winter; some goosefeather pillows; rag rugs that she had sewed; some heavy white dishes, with a brown rim, and a clover leaf in the centre, that she and Mollie had picked out in the store in Richland. August and Emma drove into town one day and got what furniture they would need: a black walnut bed and commode; a kitchen table and stove; chairs; a parlour stand. There were wedding presents. Emma's father gave them a clock, and her mother a feather-bed. Hans Stille, who was known as "quite a carpenter," made them a tall narrow desk and bookcase of home-grown black walnut. August's sister Mina sent them a "splasher" for the commode on which she had worked in red outline stitch some ducks and waves. The Stille boys gave them an album with orange plush covers, and Mollie and Herman Klaus, who were going to be married soon, bought them a set of vases, with cat-tails encrusted in gold on the sides. Their living was done in the kitchen and bedroom. The front room, which had the rag carpet, the stand, the vases, and the album, and a large German Bible, they kept shut off.

They could not afford help. August did most of the work himself. He got up at daylight, or earlier, and it was dark before he finished his chores in the evening. He was "one of the best workers around," people said. He was going to have a good place here some day. One or another of the Stille boys came over and helped when the work was heaviest. Emma had to help him in the field. August saw nothing unusual in that, although most of the farmers' wives here were not seen in the fields. All "the womenfolks" had had to help over in the Turkey timber. He had always seen his mother and his sister Lena out working with the men. He expected it of his "woman."

There was not much but work for them these days. They had no buggy at first, only a wagon. But they drove into church when they could on Sunday mornings. Church—that was somehow part of doing well, of living the way they should and getting prosperous. They couldn't go off the place often, since they had no one to leave with the stock. And when they did go, they must always be back in time for chores. August got away more than Emma did; he had trips to make into town. Emma soon found out that he was not the kind who would take her with him. His mother had never gone to town. He did all of the buying. He had a shrewd, hard feeling that he must keep things in his own hands if he was going to get ahead. He had that thrifty, bull-headed Kaetterhenry streak in him that showed in his attitude toward the woman. Emma hated to ask him for things. She went out to the wagon timidly, said, "August, do you think you could get me a little of that calico, maybe?" He grunted. He would get it if he thought she needed it, but he decided that.

Emma settled down quickly into a young farm wife. She "lost her giggles," as the family said, and got an air of timidity that was an accentuation of her old shyness. She was thin, with skin burned dark, and tired, hollow eyes. She seldom got out of her wrappers. August was close; he did not tell her things. He expected a good deal of her. But, still, as her sisters told her and as she knew, she had got a good man. He would have a fine farm some day, and then she would be glad that they had worked while they were young.

Then the children were born, Frankie, Mary, Elva, Carl. That kept Emma busy enough. While she had only the first two, she still helped in the field. Frankie and Mary were easy to manage. But when Elva was born, Emma had a hard time. It had to be right in haying-time, the men there, and no one to feed them, no one to look after the other children. They got August's sister Mina, a fat, kind, melancholy woman now, who worked at anything that she could find to do; but the old lady Stille couldn't stand it to have any of August's folks there. She came over, "nosing in," as August said, and she drove out even Mina, who was used to all kinds of treatment. Emma had to get up before she was ready and go to work again. There was no time for rest these days, she said, even if a person was sick. But she was never quite so well from that time.

After the first two, she had to stop helping August outside. She still helped with the milking, took care of the chickens and geese and the milk and cream, and made butter. She had all that *she* could do in the house. Wherever she went, the children were following her—in dingy, much-washed blue dresses, made too large, so that they could be handed along and fit the next one—little, frowzy-headed country children, toddling after her, pulling at her skirt, under her feet wherever she stepped. The older ones could play outdoors by themselves, but there was always a baby in the red high-chair beside the stove while she cooked or ironed; and she would have to stop to change diapers, cry, "No, no, you can't have that!" snatch the child hurriedly up, murmuring, remorsefully but a little fretfully, "Come on now. No, mamma ain't forgot all about you. Did you think she had? Can't you let mamma get back to her work now?" Sometimes she was fretful and anxious. But Emma never seemed to get really cross. She never sprang up and "took a whack at them," like Mollie, and then got ashamed of herself.

Emma did not look so strong, but she could keep going.

The two oldest children, Frankie and Mary, had always been "real good." Emma had never had any trouble with them when they were babies. They were both quiet, slim, dark-haired children, like some of the Stilles. They would always play together and amuse themselves, Mary especially. Mary was always a great one for school. When she was a tiny thing she used to play school out near the corn-crib, with the ears of corn, with their long silken hair, for "scholars," all arranged in a row before her, their hair braided, wearing little hats of leaves trimmed with clover blossoms, which she carefully removed when school began. She tried to read before she knew one letter from another; anything, the texts on the coloured Sunday-school cards, seed catalogues that came to the house, the labels on baking-powder cans. "She must be going to be a school-teacher when she grows up," people said.

Elva was the odd one. She didn't seem to belong to the rest of the family. Perhaps it was because she had been sickly when she was a baby and had had some "spoiling." She had been twice as much trouble as the other two put together. When she was a baby she used to have spells of holding her breath, and even her father had a hard time to manage her. She had fine, red-gold hair and a very white skin, although she was never exactly pretty. She liked to get out of things and to leave Mary to do them.

She still took more care than Carl, when he was born three years later. Carl was the one who took after his father most. He had the light hair, ruddy skin, blue eyes, and was stocky and sturdy. He kept things to himself, too. Carl was August's favourite. August was never much of a hand to be around the children, but he paid more attention to Carl.

August wanted his children to have what other children had, but he thought they ought to help. Frankie had to help his father out in the field as soon as he was big enough to go out there. August wasn't going to pay for help when he had boys of his own. "My, how those Kaetterhenrys all work!" people would exclaim. They would see this little fellow out in the field, in the burning sun, working just like a man. Looking like a man, too, in his blue overalls and big straw hat. It didn't seem to August that his children had it hard. He remembered his own childhood and how his father had made all of them slave. He didn't work Frankie like that. August wouldn't have thought of having Frankie go and hire out off the place, as he had had to do. Frankie didn't know what it was to have to get along as his father had done at some of those places where he had worked, Grobaty's, for instance, where he used to sleep in the straw. August could not see that he was hard on the boy. But other people said that

Frankie was a man before his time. A short, dark, sober boy with brown skin, always looking a little stunted, especially in that best suit of dark, thick cloth, the blue tie, and the brown felt hat, that he wore to Sunday school.

August never required Mary to help on the place, as his oldest sister had done. That hadn't hurt Lena any. Look at her now, a big stout woman, mother of seven children, stronger than it seemed Mary would ever be. Mary was obedient and good, and she was a great help with the housework and the little ones. The trouble with her was that she didn't have her mind on what she was doing. She always had to have her nose in a book, anything that she could get hold of, the big German Bible, a "History of the Civil War" that August was once inveigled into buying from an agent, the mail-house catalogues. Those catalogues opened up worlds to Mary. She could hardly wait for her father to go into town to the post office when it was time for a new one to come. She couldn't bear to go past anything that had printing on it. When they were driving along the road and saw a piece of newspaper, she would beg to get out and capture it. August thought this was silly. He could see no sense in a girl's wanting to read and study so much.

"*Ach,* what do you always have to be reading for?" the others said.

But the oldest girl in a family like theirs didn't get much chance to read.

The country school was two miles from the Kaetterhenry farm. August always "aimed" to let the children go. They walked the two miles back and forth, taking their lunch in tin pails. They went "pretty regular," except when they were needed at home, Frankie for the farm work and Mary to help with the babies. Elva didn't care much for school, but Mary made a terrible fuss, they said, when she had to miss.

That school seemed pretty fine to August when he thought of what he had had. That old Turkey Creek school with teachers coming and going! This was a nice frame building, painted pink, with desks and seats like those in the town school. And then they had a teacher for the whole term. A high-school girl from Richland usually (the high school there gave a two-year course) who was teaching a few terms of country school before getting married. Mary was always talking about town school, but August couldn't see but that they got about as good as what they'd get in town. All they needed, anyway.

August and Emma wanted to do the best for their children that they could. It worried Emma that they couldn't always get in to Sunday school; that was more important than the other school. That was bringing the children up right. August bought a buggy so that he could take them. They drove in on Sunday mornings—August and Frankie on the front seat, in the back the two girls, and Emma holding little Carl on her lap. Often they got there too late for church, but they were in time for Sunday school. Mary and Elva in funny little dresses too long for them, stiff best hats with elastic under their chins, hair in tight black and blond braids tied with little pieces of narrow blue ribbon. Frankie clumping in heavy shoes that smelled of blacking, looking too old for his age in his heavy dark suit with "long pants" and a brown felt hat like his father's.

They prized the coloured cards that they got, with pictures and the golden text on them, showing Christ, with brown curly hair, in white robes, the disciples in blue and red (blue for John, who was pictured as almost as pretty as Jesus). Their Sunday-school papers were treasured during the week—*The Boy's Friend, The Girl's Friend, Dew Drops.* Mary read the stories avidly. Even Emma got into the habit of looking at the serials in *The Girl's Friend,* although she never actually finished one.

The children were shy, and wouldn't say much in Sunday school, Mary and Elva because of the town girls, who wore better dresses than they did. But they all looked forward to Sunday school, loved the cards, the papers, the drive to town, the hymns, jingly Methodist "Sabbath-school" hymns, "There Is Power in the Blood," "Jesus Paid It All," "The Old-time Religion." Mary wished that they had an organ so that she could learn to play these songs at home, and Emma admitted wistfully that it "would be nice." When they went to Henry Stille's, where there was an organ in the closed, chilly front room, Mary went in and learned to "pick out the tune," or something like the tune.

"Until they got all this paid for once"—that was the answer to everything, new house, new furniture, organ.

The old Stilles did not like it very well that their grandchildren were going to "English church." August and Emma did not speak German in the home, as the old people had done.

"Ach, das ist nicht recht!" the old man Stille would say sadly. He wondered what would become of them all.

II: GRANDMA AND GRANDPA

THE HOUSE simply wouldn't hold them all. Three years after Carl there was Johnnie. And then the old Stilles wanted to give up their home and come to live with August and Emma. August hated to do anything with the house until he had a better barn, but there was no way out of it. The old Stilles would help a little.

Hans Stille was working over near "Wapsie." He was the only one who never married, a little, shy, dark-haired man with shining, dark-brown eyes and timid, gentle ways. Mary was like him in some ways, the Kaetterhenrys said when they were provoked at Mary. He never seemed to settle down and get anywhere, but there was not much in the line of handy things that he couldn't do. He stayed with August and Emma all that summer and the next. They moved back the old house, used the two old front rooms for kitchen and bedroom, and built on three new rooms in front and an upstairs with two rooms. It looked like a nice modern house when they got through with it, although the upstairs was never fully finished—white, with pink trimmings, a narrow porch, a triangle of wooden lace under the peak in front. The next summer Hans made over the two old back rooms into a corn-crib and tool-house.

Then there had to be new things for the house, of course. They ordered some new furniture from the catalogue, a combination desk and bookcase for the front room (they used the old one that Hans had made for a cupboard), a new stationary rocker upholstered in green-flowered velvet. They got a new bedroom set for themselves, dresser, commode, and bed of golden oak, the bed with a high head-board. They put the old walnut things in the boys' room, the big end room, left half finished, used as a store-room, too.

When the old Stilles came they brought some of their things with them,—their long extension table and some chairs for the dining-room; grandpa's old German books, queer ancient things with faded black and brownish bindings, religious books; some old home-made walnut beds and feather-beds; ancient quilts of dark woollen pieces. The little old downstairs bedroom in the back now became "grandma's and grandpa's room," a small, dark, stuffy room with an uneven floor, one dingy, small-paned window. They set up an ancient walnut dresser with a little dark-framed mirror hung above it, an old rope bed piled high with billowy feather-mattresses, with dark-looking musty-smelling quilts over them; and on nails in one corner, grandma's and grandpa's clothes—an old brown waistcoat, the coat in which grandpa had done his preaching, some big gaping country shoes, and grandma's dark dresses and stealthy-looking grey shawls and old black petticoats. The two big wooden rockers stood there, and beside one of them an ancient brown spittoon.

One thing that the old people brought was an organ. One of the old carpeted pedals would not work. It was put into the sepulchral front room, and August declared that he could pay for no lessons. But somehow Mary managed to pick out a few hymn tunes on it. Maybe some day some of them could "take."

The old people had had misfortunes. After getting together a good-sized pile of money from his land, grandpa had made poor investments. Some he had lost in Colorado gold-mines; and a German Methodist insurance company advertised in the flaming German monthly which he took, *Die Flammende Fackel,* had swindled him out of more. His son Willie took the home farm, but some of the rent would have to go to make up losses. Old Wilhelm Stille had long been on the verge of joining a communistic colony in Wisconsin of some wild Methodist sect, but the old lady had kept him from it; and now that he had so little money to put into the common fund, the colony seemed much less eager to get him. So he went instead to his daughter Emma's. The old lady shrewdly suspected that her son-in-law August was likely to have the best home for them in the long run.

They moved over soon after the new house was finished. August was close, but he would do what he must. He realized that he owed some of his start to his wife's people, but he determined that the old lady should know her place.

The old folks were now "Grandma" and "Grandpa" Stille to everyone. They had aged greatly in the last few years. It seemed as if grandpa had changed, now that he no longer had farm affairs to attend to, and that his "religious side" had come uppermost. He was thin, with a lean face, a large nose, scant, straight silvery-white hair that grew long, a white beard, and deep-set, mystical, dark eyes. His thin voice was gentler, had a far-away sound. He was feeble, and when he first came, they feared that he wouldn't last long. He couldn't do much but sit in the wooden rocker with the calico cushion, smoking a black pipe and reading his old German religious books and papers.

The old lady was squatter, craftier-looking than ever, with that round, wrinkled face, the smooth hair showing the broad, worn white parting, the round ear-rings, her eyes now two slits in narrowed, lashless rims. She went softly about in slippers, in a shapeless dark-grey calico dress and dingy, black apron, a scarf tied over her head. At first she tried to run things. She tried to tell the children what they should do and she protested against every cent that the family spent, wanted them to live in every way just as she and grandpa had lived.

Emma was going to submit to grandma's interfering at first. The old lady had always had all of the children—and grandpa, too—under her thumb, ruling them through their fear of her meanness. But August had no intention of letting grandma get the upper hand. He had stood things from grandma before, when she had come snooping over to see how they were running the farm and to exclaim at the waste. But things were changed now. He had finished paying for the farm a good while ago, although he had not actually admitted it to Emma, thinking the less the womenfolks knew about that sort of thing the better. This was his own house now. No woman was going to come around and tell him how to run it.

Grandma soon found that there was one person whom she couldn't rule. All her schemes, her craft, her sullenness, and her tantrums, which had always got her what she wanted as a last resort, were powerless against August's stubbornness. She was a little afraid of August from the start. She tried to get in her work without August's knowing it, when he was out of the house; but when he came in and found out what she was up to, then there were battles. The children sat in terrified, wide-eyed awe, and Emma wept a little, silently and tremblingly, while grandpa pleaded, moaning sadly, "Ma—*Mutter—ach,* no! no! no!" The children had never seen anyone like grandma at these times. The old woman could be a fury. But August was stronger than she. She found that she could not conquer him as she had the others. She was reduced to impotence, to angry mutterings, while she eyed August with a bitter, vengeful, helpless glare.

She had always had sullen times when no one could do anything with her. She had them now—times when she would not eat or move or speak, when, after grandpa and Emma had vainly tried to call her to meals, the children were sent to the door of her room. They found her sitting there in her old wooden rocker in the gloomy, low-ceiled room, among her old household things and her shawls and dresses, a tragic, baffled, ominous old figure, shapeless and huddled together in her dark, dingy old clothes, with her feet in their spreading, black felt slippers, rocking, and muttering, in guttural German, things that they could not understand.

This was the only revenge against August that she had. He let her be when she was like this. But she knew that even in this she dared not go too far. August was the only one who had ever been able to manage her. Far down underneath her anger and bitterness there was a kind of admiration of him. He was hard and thrifty and strong and a good farmer. She secretly despised her other son-in-law, Herman Klaus, beside him—Herman, a little, dried-up, undersized man who let Mollie have the say-so. August was not a "blower." He was close-mouthed, and the old woman admired that. And she secretly approved of his looks. You could tell from them that not many people were going to get ahead of him. Sturdy, square-set, heavy, but not fat, in his old blue shirt and overalls, with his ruddy face and blue eyes and the harsh outcropping of golden beard upon his sunburned skin, and the golden hairs on his thick brown arms. His hair was not so heavy now; there was a bald spot on top, but the old lady thought contemptuously that he looked younger than Emma did. She secretly thought that he was too good a man for Emma, whom she considered weak and *läppisch*.

Having the old folks there made more work for Emma. Her father she didn't mind. He made no more trouble than he could help. He tried to come out of his dreams to do what he could for her. He gathered the eggs, helped to hitch up the horses, kept the little ones out of the way sometimes when she was busy. Marguerite, the youngest, who was born after grandma and grandpa came, was his favourite. A pretty, wilful little baby, knowing very well that she was the youngest and had privileges, with a fuzz of golden curls and bright blue eyes. She was the only child born in the new house, and she seemed to come into a different order of things. Even her father was less severe with her than with the others. Grandpa put aside his old papers, trotted her on his knee, sang old German hymns to her in a faint high-pitched voice that seemed to come from a different world, took her out obediently to see the "calfies," made Johnnie give up his playthings to her. Emma had plenty to do besides, and was glad to have grandpa look after Marguerite.

Grandma had always worked hard at home, but she wanted to say how things should be done. Here she complained that she was useless; no one paid any attention to her. She would have helped with the cooking. But, "*Ach,* I don't know," Emma told Mollie. "Ma has her old ways of doing things, and the children they don't seem to like what she makes." She clung more than ever to her old ways now, spoke almost nothing but German, would not leave the place or ride in the new buggy, would use none of the "new-fangled" things except the telephone. That was grandma's one solace. She could sit "listening in" for an hour at a time, a look of stealthy gratification on her face, hearing everything: her daughter Mollie call a neighbour, Herman call in from town to Mollie and say what he was going to buy for Sunday, long conversations between two country women, deals between men. But they could never get her to speak into the telephone herself.

Grandpa had been the one who was ailing when the old people came. But, although he stayed somewhat feeble and tremulous, when his troubles and farm worries were off his shoulders at last, he seemed to get better and sink into a kind of irresponsible sweet content, dreaming, reading his old books, playing with Marguerite. It was grandma who was ailing now. They didn't know what was the matter with her. She took more and more looking after. One morning when she got out of bed she fell, and couldn't get up. They had to have August come in and lift her. Afterwards they thought that it must have been "kind of a stroke." She seemed to get all right again, and yet they thought that it was hard for her to lift her feet, and that she mumbled a little sometimes when she tried to talk. Always in Emma's mind was the fear of the time when her mother might be helpless, like the old lady Schuldt, and have to be taken care of.

It all came on Emma. Grandpa helped a little, but there was more washing, more cooking and more cleaning. It seemed as if she lived more than ever in the kitchen. Neighbours consoled her. "Well, now you can go more. You can leave the children with grandma and grandpa and get away." Maybe they did go a little more than before. They had a nice, big, leather-topped, two-seated buggy now. There were the boys to help August with the chores, so that he didn't have it all to do.

They went into church often on Sundays, leaving the two smallest ones with grandpa. August and Emma joined the Bible class, which was taught by the Hon. H. G. Bossingham, who had served a term as State representative and got the "Honourable" before his name. August never talked in the class, but he enjoyed it more than anything since he used to attend the old German country church near Turkey Creek. Emma liked it, but she didn't always feel like coming. Either she or Mary had to stay at home and see about the dinner, and it had better be she, since, if she came, she felt uneasy about grandma.

They had their outings, like the other country people. They drove in to the Fourth of July celebration at "Wapsie" on a blistering hot day, leaving their team and buggy at the park and tramping the burning streets, where red-white-and-blue bunting was hung between the telephone poles. A silent country party, ill at ease, the girls in home-made lawn dresses of blue, with cheap lace, the boys sunburned and short, like little old men in their heavy clothes and felt hats. The hot cement burned through their stiff Sunday shoes. They listened to the band concert and the speech in the park. They brought their dinner in a big pasteboard box, and they and Herman's family ate together on the grass, fried chicken, thick bread and butter, pickles, coco-nut cake. The children teased for ice-cream, which the Baptist Ladies'

Aid were serving, but August said there were too many of them and that they had enough without. The children liked to come, but there was all that work beforehand getting up the big lunch and getting all the children ready, then looking after them while they were there and getting them all together to go home again. Emma and Mollie said that they'd almost as soon stay at home.

They went to the county fair, held every September in the fair grounds at "Wapsie." They drove, and Herman and Mollie drove, and they took big boxes of lunch again and ate together. The men enjoyed the races, but the women liked to go into the big, flimsy wooden building, where the fancy work and cooking-exhibits were held, walking about and looking and murmuring to each other, "There's Mrs. Lempcke's quilt. It didn't get a prize. Look at that big pincushion with the blue tag on it. Do you think that's so pretty as all that?" Mollie brought some things once or twice, but Emma said, "*Ach,* I ain't got time for all such things."

The children always teased for more money than August would give them—wanted lemonade and wanted to go into all the shows. The older children now began to go by themselves. Mary and Elva went with two "fellows" in a buggy, and Frank teased for grandpa's old one-seated buggy so that he could take his girl. The parents would meet the young people about the fair grounds, four or six going around together, Elva always giggling and "carrying on" until Emma was ashamed of her. They saw them at the lemonade and the ice-cream stands, and saw them carrying toy balloons. But they never met Frank and his girl. They didn't know where those two kept themselves.

August and Emma never went anywhere without the children except once to "open-air conference" down in the Turkey timber. While they were gone, Elva and the two little ones came down with scarlet fever. Emma said she'd never try that again. It was worse than staying at home.

Then grandma had the "stroke" that they had all been looking for. She was completely paralysed, and never got out of bed again. She didn't seem to realize much, but she never let anyone but Emma do things for her, except that she wanted August to turn and lift her. She was in bed for five years.

Emma lived between bedroom and kitchen, the kitchen a narrow, low-ceiled room, calcimined in green, the little window with geraniums in tin cans looking out across the back yard to the small orchard.

Emma always said that these were the hardest years of all.

III: LOOSENING UP

THINGS WERE a little easier after grandma's death. At first Emma could scarcely realize that she could really leave the place, that when she worked she needn't always have the feeling that she ought to go in and look at grandma. In a way she missed the fact that grandma no longer needed her. But grandma had scarcely been a person to anyone for the last five years—only a responsibility, a gnawing sense of worry under everything. Nearly all the feeling connected with grandma had been fear, defence, rebellion, care, worry. Emma could not help feeling the relief that slowly seeped through everything.

Grandpa they didn't mind, he made so little trouble. He stayed about the same, as Emma told people, except that he seemed in a way to have withdrawn himself to a greater distance, that he seemed to be living in some region of his own. Only when some old friend or neighbour came out occasionally, and they got to talking of religion, he would come out of his dreams. They could hear him praying aloud in his room sometimes, the children coming in wide-eyed and whispering, "Mamma, listen to grandpa in there!" *"Unser Vater . . . in dem Himmel,"* the German words sounding rich, feeling, even in his thin, high-pitched voice, with long pauses between. He sat nearly always in his own room. Marguerite was bigger now, she didn't need him. He looked just about as when he had first come to the farm—tall, thin, bent, with his narrow, lined face and white beard, thin, silvery hair, his deep-burning, dark eyes.

August was getting a few things now. He was putting improvements on the place. He had put up the big new barn, and Hans Stille, who was keeping some bees now and doing a little farming over on the other side of Richland, had come for the summer again and made over the old buildings. August had all the farm buildings painted white, but the house would have to wait awhile for its new coat. They had a good milk-separator now, and Hans had fixed up a milk-house for them. August kept everything in fine repair. He kept all his machinery under cover, had no old ploughs and shredders standing about in the grove, like Herman Klaus and some other farmers. But he did not do much to the house. He had put in a sink in the kitchen, with a wooden cupboard underneath, and a soft-water pump. That was about all.

August and Emma had been too busy really to know that they were getting older. They had to look at the children to realize that. Emma looked older. Her hair was getting grey. She had always been slender, but she began to take on flesh now. People joked her about it, said, "You're getting fleshy, ain't you? You must be makin' the girls do the work for you." She said, without rancour, that she guessed she'd always been on her feet too much to get any flesh before. She'd run it all off. It made her look older instead of younger, dumpy and shapeless and middle-aged. She had to put on glasses, too. She should have done so long ago. She ordered a pair from a man who came around with a little card testing eyes, and who fitted people out with glasses cheap. But when farmers who had known August Kaetterhenry around Turkey Creek happened to meet him in town, they said, "Well, you ain't got so much older a'ready, August." He looked a little heavier, his neck creased and red, but in general about the same.

It was the children who were changing. Frank was a man now, they had to realize, although he was a short little fellow and didn't look any older than Carl when you saw them out in the field together. He had once wanted to be a mechanic, but he had given up that notion and was going to get married and settle down to farming. He had been going with the same girl for five or six years now—Lottie Schenck, a heavy, coarse, hard-working girl. People were all asking when the wedding was to be.

August would miss Frank when he left the place, but Carl and Johnnie would help. Johnnie might take hold better if Frank wasn't there to do things. He was the restless one. Neither of the other boys could be relied upon quite so much as Frank. They hadn't been brought up to work so hard. But August always believed that Carl would make a better farmer than Frank when he settled down to it. It was hard to tell about Johnnie.

Frank was looking around for a place to farm. August was doing most of the looking, however. He had always wanted to get hold of the next piece of land, where those LaRues had lived, and now, finally, the last of them was pulling out and going to Colorado. He took the farm for Frank. Frank was to pay him back eventually in the form of rent. August wanted to see the boy get a good start. He might be realizing a little, although he didn't admit it, that he had been harder on Frank than on the other boys. And he didn't mind having that other two hundred acres. It was a good investment, and made him the owner of four hundred acres of the best land, all there together. It gave him an excuse, too, to say to the family, who were getting to want too many things, "Needn't ask for that until I've got back some of what I paid for Frank's farm."

Mary was the one who was giving them trouble. More than Elva now, who had been inclined to be wild and to run around with fellows whom her parents couldn't approve. Mary had always been such a good child except for that weakness for reading. The only time they had had any trouble with her had been when she'd been determined to study to be a teacher and to go to the little Methodist academy at Wesley. August had said that she could teach country school without going there. He had too many children to send them away to school. She'd settle down and marry like the rest of them, and there'd be his money wasted. She had seemed to give that up and not to say anything more about it. She had taken to dress-making a little, had gone about to the neighbouring farms as people called for her. Of course she hadn't made much at it, because she was just Mary Kaetterhenry, someone whom they all knew; but it had given her something to do and got that crazy notion out of her head.

But now she began to have some queer spells. No one knew what to call them. The neighbour women were all interested, wondered if they could be fits, wanted to know all the symptoms. She would get pale and seem to stiffen out. The neighbours all advised different things, brought over remedies that had helped them. August and Emma bought her large bottles of "nerve tonic" at the drug-store, but that didn't seem to help. They were frightened, even to the extent of hitching up and taking her in to old Dr. Bowen's office in Richland. He gave them a prescription, but he didn't seem to know much more than they did what was the cause of the thing. They "kind of lost confidence in Bowen," they said. A neighbour told them about this new "rubber doctor" in "Wapsie," and how he had cured her brother's wife. Mary wanted to try him. They took her into "Wapsie." He told them that some bone was out of place and was pressing on a nerve; and although they didn't see how that had caused the spells, they thought they'd try him. He wanted Mary to come in twice a week for treatment. $1.50 a treatment, a lot of money to pay for that little rubbing, but they were worried now. For a time it seemed that the treatments were helping her. Then all at once she got worse than ever. They heard of a place over across the river in Wisconsin where they gave mud baths that were supposed to cure anything. Despite the expense, they sent her there. When she came back she was better—she had never been away from home before—but she was told to take it easy, not do much of the work.

It had shaken them up a good deal to have Mary go back on them. It made them more careful with the other children. Elva was going with Roy Robbins, but it didn't seem as if Mary was going to get married. They let her go over to visit her Aunt Sophie Klaus at

Turkey Creek. Then August let her go in to Rapids City and take a sewing-course. That was the most like going away to school of anything she had ever had. She improved after that, but she was not strong. She was like Grandpa Stille, tall, slender, black-haired, with bright, shy, dark, intelligent eyes.

Elva married when she was just a girl. She had stopped the country school long ago. Her parents wondered how she would like it when she had everything to do herself. They thought that she and Roy would make a queer set of farmers. They were both so flighty. But they started in immediately to raise a family, and that steadied them down.

Elva was the one who complained most that the younger ones "had it pretty easy." It was true; August was not so hard upon Carl and Johnnie as he had been upon Frank. Things were easier on the farm. Carl and Johnnie didn't have to stay out of school and help with the farm work, as Frank had done.

Frank felt himself at a disadvantage with the younger boys. They grew up into big, blond, good-looking boys. They didn't mingle much with the older ones. They kept to themselves and seemed to enjoy things together. Frank was a little shy with them because they had gone to school so much more than he had. Frank had had to quit the country school at what would have been about the seventh grade in town.

The roads were better now. It was easier to get about. There were more horses on the farm, and there was grandpa's old one-seated buggy. August let the boys take that and Nell, one of the old horses, and drive in to Richland to school. More and more country children were doing that now that the high school gave a full course. The boys took Marguerite as far as the country school. She was too little to go into town yet, and by the time that she was ready, probably they would have this new consolidated school against which August was voting because of the taxes.

August didn't know how it would be in the winter. The first winter the boys tried to drive back and forth the five miles. The next year they stayed in town until spring, at the Henry Stilles', where they kept the fires going and looked after the chickens and the cow and chopped the wood. They could go to the high-school parties, and play basket-ball, go around with the town "kids." Johnnie had a town girl, and so did Carl part of the time. But he still went to see Clara Josten, in the country, when he and Johnnie went home on Friday night, and he took her to box socials in the country schools. August grumbled about the boys—*ach,* they thought they had to have everything; didn't know anything but basket-ball any more. But he was proud of them.

It was entirely different with Marguerite than with the older girls. She had everything, it seemed, that Mary and Elva hadn't had. Elva grudged it to her, said, "I'd like to see what pa would have done to us if we'd asked for just half the things she does!" But she was so much the youngest, the baby and the pet, that it seemed natural that they should give her things. Mary made all her clothes for her, fitting her out regularly every spring and fall, and watching the dresses of the little girls at Sunday school to get ideas for her. They liked to "dress baby up." The whole family were proud of her hair, a thick, blond fuzz that couldn't be braided, and at which everyone looked, saying, "Hey, there, curly-head!" They all knew that "baby" could get things out of August. He grumbled, but when he knew that the cloth that Mary wanted to buy was to make "baby" a dress, she was sure to get it. He even let Marguerite take lessons on the organ from Miss Grace Bracebridge, who drove about through the country with a pony and buggy teaching music.

August listened to the younger boys as he had never done to Frank, although he was still close and kept things in his own hands. The boys saw how other people did things. They tried to get their father to "loosen up a little," to get things that other farmers were getting. When they talked with their mother about it, she said, looking frightened, *"Ach,* how can we afford all that?" The boys hadn't grown up with any such awe of money matters. Emma had no idea of what the family resources were; she would never have dared to ask. But the boys seemed to know, somehow or other, what their father could do, how much he had. They scoffed, to Emma's scared delight, and said, "Aw, pa could have lots of things if he'd just loosen up and get them. We don't need to do things this way. Pa's so afraid he's going to take a cent out of the bank. He's got more than most farmers have. He could put up a silo if Uncle Willie did. Why couldn't he?" *"Ach!"* Emma said, frightened; but it pleased her.

They were beginning to get things. August began to try out new machinery. He put up a silo. One thing meant another. The boys kept talking gasolene-engines. It was crazy to pump all their water and turn the separator by hand. They couldn't get August to say anything. They needn't think that he would do whatever they wanted. But he had been talking to Art Miller in Richland, who was handling the Porter lights, and one summer he had his own electric plant installed on the farm. He didn't have the house wired at once, but they had lights in the barn and ran all their machinery by electricity.

August wanted his farm to have what other farms had, but he hated to dig into that pile in the bank. He knew how much work it had taken to put it there. No one worked harder for their money than the farmers did. He must think of his old age. They wanted to take it easy some day. He didn't want to find himself with as little as Grandpa Stille had.

He kept on digging. He worked as hard as he had ever done, except that he had the boys to help.

The greatest change came when he bought the Ford. August had been one of those who kept his old horses as long as he could, but he had to come to the automobile, like the rest of the farmers. He went into "Wapsie" one Saturday and looked at cars. He had the agent take him out and teach him how to drive that afternoon, and he drove the car home at night. The family came out into the yard. The children shouted, "Mamma, see what pa's got!" August drove proudly, scowling, not sure whether he could miss all the buildings and stop where he wished. The boys ran up to ask excitedly, "Can you stop her, pa? Hey, look out for that wagon! Where'd you get her? How much was she?" After August went into the house they stayed out there, looking the little five-passenger car all over, testing the wheels, examining the engine.

"*Ja,* I s'pose they'll think it's theirs now," August grumbled.

Emma declared at first that she would never go in the car. Her timidity delighted all of them. The boys could take the auto; she would drive with the horses and the old buggy. "*Ach,*" she said, "I don't trust those things. You read about accidents all the time." "Well, mamma, horses can run away, too. Old Dick ran away with Frank." "*Ja,* but then——" But the children teased her so much that she finally consented to get into the car. "Now, ain't this better than the old buggy?" the boys demanded. "*Ja,* well it ain't so bad, I guess," was all that they could get her to say. She never really liked the car. She was always nervous and looking out for accidents. For some reason she didn't believe that August could learn to be a good driver. "*Ach,* it's so late for him to learn!" She had never been afraid when he had a hand on the reins when they had gone out with the horses. After the boys learned to drive, she liked it better. She said it seemed more natural for young folks to learn things like that. She had faith in Carl and Johnnie. But when she went with August, she always kept one hand on the seat ready to open the door and jump out. And although he got to handle the car in any kind of weather and on any kind of roads, as all farmers did, August never did drive as well as the boys. They could seem to get the thing cranked when he couldn't.

It was a knack they had. Emma noticed that he was ready to let them do the driving when he could.

The car meant that they could get away from the farm. They went into town oftener. They drove to Elva's and Frank's and Mollie's. The relationship nearly always had Sunday dinner together now. They went into church more regularly, and to other things in town—basket-ball games to see the boys play, the lecture course.

They even took a little trip, the first time they'd really been away from the farm. Once after harvest they left the boys to look after the farm, and August and Emma and Marguerite drove down to Turkey Creek and visited all of August's folks. The old man Kaetterhenry was dead, of course, but most of August's brothers and sisters were still living about there. It was a beautiful time of the year. The autumn was lovely there in the timber, among the hills. They all drove out for picnics together. They made plans with Sophie and her husband to drive to the "Picture Rocks" on the Mississippi some year, stopping at the little old town of Guttenberg, where their folks had stopped when they came up the Mississippi and had bought their first farm implements.

Then the road past the farm, between Richland and "Wapsie," was made a highway. That dreadful hill by Ed Hunter's farm was graded down so that no one need be afraid of it any more. The old country road was widened and ditched and gravelled; the tall black-eyed Susans and the sweet clover were ruthlessly slashed down into dusty stubble. Although August fought the highway and joined other farmers in grumbling at the taxes, still "it made it handier." They went into "Wapsie" often, although they still did most of their trading in Richland, believing it must be cheaper there, since the stores had fewer goods and they were set out with less style.

That used to be a country road along which occasional wagons and buggies jolted. Now it was a gravelled highway, "Primary Road 5." Cars flashed down it all day, and on Sundays in the summer there was a constant stream of travel. Head-lights and wind-shields gave off sharp white flashes as cars whirred past on the light-coloured, glittering gravel. It was a wonder to Emma to sit on the porch on Sunday afternoons and count how many vehicles went by. But Grandpa wouldn't even try to count. "*Ach*, no! no! no!" was all that he would say. This was all so wicked on Sunday!

August had kept his hands on other things, but he couldn't keep the boys from using the car. When they took their girls, it wasn't an all-day occasion, as when Frank had got grandpa's old buggy to drive Lottie to the fair. They went out on Sunday afternoons when they felt like it. August would go out and find the car gone again. It was no use trying to stop them. Emma thought it dreadful for the boys to "pleasure-drive on Sunday," against which the Richland Methodist church was making a last futile stand, as against cards and dancing; but both she and August got used to it. All the young people seemed to do it. But one thing August said: if he ever heard of his boys driving to a Sunday base-ball game, they could never have the car again.

Grandpa never grew accustomed to all this. He was now too mild, too feeble and withdrawn, to protest much against it; but he would say sadly, when he saw that the boys were gone, *"Ach,* no! no! *das ist nicht gut."* And sometimes, sitting alone in the big rocker in his gloomy little room, he would mutter, *"Nein, nein, das ist nicht gut."*

IV: THE WAR

THE FIRST years of the war didn't affect the Richland farmers very much. It seemed far away from them. *"Ach,* over there in those old countries——" August said with a kind of contemptuous blankness. The men talked about it down at the implement store and at the produce house. They said that this country would never be involved. They were opposed to that, the farmers, as they were opposed to anything that seemed unsettling. They were a conservative bunch about Richland.

August had at first only a slight German feeling. Many of the farmers around Richland were English, and there had always been a little line of cleavage between the English and the German farmers. Sometimes, when August heard old Roland Yarborough "blowing off" about how wicked the Germans were, and that they ought all to be exterminated, it made him hot for a moment, made him feel that he was a German. All the feeling that he had was naturally and instinctively on the side of Germany. But most of the farmers were agreed. "Well, they've got to fight it out among themselves. It's their business; 'tain't ours." That was the way that August felt. He went about his own business.

Grandpa was the one who got excited. The old man, so withdrawn, his inner life known now to no one but himself, buried in strange dreams and prayers and fervours, now suddenly came back to the world. It was as if all at once childhood things, which had long been buried, came surging to the surface and overwhelmed him with memories. He went back to his boyhood in that little village in Mecklenburg whose name the boys had never heard before. Now he was always talking about it—Gultberg. *"Ja,* in Gultberg den——" "Gultberg? What's that? What's he talking about?" the boys asked, half amused. This was all far away to them. It tickled them, they said, to see "grandpa get himself all worked up" over something he had painstakingly read in the paper; come tottering out from his room, in his old felt slippers and patched brown trousers, his dark, sunken eyes burning, shaking one long, bony finger and pouring out a lot of broken English and German that they could only half understand. "Are de Germans so bad, den? *Mein* oldt *Vater, mein* Uncle Carl, I remember in de old country, were dey den all such bad men? No, no." They would listen, grinning a little, until he was exhausted and would go back to his room, shaking his head and mourning sadly, *"Ach,* no, *nein,"* to sit in the old rocker, sadly, his hands in his lap, muttering as he used to do about the Sunday travel.

Emma tried to calm him; she was afraid that the excitement would hurt him. She couldn't see why he was so affected by this, by things so far away; but of course he was thinking about his old home.

But when this country went in, all this was changed. Then feelings that had never been known before were all about. Then the taunts, the talk about Huns and *Boche,* made farmers like August for the first time actually realize their German ancestry. August had always taken it for granted that he belonged in this country. They awoke a deep racial resentment that could not come flaring out into the open but had to remain smouldering, and that joined with the fear of change, the resentment at interference, into a combination of angry feelings.

This centred chiefly in a deep opposition to the draft. To have someone tell his boys to do this and that! To take away his help on the farm just when he needed it most! To have somebody just step in and tell them where they had to go! Was that what happened in this country? Why had his people left the old country, then, if things were going to be just the same?

Carl was twenty-three now, Johnnie twenty. Carl's was among the first three names drawn in Richland, where he had to register. It was on the list in the post office—Carl Kaetterhenry, along with Ray Powers and Jay Bennett, the preacher's son. August stormed, wanted to know what right the Government had. But Carl took it quietly. There was no use kicking, he said. His name happened to be one drawn, and that was all there was to it.

What roused August to the greatest anger was that Harlan Boggs, the banker's son in "Wapsie," should get exempt, while his boy had to go. Harlan Boggs had appealed to the board and got exemption on the grounds that he couldn't be spared from the bank because of Liberty-bond work. But it didn't matter to the board, August said, that he couldn't get help and that they should take his boy right in the midst of the harvest season. Johnnie was working for Frank that year, and Carl was the only one he had on the farm. They said, "Produce, produce," but how was he going to do it when he got no help? There was all this talk about the women working on the farms, but August didn't see many of those high-school girls from Richland coming out and offering to do his threshing for him. Where were all these women working, then?

Grandpa quieted down after he learned that this country was in the war; regarded with a hurt, sorrowing, bewildered wonder that it should be fighting Germany. That was all that mattered to him, all that he could see of it. Carl went in to say good-bye to him, embarrassed and a little afraid of what grandpa might do. The old man rose from his chair, holding it by one arm, and quietly shook Carl's hand. Then he returned to his solitary brooding. It was strange and remote, the touch of that dry, aged, bony hand, although grandpa had been there in the house ever since Carl could remember.

The train left in the early morning. August drove his family in, Emma and Carl and Marguerite. Johnnie and Frank and Frank's wife came in Frank's car; Mary and Elva and Roy in Roy's. There was a little group at the small wooden station: the other two boys and their families, a few people from town, one or two detached travelling men. The family stayed awkwardly in the depot, didn't know what to do or to say to one another. Johnnie and August went out to see if the train was in sight.

Just before the train came—the morning *Clipper,* the Chicago train, by which clocks were set and rising timed—old Jerry McGuire the postmaster, an old Catholic who had come into office when "the Democrats came in," lined the three boys up on the station platform and read the President's Proclamation to them. It was a strange, solemn, unreal scene. Even the people who saw it didn't believe in it. The three boys standing there, their figures against the dim red of the harvest sunrise, with solemn blank faces, frowning a little to keep down any signs of emotion. One of the mothers sobbed. Emma wept only a little, effacing herself even now. Carl looked big and fresh between the other two boys, Jay Bennett, a thin boy, dissipated in a small-town way; Ray, gawky and sunburned, with a wild head of hair. Carl was such a big, sturdy boy! He had his father's fresh-coloured skin, only finer-grained, rough light hair, full boyish lips, and clear blue eyes.

The little town was silent. Away from the station stretched pastures, the dew lying wet and heavy on red clover and tall weeds. The train came bearing down upon them, puffing out blackish smoke into the pale morning sky. It went black and big into the red prairie-sunrise. The fields were left silent again. The scattered group of people on the platform got into their battered cars and drove back home to the morning chores.

When Johnnie had to go, they were more used to it.

It was a queer time at home. It was so strange to be without the boys! August was a big, vigorous man, but now he realized for the first time, now that he had everything to do alone, that he was getting older. He had never stopped working hard; but now he saw that, strong and dogged as he was, he couldn't quite do the work he had done in those days when they first went on the farm. He didn't even think of getting Emma out into the field now. "Mamma" belonged in the house.

The feeling of the neighbourhood against the German farmers had grown to a degree that would have seemed incredible at the beginning of the war. August "got off easy" compared with some of them. He had two boys in the service, he could keep his mouth shut, he bought Liberty bonds, although he didn't like to be told to do so. If it had not been for Carl and Johnnie in the army, he might have refused, like old Rudolph Haas, out of pure Kaetterhenry stubbornness. It was the thought of Carl and Johnnie that kept him from flaring up too fiercely when the boys yelled at him, when he drove into Richland, "Hey, Dutchy! Old Dutchman! Old Dutchy Kaetterhenry!" Once or twice he threatened, and started after them; but usually he only glared at them, smothering his impulse to fight. Some of the other German farmers came up before the board because of things they had said, or were reported to have said. Old Haas's corn-crib was burned. But nothing worse happened to August than being yelled at on the street and finding painted in crude red letters on his barn: "Old Dutchy Kaetterhenry. Hun. Bosh. Look Out."

They were having terrible times down around Turkey Creek, which was solidly German, and where there had been more resistance to the draft. One of August's brothers had been threatened. A mob of boys and men from "Wapsie" had gone down there one night and tarred and feathered the preacher at the old Turkey Creek German church.

August kept himself in hand because of the boys and because of the way Emma worried. And underneath all his anger was a strange, hurt, puzzled incredulity. Hadn't he lived here all his life, been born twenty miles from here? Didn't everybody know August Kaetterhenry? Hadn't he been a good farmer and citizen and church-member all his life? There was at the same time something fiercely real and yet utterly incredible about the whole thing.

Emma worried about the boys. She never heard the telephone ring that she didn't think it might be a message for them, as their neighbour, Mrs. Griffin, had got. She knew now that of all the children Johnnie was her boy, just as Carl was August's. Carl was steadier and more level-headed. She had a feeling that Carl would take care of himself, that nothing would happen to him. But Johnnie—he would go rushing into everything.

It was long since she had done the milking and all such work. Despite having less cooking and washing to do, it was hard on her. She was ailing more or less, although she kept up. That old trouble that she had sometimes had before came back on her. "Spells with her stomach," she called it. The family had long supposed that these spells were just something that mamma had, but now she told Mollie that August wanted to get the doctor out for her. She always said, "*Ach,* no. Wait awhile. I guess it won't last long." Then she would feel better again.

Things were strange all about these days. One of the queerest things that happened was Mary's marriage. Years ago Mary had gone with Joe Fields. He used to take her to the county fair when Roy took Elva. But then Mary had wanted to go to school, and Joe had married Ada Griffin. He was a widower now, with four little children. Mary was "sewing around." People hadn't even known that Joe was "looking in that direction" again. But all at once he and Mary turned up at the Kaetterhenry farm married! Well, the family were glad that she was settled, although they didn't see how she was going to be strong enough to do all that work and look after those four children. But she and Joe, it seemed, had always liked each other, although once Mary had wanted a different kind of man from Joe. The family thought it was a good thing to have her settled down at last. This was something to write the boys, if it didn't take them so long to get their mail that it would be old before they heard of it.

Carl had gone into the army first, but Johnnie got across before he did. Carl had his father's knack with horses. They kept him down at one of the Southern camps training new recruits to handle the horses. Johnnie was in the machine-gun division. He was right in the thick of it, as they thought Johnnie would be sure to be. He was wounded once, but his family didn't hear of it until he was back in the fighting again. Carl just got across when the armistice was signed.

Carl came back, ready to settle down for good, saying that this old Iowa farm looked better to him than any place he had ever seen or hoped to see. That went far to soothe August's anger. Carl hadn't been at home three weeks when he married his old girl in the country, Clara Josten, and brought her out to the farm until he and she could find a place of their own.

But Johnnie was different. He was restless. He was reported cured of his wound, but they could see that he was nervous, jumpy, not the boy that he used to be. He couldn't seem to be still a minute. He was always running off with the car and going to town. The car was the only thing in which he was interested. August, who was a cautious driver, grumbled about the way that Johnnie drove, with all the gas on, muffler open, fenders rattling, making that old car go at top speed every moment. Johnnie went over to help Frank again. They thought that maybe that might help to give him a change and quiet him down. But at the height of the season he suddenly walked out and went into Richland, where he got a job at the garage with the Beal Brothers.

August shared in the high prices and the land boom that raged in Iowa after the war. He had an offer of five hundred dollars an acre for the farm. It dazzled him, but still August was too cautious to sell. And if he did, then what would he do? It was a better piece of land than he could pick up again. Roy Robbins and Elva did sell their farm, but then the slump in prices came, and the man couldn't make payments, and they had it back on their hands again. There was a piece of land down near Turkey Creek, however, that old Casper Kaetterhenry had left to the children; the second wife had got the home farm. August and his brother Heinie bought that piece from the others and sold it when prices were at the peak.

War-time feelings died out, but a little of the old resentment stayed. August never felt quite the sense of home and security in Richland Township that he had felt before.

PART THREE

I: OPERATION

CARL'S WIFE was a great help in the house. She was much like Carl himself, fresh-faced, light-haired, rather quiet, but good-tempered and sturdy and vigorous. At first Emma tried to treat her like company, but Clara said that she was used to doing things and really tried to take some of the hardest work off Emma's hands. Emma had always had the feeling that she must be responsible for all that was done in the house. But now she let Clara do things for her. She told the relatives she "liked Carl's wife real well. She was nice to have around."

The family thought that Emma might get to feeling better now that the boys were at home again and she didn't have all that worry. But she was still miserable. People noticed that she didn't look well; said, "Ain't you thinner than you been the last few years? What they been doing to you?" August was slow to believe anything really wrong with any of his family. But he did see that Emma didn't look right.

Then she was "right down sick." August didn't know when Emma had ever really given out before, and it frightened him. He asked her if she didn't want to try that place where Mary had gone. The neighbours and relatives all came in to help and advise. They all said wisely that it was something that had better be looked after. They told about Mrs. Ed Kohler. None of these doctors could help her, and old Bowen had said she was dying, until she had gone up to the clinic at Rochester. Others had gone there, as formerly they had tried patent medicine and mud-baths. People talked Rochester, Rochester, until August asked Emma, "Well, do you think you'd like to go up there, then?" She said, as she always did, *"Ach,* I don't know." But he could see that she rather wanted to go. All the children urged it. They wanted August to take her there. Carl and Clara could look after the farm. Finally August said he guessed he'd take her up there.

It was the greatest journey that they had ever taken together. August had gone to Chicago once with stock during the war, and when she was a little child Emma had come out to Iowa from New York with her parents; but they had never gone farther on the train together than to Dubuque, about thirty miles away.

Everyone knew that he was taking her to Rochester. People who had been there, or had had members of their family there, came over to tell Emma details of operations. When they saw that she was getting frightened they said, "Well, now, maybe you'll find it's just some little thing that don't need an operation, like Myrtie Rohrer."

It seemed to Emma and August that they were taking a terrible and final journey. Carl drove them to the station. They were taking Marguerite with them. Clara stood in the kitchen doorway, her arms hugged in her apron, because the March wind was cold. As Carl cranked the car and hurried around to the side to get in, she waved her arm and called, "Don't worry about your chickens." Emma asked fearfully, "What's that she said?" "Said not to worry about your chickens, mamma." They drove out through the deep, black, sticky mud of their own drive, out to the highway, with its brown gravel gritty and wet in the sharp, windy March air.

At the station they felt a faint importance and pride when August told the people who inquired, "*Ja,* I'm takin' her up to Rochester; see if those fellows can't help her some a'ready."

The children, too, felt pride in the clipping from the Richland *Banner* that they sent on to the folks up at Rochester.

> "Mr. and Mrs. August Kaetterhenry left Tuesday for Rochester, Minn., to consult the Drs. Mayo in regard to her health. Mrs. Kaetterhenry has been in poor health for some time, and it is hoped by her many friends that she will find speedy relief at this famous establishment."

The trip up to Minnesota, bleak and sharp as the weather was, had interest for them. It was almost the first time that they had been in any other State than Iowa. August was in the smoking-car. He came back and said to Emma and Marguerite, "Do you know you're in Minnesota a'ready?" "Oh, are we?" Emma looked out of the window. She thought with a thrill, "We're in another State!" August kept watching to see how the country looked, and whether things were as far along up here as he had left them back there. He saw some nice farms, he said. But the land was flatter than around home, and a fellow to whom he had been talking told him that they had more wind up here. August said he didn't think he'd like to live where they were all Swedes and Norwegians. He hadn't seen any farm yet that looked better than his own in Richland Township.

They took the journey in the day coach and thriftily ate the lunch that Clara and Lottie had put up for them, taking the fried chicken out of the pasteboard box and telling Marguerite to brush the crumbs off the dusty, red plush seat. They looked like country people, August heavy and silent, his farmer's red neck showing rough and creased above his collar in the back, in his heavy coat and overshoes and cap; Emma subdued and uncertain over the journey, looking with a kind of fearful curiosity at the other people in the train; a sickly woman with greyish hair and old-fashioned glasses, in a stiff, black velvet hat and an old black coat of some imitation fur with old-fashioned sleeves gathered slightly at the top, a black skirt that came down to her rubbers, black golf mittens. Even Marguerite looked a little coarse and sullen, with her blue knitted tam pulled down upon her bright fuzz of hair.

They went to a boarding-house where some of their neighbours had gone, one that was said to be clean and that didn't charge as much as some. It was just as good as anybody'd want, Mrs. Griffin had told them. It was snowing when they got there, as they wrote back to the children, and they trudged up through the dismal streets, with their left-over dingy snow, August carrying the two suit-cases that Carl and Johnnie had let them have. The boarding-house was an old-fashioned, brown frame-house close to the medical buildings. Marguerite shared a room with an excitable, talkative woman who took pride in being in Rochester for the fourth time. She told Marguerite all about her different doctors, saying happily, "I said when I come in, 'Well, doctor, you've got me back again, you see.' Dr. Barnard knew me right away. Well, he'd ought to; this is the fourth time I been in Rochester. He's had to examine me twice before his-self. He says, 'Well, Miss Parmenter, I see I have. What do you mean by this?' He's awful good-natured; not like some. Always a-jokin' you when you come in there."

The Kaetterhenrys had nothing to say to the other boarders at first. They ate in silence, asking one another in hushed voices for butter or bread. But they had to wait several days until they could have their turn at the clinic. One of the women who sat in the shabby boarding-house parlour, with its ancient furnishings, began to talk to Emma. "You here on your own account?" she said. "I thought you was the one. What's your trouble?" They talked over symptoms together. The woman told Emma what she must expect in going through the clinic, and terrified her with descriptions of all the tests that she herself had had to have, leaving out no detail. She thought that Emma must have just what her cousin's wife had had, and she had spent four months in the hospital and now was going to have to come again. At night Emma and August talked over the boarders together in their room, in hoarse whispers, Emma telling what she had gleaned of where this one lived, what that one's husband did, what was the matter with another one.

They started in at the clinic at last, when Emma was afraid that "mister would get restless and want to go home if they didn't get in pretty soon." When the girl at the desk asked them for what they had come, they said—looking at each other as if the other one might know—they didn't know, that was what they wanted to find out. She sent them patiently to the abdominal section, which was a good guess for most farmer people. Emma took the tests, while August stolidly waited in the lobby of the clinic building, with his overcoat thrown open and his cap on his knee. Emma wanted him around. He did not take an interest in watching the people, as she would have done, but he liked to see how the building was put up, to calculate how much space and how many rooms they must have and how many people there must have been going through it to-day.

He was just where Emma had left him. He said, "Well, what'd he tell you?" *"Ach,* I got to see another one to-morrow."

Gradually they felt themselves drawn into the life of the place. It was an experience to them, more than the mud-baths had been to Mary. Although they were bashful and ill at ease away from home, it was not so hard getting acquainted as they had thought. People talked to them—the boarders, people who happened to sit near them in the clinic—and wore away their country shyness. Emma felt a kind of enjoyment in talking over the tests she had taken, and the doctors she had seen, with three or four other people who sat in the boarding-house parlour with the landlady and talked. Her ailments had never had any importance before. They always asked, when she and August came in, "Well, still taking tests?" *"Ja,* I guess that's what she'll always be doing," August answered. Emma smiled shyly. The boarders thought that that Mrs. Kaetterhenry was a real sweet little person. Even August fell into conversation with a fat man who sat next him in the clinic and who was also waiting for his wife. They talked about their wives' illnesses, and the man told how the crops had been in Wisconsin. August had some conversation with a fellow from Texas that gave him a travelled feeling. Marguerite went to the movies and into the shops with Miss Parmenter, who flew about town buying squares to make drawn-thread handkerchiefs in the intervals of examinations.

The strange and unaccustomed thing was the importance of Emma. August and Marguerite counted for nothing beside her here, were merely here to be with her. It was a new idea to both of them, and to Emma, too. August went in with her to the doctor who had examined her to hear the verdict. He did not make a murmur about the expense, although it was all so much more than he had figured on. Emma's value was strangely enhanced in his eyes when the doctor, a large, well-groomed, imposing man with a courteous manner that made Emma admire him, spoke respectfully of "Mrs. Kaetterhenry," outlined her condition, and said that she must go at once to the hospital.

The boarders all said, "Gall-bladder operation! Well, that's just what I thought from what she told me," although the woman who had thought that Emma had her cousin's wife's ailment was disappointed and unconvinced. This was a respectable and well-known operation, and it, too, seemed to raise Emma's value in some strange way. The boarders were interested, helped Marguerite to pack her mother's suit-case for the hospital, reassured, and condoled.

Emma seemed still more removed from their common ways of life when she entered the hospital. August went into her room for a while, a small double room, Emma's bed across from another bed where a woman with a long, meager braid lay and talked in sepulchral whispers with a visitor in a hat with green plumes. Emma looked changed, in the narrow, white iron bed, so immaculate, different from their puffy feather-bed at home, without her spectacles, her thin grey hair neatly parted and braided by the nurse. Both she and August felt a mysterious fear of "the sisters" who glided about the halls in their robes and rosaries. They had always felt a fascinated horror of the wickedness of the Catholics.

"It kind o' makes me creepy to have them around here," Emma protested.

"*Ach,* I guess they're all right. He wouldn't 'a' sent you here if they wasn't," August said.

All this whiteness and immaculateness seemed great splendour to them.

Emma had her operation the next day. August was really frightened then. The boarders all reassured him, all told of the wonders of the surgeon. August had seen him for a moment in the hospital—a short, plump, very clean man, exhaling a kind of unshakable vigour. August felt a tremendous awe of him. They both trusted him in the blind way that they trusted their Methodist God, because they must. It helped August, fed his pride, that his wife was to have a famous surgeon. But, although he said little, he was shaken. Emma had made him promise to be right there. It seemed now that August mattered more to her than Marguerite.

He waited in the sun parlour. He had never gone through such an endless morning. He tried to think about the farm, about what crops he would put in this summer; but under everything was a sinking, sickening dread in which he would suddenly be submerged. He was silent, turning his cap upon his knee. Marguerite sat restlessly beside him. She could not keep her hands still, fingered her dress and her beads and her handkerchief. People were wheeled past from the operating-room—mounds of white, some silent, some moaning. August looked at his watch. He went through terror. It shouldn't have taken as long as this. Something must have gone wrong. He tiptoed down the hall to Emma's room. Her bed was still empty.

The nurse came for them at last. They went, solemn, shaken, on tiptoe, into Emma's room. They felt awed, taken aback, at the sight of her strange, pinched, colourless face at which they stood awkwardly gazing.

"You can speak to her," the nurse said encouragingly. August was terribly in awe of Emma. He did not know what to say.

"Well, it's over," he said finally.

"*Ja,* I guess so," Emma whispered.

Marguerite stood looking sullen and angry in her fright. She hardly dared go near her mother, kissed her quickly, barely touching her cheek, when the nurse said that she might. They stared awhile longer, tiptoed out.

The excitement of the day died down. The boarders all said, "Well, she got through it all right, I see. Sure. I knew she would. Well, now you must telegraph the folks at home. I expect there'll be some pretty anxious folks."

It was the first telegram that August had ever sent. "Operation over mamma doing fine." That, too, gave him importance.

After that August and Marguerite went twice a day to the hospital in the motor-bus that ploughed clumsily through the spring mud. August always felt big and awkward and out of place in that silent building, but he got to know the faint odour of drugs. He recognized some of the people who always went up in the elevator with him and felt a kind of kinship with them. He even felt less awe of the gliding sisters. He wasn't dreadfully abashed now at the woman in the other bed, who talked to him and Emma, called him Mr. Kaetterhenry.

Emma now seemed to belong to the place. She said that they were nice to her. She took with shy gratitude the first attention and petting that she had had since she was a girl, with a kind of feeling that she, a married woman and mother, shouldn't have it, but a feminine pleasure in it. The nurses liked her. They were good to her, petted and cared for her in a way that made Marguerite look at them wide-eyed, remembering that this was mamma. It was so strange to see mamma waited on and of first importance! The other woman in the room was fretful and exacting. Emma was such a contrast to her that the nurses appreciated her all the more. They told her she mustn't be afraid to ask for what she wanted, and they liked her shyness and fear of giving them trouble.

For the first time Emma had a life in which family were outsiders. She had a kind of intimacy with the nurses, and with the very spruce, black-haired young intern who came in and jested with her in a kind of fond teasing way that greatly flattered her. He never did learn how to pronounce her name, and called her blithely "Mrs. Katterhenry," at which she was too shy to protest.

As Emma grew better and his fright died down, poor August hardly knew what to do with himself. He never had been without work before in his life. He had never had a real vacation from the farm except that drive down into the Turkey timber, and then he had had the car to look after and had still talked crops with his brothers. When he could not be at the hospital, he hung about the boarding-house, yawned, sat drearily while the others were gossiping. He had never been a talker. He couldn't find the interest in the discussion of ailments that the others did, since he had never had any of his own. Now that he knew what it was, that Emma was getting better, he was no longer interested. There was no one just now to talk crops with him. That was the longest three weeks he had ever spent. He would rather have been threshing. The boarders said, "Well, I expect you're getting anxious to get back to your work now, Mr. Kaetterhenry." He said, *ja,* he was. He worried about how Carl was managing the farm. He would have gone back if Emma hadn't begged him to stay.

The boarders said encouragingly, when they saw his restlessness, "Oh, the vacation'll do you good." *"Ja,* but I've had about enough of it, though," he said.

Emma, too, said that she was anxious to get back home, but in a way she was having the best time that she had had for years. She was taking her leisure with a clear conscience. She had never been treated with such consideration. She really hated to leave the nurses and the young intern.

When she got back to the boarding-house most of the boarders who had been there before her operation were gone. Miss Parmenter had left much disappointed because they had told her that she didn't need an operation; a little medicine was enough. Dr. Barnard had gone down in her estimation. Emma missed the care and attention which had embarrassed her so at first. She missed the visits of the young intern, with his flattering jests. The boarding-house seemed dreary.

The specialist at the clinic had a talk with August before they left for home. August listened, subdued and respectful. The doctor said that he "anticipated no trouble," but that Mrs. Kaetterhenry must do no heavy work this summer and must take things very easily. August heard him uneasily, agreed, *"Ja,* I guess we can manage that." Something in it appealed to his sturdiness and reliability, his feeling of protection. Down underneath was a little feeling of bewildered guilt. This thing had opened August's eyes a little.

They went back to Richland feeling journeyed and full of Rochester. August was glad to get back to the farm and plunged at once into the late spring work. Emma was fearful of her strength at first. She remembered the admonitions. Clara said, "Now, mamma, we mustn't let you overdo." But when Emma got home, into the familiar routine, she threw off invalid ways. She had always worked here. They couldn't keep her from doing things. No one knew the people of whom she talked in Rochester. The surgeon, the doctors, meant nothing to Clara and Carl. The event of her home-coming was soon over. She settled down into the old ways again. She didn't go around telling everyone of her operation, as Mrs. Griffin had done, but the experience stayed, sharp and momentous, in her mind.

August, too, was a little different. He seemed to accept with relief her settling back into the rôle of mamma. But he was more thoughtful of her. He asked her if she couldn't let Clara do this or that. He saw, they all saw, that she wasn't equal to the things that she used to do.

August had worried about the farm. But when he came back to it he couldn't find anything very wrong with Carl's management. Things seemed to look as usual. That summer Carl kept on with some of the things that he had been doing that August had never entrusted to any of the boys before.

Those years of the war, when he had had everything to do, had tired August. He had always intended to retire, take it easy, when he could afford it; but all these things brought him to it now. He announced to Emma one day that they might move into town and leave the farm to Carl.

II: TOWN

THE CHIEF question was what they should do with grandpa if they left the farm. He had lived in that little room so long! He was over eighty now. It would be hard for him to make any change. He wouldn't want to go to town with them; he was used to the country. Clara and Carl said, "Let him stay here," but Emma hated to do that. He was getting so old now and might need a good deal of care before long; and they were young people, and didn't want to be tied to the place. Grandpa ought to have some of his own children to look after him. August thought that Herman and Mollie ought to take care of him now. They had let Emma have the whole care of both grandma and grandpa always. Now it wouldn't hurt Mollie to do something for her father. The old man would be no expense to them. He had a tiny income from bits of his land that had been left to him, enough to buy tobacco for him and *Die Flammende Fackel,* and the few clothes and things that he needed. Now August and

Emma were going into town to take it easy. Emma wasn't going to be saddled with the care of grandpa, August said, as she had been with grandma.

They took grandpa's belongings over to Mollie's one day in the motor-truck that Johnnie had assembled from an old engine and various miscellaneous parts: the ancient rope-bed with the feather-mattresses, the two wooden rocking-chairs, the commode and little old mirror, the air-tight stove, the ancient, faded books. Mollie and Herman made little trouble about taking him. They would probably not move off the farm for years yet. They couldn't afford it. Herman hadn't done as well as August had. The Klauses had taken things more easily all along, were more happy-go-lucky and not such workers as the Kaetterhenrys. They were easy-going people, Herman a little, lean man with kindly, childlike eyes and a kind of innocence of speech, Mollie short and fat and shapeless, waddling, good-hearted. Their farm had a dingy old-fashioned house set close to a scraggly, tangled willow grove where the ground seldom got a chance to dry and the blackbirds were noisy. They used a gasolene engine for some of their work, but they had no silo, no lights, and only the old red-painted barn. Farm implements stood about the worn, grassless farm-yard. August had always despised Herman a little for being so easy-going and not getting anywhere. They put grandpa's things into their own downstairs bedroom, moving up themselves into the room that Ernie, their son, had had, and saying, "*Ach,* we don't care. We can get along anywhere."

Emma felt a dreadful sense of guilt and desertion in leaving her father there. Not that Herman and Mollie wouldn't be good to him. But she knew how things went at Mollie's. It didn't seem right to have him anywhere but in that room where he had lived so long. But August said it would have to be that way.

The Kaetterhenrys moved to town in the late fall. There was no house that they could get to rent. They had to take rooms in old Mrs. Freeman's house until they could get a place of their own. Houses were scarce in Richland, where little business was done. This was a small house in the south part of town, the old and hilly part beyond the railroad tracks. It was half-frame, half-brick, painted a cream-yellow. They lived in the brick half. There were three rooms. They did their cooking and eating in one, August and Emma slept in another, and Marguerite had a cot and dresser in the third, which was their sitting-room. The rooms had the old square, small-paned windows, close to which some oak-trees rustled dry leaves. They had to get all their water from the pump next door. They had a stove only in the room where Marguerite slept, except the little oil-burner in the kitchen.

Emma didn't know just what August intended to do, whether he meant to buy or to build a house of his own. He still kept all such things to himself. He managed all the money. Once Johnnie said to her when he came over, "Heard pa was trying to buy one of those lots over by Cunningham's." *"Ach,* is he?" she said. *"Ja,* he don't tell me nothing." She did not think of making a fuss, as some would have done, but no one suspected the resentment that lay deep under her silence.

The children all said cheerfully. "Well, mamma, you can take it easy this winter. You ain't got much to do here." She said a little complainingly, "No, I should say I ain't. I wish I had a little more." These three small rooms were nothing after she had looked after a farm-house. Of course there were the meals to get, and they were hard to cook on this little three-burner oil-stove, when she was used to her big range. Johnnie ate with them, although they didn't have room for him to stay there.

But she had all afternoon to herself and she hardly knew what to do. It was a long, snowy winter. There were not many side-walks in this part of town, and it was hard to get out anywhere. She didn't see the children as often as she had in the country. She didn't get out to Mary's once all winter. She knew a few people in town—her two sisters-in-law, Mrs. Henry and Mrs. Willie Stille—but this was too far for them to come and see her much. She had a cold, and didn't even get to church most of the winter.

Once she said to August:

"Johnnie says you're buying one of them lots over north."

"Ja, I guess maybe," he admitted.

"Well, are we going to build?"

"I guess we better build. They ain't no good houses for sale. Why, don't you want to build?" he demanded.

"Ach, I'd like it, I guess. I just wondered what you was doing."

He grunted. But she had to find out from the children that he had actually bought a lot and that he was ordering lumber from the Great Western Lumber-yard. Elva demanded angrily, "Why don't pa ask you something about it? You ought to have some say-so about your own house, I should think. I'd like to see Roy do that." She said, *"Ach,* that's the way he always does." He did mean to let her have something to say about the way the house should be built, but buying the lot and things like that—he couldn't see how they concerned her. The house did, of course. She often wondered how much he had to pay for the lot, but she never asked him.

August's interest was all in the new house now. It was something to build up, as he had built up the farm. There were some pictures of houses in the window of the bank, a large card showing four of them, all planned by the same company, all more or less on the bungalow type. August went in several times to look at them. The banker always said, "Sure! Any of those appeal to you, Mr. Kaetterhenry?" August replied cautiously, "*Ach,* I don't know. I ain't quite ready to build yet a'ready." "No, no. Well, they're pretty nice little houses." "*Ja,* they're pretty nice all right."

When he had got his mind pretty well made up, he asked for one of the sheets with the pictures and took it home to show to Emma. "How'd you like to live in one of those?" he asked. He had always had a kind of idea that when he came to town he would put up a big house, one like Mr. Nixon's, the banker's, that had a porch all the way around. But it seemed that they weren't putting up many of those houses now. Mr. Nixon sent the contractor, Herb Carter, to see them. "Heard you folks were thinking some of building." Herb tried to get them to put up a pebble-dashed bungalow, like the one he had put up for Dan Myers the summer before. But they wouldn't agree to that. Emma wanted an upstairs. August wasn't sure that he liked this pebble-dash. It was a pretty new thing, and he wasn't sure how it would "hold." They compromised on a kind of semi-cottage with no attic and three small upstairs rooms.

That was a good part of town where their lot was. It was where the building would be going on now. The banker's son, Clarence Nixon, owned the lot next to theirs, they had heard. He would probably build as soon as he got married. There was no house so far on their side of the street except Tom Cunningham's, on the corner, and that faced the other street. There were no trees either—just a short, vacant block, beyond which were pastures.

They began work on the house as soon as they could in the spring. Herb Carter had a lot of houses to build. He always promised more than he could do. But they got along because August did so much of the work himself. He got a wagon and team from the boys and hauled his own sand and earth for the yard. He was a pretty good carpenter, handy, as many Germans are, and he helped with the lathing and siding. It kept the men on the job, too, to have him there. There wasn't much fooling with August Kaetterhenry, as people who had

had to deal with him knew. He meant to have the house ready, so that they could move into it before winter.

The boys said laughingly, "Thought pa was going to town to take it easy. He's working as hard as he did on the farm. I'd want to be paid good and plenty before I'd take to hauling all that dirt."

But August liked it. The house filled up the blank left by the farm. It fed his pride to be putting up a good house, showing people that he could afford it. There was the thought that he had worked hard for this, that he owed most of it to himself. People said, "You always see Mr. Kaetterhenry going back and forth from his new house. It must be going up pretty fast. They say it's going to be nice."

It was up now, although the finishing wasn't done inside. The *Banner* had an item about it:

> "Mr. August Kaetterhenry has put up his fine new house in the north part of town and is about ready for the finishing. Mr. Kaetterhenry says that the first of October will see them established in the new house."

He went over to see it in the early summer evening, to take some more boards over, so that the men would have them there in the morning, but really to see how the place looked when he wasn't working on it.

The house stood, new, bare, bright, on the raw earth that was littered over with boards, shavings, pails of dirtyish mortar. It had had its first coat of paint, the upper story yellow, and the lower white. The shingles looked brown and fresh and had a woody smell. The porch roof sloped, and there was one of those dormer-windows in the centre that looked as if it had slipped down half-way. Narrow planks that bent a little led up over the porch steps and to the shining front door. The door was locked now. The house was past the stage when little girls could go in and find shaving-curls to hang over their hair, and when women could go there looking around and speculating on which room was which.

Inside, the house was new, echoing, still. The unstained floors and woodwork made August feel that he shouldn't be stepping about in his heavy shoes. The walls were rough, white, untinted. The bathroom was finished, although chunks of plaster lay around. He was proud of the shining pipes, the white porcelain of the fixtures still unwashed, with labels sticking to it. Another thing that he admired was the colonnade between the dining-room and the living-room. It seemed queer to both of them not to have a parlour, but that was the way that houses were being made now. Although he had worked on this house, August could hardly believe in it, somehow, and that he was ever going to live here.

There were some small boards laid over the stairs to keep them clean. He thought he'd go up and see how it looked up there. But he did not stay long. It was dim up there, more silent, and his shoes made a fearful noise as he creaked from room to room. He had a stealthy feeling, as if someone would catch him there. These rooms kept the heat of the day. He was proud of the shining bronze-and-black registers in the walls.

Well, he guessed there was nothing he could do in here. He'd seen it all often enough.

He went outside. In the early summer evening there was a kind of sadness and bareness in the new house, standing stark against the pale evening sky, the new boards around, the raw dirt, the tools thrown down wherever the men had happened to drop them, the vacant lots beyond, and then the pastures stretching away, damp and fresh with dew, and the slow-moving forms of cattle.

They had wanted to move in in September, but it was the middle of October before they could. Then the woodwork was all stained and varnished—light, shining golden-oak. They had had the walls in the front room "tiffanied." In the other rooms the walls were tinted light green or blue, with stencilled borders. They had bought new rugs for the two front rooms, with bright mottled patterns, and had had the old rag rugs made up into strips for the bedrooms. They were "doing everything right."

They hadn't brought in all of their furniture. August said some of it wasn't worth carting. The combination desk and bookcase, their bedroom furniture, the standard rocker, and three or four others—all these they had. The old rockers and the little old stand they put upstairs. Grandpa's old German Bible and the album and other old things went into the small store-room at the head of the stairs. Downstairs, as people said admiringly, half the things were new. The dining-room furniture was all new—a round table and four chairs with leather seats. They had kept some of the old chairs to help out when they had company. They had a new set of dishes, too, although they themselves used the old ones. The new ones were white, with scalloped edges and a thin gold line. The dining-room table remained immaculate, on it a round, embroidered crash doily and a plant. They would do their eating in the kitchen. In the living-room was the piece of furniture that the children admired—a large brown davenport upholstered in stiff half-leather.

People went in to see the Kaetterhenrys. They said they were "fixed real nice."

At first it seemed queer to the children to see ma and pa in this brand-new modern house, with the shining floors and white plumbing and new furniture. But they got used to it quickly. Now, when they came into town, it was a settled thing that they should go to the folks' for dinner, and leave the babies there while they did their buying. They came in on Sundays to church, and all ate in the new dining-room, the daughters holding babies on their laps.

There was one thing that disappointed them, Emma especially. They had fixed up such a nice room for Johnnie and had thought that they could have him with them again. He had been rooming over in an old house near the garage. But just before they moved into the new house, he had driven over to "Wapsie" one day with his landlady's daughter, and had come back and announced himself married. Emma felt dreadfully, both because of the girl he had married and because he hadn't told her and his father about it.

They hated to think of his marrying "such a little flip," as people in town called her. The other two boys had married good workers, good sensible girls, although in some ways they didn't care much for Frank's wife. This Bernice was only a junior in high school, a silly, rather pretty girl, with a large, soft, powdered face and great buns of dark hair showing the rats, melting, foolish brown eyes. She wore sleazy over-blouses moulded by her large, soft breasts, and knee-skirts showing her fat white legs in cheap, thin silk stockings that had a brownish cast. She didn't know how to do anything. She and Johnnie were to stay with mamma.

If Frank had married a girl like that, August might not have forgiven him for years. He did storm and say that he wouldn't do anything more for Johnnie. But, although the marriage was known as a great disappointment to the Kaetterhenrys, August's anger didn't last. In a way this crazy action of Johnnie's, while it hurt August, partly satisfied his old grudge about the way he had been treated in war-time, the peremptoriness of the Government in taking his boys off the farm, being called "Old Dutchy Kaetterhenry." If Johnnie had not gone to war, he would never have done such a thing. He had not been the same boy since, as anyone could see.

Johnnie quarrelled with Bernice's mother, an old Tartar, and he and Bernice went to live in some rooms up over the hardware store. Their baby was born soon after that. Women whispered how long it should have been before the baby ought to have come. But Junior was the prettiest, sturdiest, fattest baby in the relationship. It gave Emma something to do to go over to Johnnie's rooms and clean up and help Bernice with the baby.

Johnnie seemed to be settling down now. Being older than Bernice made him seem older and more staid to himself. August said that if he had really made up his mind now to stay in the garage business, and not just tinker, they'd see what they could do for him.

PART FOUR

I: RETIRED FARMERS

PEOPLE ASKED the children now:

"Well, how do the folks like it in town?"

"Oh, pretty good, I guess," the children answered. "Mamma likes it a lot better since they're in their new house. I guess pa kind o' misses the farm, though."

"I guess Marguerite's glad they've moved in."

"Oh, sure, *she's* glad. It suits her just fine."

The Kaetterhenrys were settled in town now, retired farmers.

Marguerite was the one who had profited by the change. She was a town girl now. Her sisters said that she acted as if she had never lived in the country. She was in high school now, where she played basket-ball and went around with the girls. Marguerite Kaetterhenry was a good-looking girl. She was tall, large-boned, but still thin, with a fresh skin that was apt to break out a little. Her fuzz of bright light hair she wore in huge side-puffs. She was very particular about how her clothes should be made. She wouldn't buy shoes at one of the general stores in Richland, but made her father take her into "Wapsie," or went to Dubuque with one of the boys when they were going. She was popular in high school, had good marks in her studies, and went to all the parties, although the Kaetterhenrys wouldn't let her go to the town dances in the opera-house. But she was a kind of stranger at home.

She did not look as if she belonged to the same tribe as her sisters, when they came to town. Mary lived away out in the country, near the old mill. She looked aged and hollow-eyed, with dark skin and those glowing, shy, intelligent dark eyes. Her clothes were shabbier than her mother's. Elva took more pains with hers. She still had her white skin, but somehow her things had a country look. She was getting fat and matronly and sloppy, with all those fat white babies of hers. Clara, of course, was young and fresh-looking, and she looked well in the clean ready-made bungalow aprons that she wore out on the farm. But when she came to town, she seemed different, coarser, and she wore shabby, high black shoes with her thin summer dresses. Lottie, Frank's wife, was a heavy, coarse, homely woman, with straight red hair and a thick-freckled face. Marguerite would never be satisfied with what her sisters had had.

In some ways the Kaetterhenrys lived much as they had done on the farm. They did most of their living in the kitchen. August always washed his hands and face there, at the sink, in the granite basin, instead of in the bath-room; and he kept an old pinkish comb and his shaving-things on the shelf above the sink. They used their old dishes and ate from the oilcloth.

They had arranged to get their cream and eggs from the farm, but they found that it was very different from having those things right at hand in abundance. Emma said that she had to learn to cook all over again. They were sparing of milk and butter when they had to pay for these things in cash. They got several quarters of meat when Carl butchered, and Emma put it up in jars, as she had always done. But somehow, when they were so near town, they found themselves getting more fresh meat. Emma canned quarts and quarts of vegetables, too. The cellar was full. They couldn't use half the things. They couldn't have chickens because they might dig up the lawn, which was freshly seeded.

August had let Carl keep the old car and had bought a new sedan. They drove a little more now, oftener to "Wapsie" and to Dubuque, where they got into the habit of doing their important shopping, like most Richland people. But August used the car chiefly for going back and forth to the farm. He wouldn't let Marguerite drive it, and of course Emma never thought of doing so. They still did little pleasure-driving. They took out the minister and his wife for a drive, went two or three times to Turkey Creek. In the hot summer evenings the car was locked in the garage, although they might have been out getting the freshness from the open country, where ghostly vapour rose from the cornfields and the trees looked misty and drenched in the loneliness of evening.

They got considerable consolation from the church. Now they were among the chief and faithful members. If the Kaetterhenrys were not in their pew, the minister knew that something was wrong with them, and took pains to call the next week. They were among the eight or nine who attended the prayer-meetings. Emma had a kind of fondness and loyalty for the church because of her father, and August remembered it as the best thing in his young days.

Going to church, and being steady and a good worker, and not drinking, and paying his bills, and saving money, were all part of the same thing. August and Emma still attended the Hon. Mr. Bossingham's Bible class, where August sat dumb and Emma occasionally made a timid answer. They never said much at church-meetings, but they could always be counted upon to be there. After the evangelist had been to Richland—a modern evangelist who had a singer who shouted, "Now put a little pep into these hymns, people!" not like the old travelling evangelists who used to go around to the camp-meetings—they offered the use of their house for one of the cottage prayer-meetings that were held for as long as a month before they petered out.

But although the church was still a social and business centre in a little country town like Richland, one doctor attending the Methodist church, the other the Congregational, it didn't seem to have the importance that it had had when they were young people in the country here. The children didn't make the effort to come in to services that they had made, easy as it was for them now, compared with those old days of buggies and dirt roads. There were too many other places where people could go now. August and Emma made Marguerite go to church and Sunday school, but after the League she went walking, on pleasant nights, with her current admirer.

And, really, it was only as a kind of deep-rooted custom, a bulwark against worrying changes, an idea, that August cared for the church. He often went to sleep during the services. He did not get the sentimental and emotional satisfaction out of the prayers and sermons and hymns that Emma did. It did not fill the same place in his life. He had never questioned anything, but it was doubtful what these things really meant to him.

Emma was getting used to town. As the children said, she liked it better now that they were in their own house. She was still very quiet, but she was beginning to go about a little more than formerly. Her sister-in-law, Mrs. Henry Stille, "got her into" the Social Circle Club, a collection of elderly ladies who met every Tuesday to eat and talk. They had no program, like the Tourist Club, took up no "line of study." The club was only and frankly for social purposes. The *Banner* said of it:

"The Social Circle Club held its weekly meeting on Tuesday last at the pleasant new residence of Mrs. August Kaetterhenry. The ladies brought fancy work and, after a pleasant hour spent in social intercourse, were served with a delicious luncheon by the hostess, after which the club adjourned, thanking the hostess one and all for a delightful afternoon's entertainment."

Then there was the Aid Society. This, too, was composed largely of the older women of the church, who were still willing to get up big suppers, work at cleaning the church, make sheets and pillowcases for the missions that they supported, and raise money for the parsonage fund by making quilts which women from "Wapsie" came down to buy. Emma enjoyed these quilting-afternoons in the quiet, chilly church basement, to which she went with Mrs. Willie Stille, with all the women sitting about in old-fashioned comfort, talking over neighbourhood affairs, telling what their husbands and children had done, as they worked together at the big quilting-frame. It was like her girlhood days, when she was getting ready to be married, and they had held quilting-bees in the country. There was the crisp smell of coffee, which some of the ladies were getting ready on the oil-stove, coming in and saying, "Well, don't you ladies think you better quit working so hard and have a little coffee for a change?" She helped at the church suppers, was one of those who could be counted upon to work in the kitchen. But it was noticed that the Kaetterhenrys were always careful not to donate too much.

Emma still had the feeling that August mustn't be kept waiting a minute for his meals and that she "must be getting back."

She took more pains with the house than she had ever taken with the one in the country. It was all so bright and shining, and she wanted to keep it that way. Marguerite, of course, didn't get things out of order as the boys had done. Emma raised plants, geraniums, and coloured foliage, and a sword-fern for the front window that she hoped would grow huge, like Mrs. Henry Stille's. She did more sewing than she had done before. She used to count on Mary for that, but Mary had less time than she did now. Emma made Marguerite's clothes, under minute and fretful and exacting directions. "No, mamma, I told you I had to have the belt *down* lower. This makes me look like Lottie." She got patterns from other women and crocheted wide elaborate yokes for Marguerite's corset-covers and camisoles.

She took care of the grandchildren when the young people wanted to go somewhere. She went out into the country to help out when there was sickness at the homes of any of the children. She missed the farm sometimes—missed the quiet, her work with the poultry, the feeling of the old rooms, the country air and sounds. But she kept busy enough.

August was the one who felt that he had nothing to do. The house was finished now. Life moved along, and what else was there to do? He was taking it easy now. He made a kind of religion of the garden and the lawn. He looked forward to the meetings of the stockholders of the Farmers' Bank, in which he had an interest. He made a rite of going downtown for the mail and the meat. But all this meant nothing.

There was no club for him. For some obscure reason he "didn't believe in lodges." He paid his subscription to the church, and that was the end of it. He read the Richland *Banner* and a Dubuque paper and a farm journal. He cared for nothing else. There was no library in Richland, no place where magazines were sold, but he would not have patronized such places if he had had them, although Emma might have done so.

He didn't come right home when he went down for the mail. He got into the habit of hanging around with the other retired farmers, in at Dawson's store or at the post office. Not at the barber-shop. The "tougher element" hung out there, and at the restaurant, which had a pool hall in connection. The men talked a little about politics, but mostly about farms changing hands, and crops and roads, with minute observations on the weather.

"Well, that was just about a frost we had last night."

"Yeh. Little too windy for a frost."

"My wife thought some of her plants had been frosted."

"No. Wasn't quite a frost. Our plants didn't show any sign of it."

Most of them had a kind of seedy look. They walked heavily, without spring. They didn't know what to do with themselves.

People said, "Have you noticed how old Mr. Kaetterhenry's getting to look? He don't seem like the same man he did when they first moved into town. I wonder if he can be well." He wasn't very well. He had headaches, trouble with his stomach, once a dizzy spell. He was eating the same heavy meals that he had eaten when he was working hard on the farm, coffee and meat three times a day. August thought he had to have his meat.

It was true that all at once he was beginning to show his age. Emma looked no older now than he did. She had gained flesh again since her operation, and some of the lines had gone from her face. August, when he decided to retire, had been a hearty, vigorous man seemingly in the prime of life. But now all at once his old colour was gone, his shoulders were slack, his vigorously bright curling hair was sparse and faded, and he walked like a man ten years older. He actually looked older than Herman Klaus, who had always been a little dried-up fellow. August had never had anything the matter with him except when he had lost two fingers from his left hand in the corn-shredder. But now he began buying a patent tonic at the drug-store, and he and Emma both took it.

Emma said that she believed half the trouble was that August had nothing to keep him busy any more. He did a little hauling. There was a job vacant in the lumber-yard. He would have liked to take it, at seventy dollars a month, but his old stubbornness kept him from it. He had said that he wanted to quit work. Actually he would have been glad at times to work on the roads or the section. But no work was vital any more. No work looked forward to anything. He didn't want someone else for his boss. Everything that he had done had been for the farm. The farm had always come first. He had always talked about retiring some day, quit this slaving; but he had never really looked forward to it. He had used every energy to build up the farm. He had done it, from almost nothing, by his own efforts, and now that he had made a fine place of it, Carl was living on it and he had moved to town. Well, that was what everybody did. He would not have wanted to be like Herman, not able to do it.

The boys had speculated upon whether pa would be able to stay away from the farm. They weren't surprised to see him going out there. He made excuses at first. When he got the new sedan, he drove out just to see what Carl was doing. Then he said, "Want me to help you some with that ploughing?" Then he began to go regularly, except when the weather was too bad and he was forced to hang about the house, looking at the farm journal and trying to take a nap.

He and Emma had always thought of taking a trip, but it seemed now that neither of them really wanted to go.

The farm looked different now, more so as time went on. When August and Emma sometimes drove out there for Sunday dinner, it gave them a kind of shock when they turned into the drive. The place was theirs, and yet it wasn't. The house was different. Carl and Clara were getting new furniture. They used grandpa's old room for a store-room. They didn't like the upstairs, which was not well finished. They had a brass bed and a shiny mail-order dresser in the downstairs bedroom, which was full of the baby's things, thrown around everywhere. They had a new bright-coloured rug in the parlour, where there was none of the old furniture except the organ, which Marguerite had refused to have moved into town. Clara said she didn't know why they kept it there, since neither of them could play a note. She wanted a Victrola if crops were good this year. Carl had made a little cage for the baby, like one that they had seen in a store window in Dubuque. They let him play there on the new parlour rug, with all his celluloid animals and the little doll like one of the characters in the funny papers. None of Emma's children had ever been permitted to be in the parlour.

It was still different out on the place. August thought that Carl was doing a good deal of experimenting with new things. August had never believed in sweet clover for pasturage. He called sweet clover a weed. Now Carl had got a lot of new seed from the state agricultural college. August couldn't get used to the feeling that he couldn't tell Carl just what to do. Carl was thc boss now. He was good-tempered, didn't say much. But August noticed that he kept on with exactly what he had planned to do. He was a Kaetterhenry. August worked on the farm, but then what did that mean when he was no longer doing it for anything? The life had gone out of his work. Sometimes he hated to go out there, although he couldn't stay away.

Carl didn't like to have him come, either, as he told Frank. Pa was too used to thinking he could do anything he pleased there. They had quarrels once or twice.

Emma, all of them, thought that August was working too hard. They said, "You don't need to go out to that farm and kill yourself." He kept on stubbornly. One day he was overcome with the heat out there. Carl had to bring him home in the sedan. But even after that he wouldn't stop. Carl had to be careful, and scheme so that his father would get the easier part of the work.

"Mr. Kaetterhenry looks real bad," people said. He would not admit it. Emma wanted him to try this and that that other people recommended. The children said, "Pa'll have a stroke some day if he isn't careful."

He was never so vigorous again after that heat prostration. He knew that he was sick, but he tried obstinately not to give in, to hang on. Then one day, coming home from town, he had a kind of dizzy spell. He got home all right, and no one knew it. But it frightened him. It broke his resistance. He told Emma that he believed there was something the matter with him. The next day Emma telephoned the children that she and pa were going to Rochester again.

II: OBITUARY

It was in the dead of winter that August and Emma took their second trip to Rochester. They did not take Marguerite with them this time. She was going to stay with her uncle Henry Stille, so that she needn't miss school. Altogether the trip seemed less eventful than the first one that they had made, when everything was new.

August was not interested in the farms this time, or the country. It lay under a heavy crust of snow, the willow-trees pencilled bleak and small upon a grey sky. Although they had both had such awe of the operation before, this time there was a different fear in their hearts, down under everything, gnawing in silence.

They went to their same old boarding-house. The landlady did not recognize them until they told their names and reminded her of when they had been here before. Then she exclaimed:

"Oh, my! Well, I should say! Well, what are you folks back here for? Are you the sick one this time, Mr. Kaetterhenry? Missus looks fine, though."

They did not like the place so well as before. They were used to the shining immaculateness and comforts of their new house now. The bedroom, the dining-room, with the brown linoleum and the little step up from the ancient parlour, seemed darker and shabbier to them. They did not know any of these boarders. Somehow, it seemed to them that they must meet some of those who had been here before, that they must belong to the boarding-house.

The landlady tried to cheer them. She said:

"Oh, they'll fix you up over there. They're great folks. Not much them doctors can't do."

Emma said:

"*Ja,* if he'll do what they say."

"Oh, he will. That's what he's come here for." She rallied him: "I never thought I'd see you folks here on your account, Mr. Kaetterhenry. Ain't you ashamed of yourself? My, I remember that Mrs. Boohey that was here with her husband, had the operation on the jaw, used to say, if her husband looked half as strong as Mr. Kaetterhenry! Well, they'll have you looking that way again."

But she was doubtful. She told the other boarders about how vigorous August had been and how he had aged. She said:

"I'll bet he's waited too long before he came, just like all those old farmers. He looks to me as if he might have had some kind of a stroke. Did you notice how kind of slow he moves? Well, sir, it's that big strong kind of men that sometimes goes all of a sudden."

She frightened Emma, who had never actually noticed before how changed August was. It was hard to say what the change was, exactly. He was not thin. His face was still high-coloured. But the skin looked different; there were wrinkles; his figure was sunken, and his movements were no longer vigorous; his eye was vacant and seemed to turn slowly. The whole impression of the man was different.

Emma and the children had wondered if August would ever submit to all those tests and examinations. He had always scorned all such things. It had taken him a long while to give up, but now he had done so completely. He was suddenly not the same person. He was meek. He let Emma do things for him, turned to her. He seemed to depend upon her. When they went to the clinic, he let her make all the arrangements. And he called her in and let her answer many of the questions that the doctor asked. All the time, from the doctor's careful, non-committal manner—a new doctor, large and calm—from something that they felt, but could not name, they were afraid.

August had fought all these months against having anything done for him, against "seeing anyone." But now that it might be too late, he was suddenly ready to do anything. He went through all the tests without a murmur, and he even seemed to find a relief in having his ailments admitted to the doctor. August! He seemed to want Emma's help and sympathy. Before, he wouldn't even so much as admit that his stomach was out of order, was angry with anyone who dared to suggest it.

They had both been hoping that the doctor would say that there must be an operation. Since Emma had been helped by an operation, it seemed to them that an operation would do anything. But the doctor merely said that this condition could hardly be helped by that. He wouldn't say much about it all, only murmuring something about "blood pressure pretty high." He was going to give August a diet, and he was to do no physical work, not to drive the car, to be quiet and avoid excitement. August and Emma did not say to each other what was meant, but they knew. "High blood pressure" was a term of terror to people in Richland, although old Dr. Bowen laughed at the whole business and said there was no such thing. Everyone said that that was what had caused Mrs. Vesey's stroke. The doctor's coolness, his temperate statements, only soothed them for the time being. "Stroke" was what they were both fearing. It was the fear of all the elderly people in Richland. Time was counted from the day when Mrs. Vesey or Grandpa Granger or Fred Williams had had a stroke.

Emma was all the more fearful because the doctor kept her and questioned her closely about the time last summer when August had been overcome with the heat. She answered timidly, half consciously trying to make it sound less serious than it had been, for fear of that word. But she had to ask the doctor what he thought it had been. He would admit no more than that it might have been slightly on the order of a stroke. But he let her know that August's condition was serious.

August had a reaction from his meekness before the doctors. The night before they left Rochester he was discouraged. He let himself sink into bitter depths of hopelessness. He blamed the doctors. He said that if he'd known they weren't going to do any more for him than that, he wouldn't have come up here and wasted all his money. Just tell him to be careful! Any old fool, even old Doc Bowen, could have done that. He didn't need to come clear up to Minnesota to learn a thing like that. Emma tried to soothe him. She defended the doctors.

"Well, maybe there ain't anything else they could do. They said there wasn't anything to operate for. I suppose there's times when they can't. They gave you a diet."

"Ja, diet!" he said bitterly. "Think if I can't do anything else, then I might as well starve too, a'ready."

They admitted to the landlady that they didn't think August had got much help. It seemed to both of them that the doctors should have *done* more. August declared that he believed that stuff he'd taken last summer had given him more help. They both thought that if Emma's old doctor could have looked at him, he might have done something. "If he helped you, why couldn't he have helped me?" Their notion of medicine was still as of some universal panacea. August had looked to "operation" and "Rochester" as the last resort, the final magic independent of what he himself did. Now it seemed that there was no panacea.

They went home silent and discouraged, fearful, hating to admit to the children and the neighbours what had been said. They had not sent word that they were coming. There was no one to meet them at the little station, standing bleak in the midst of frozen winter pastures. They went up the lonely, icy street. They had had a discussion about the suit-case. Emma had been afraid to have August carry it all the way home. She had wanted to leave it in the depot. One of the boys would be in town soon and could get it. He had angrily refused. Then she had said:

"Well, let me take it, then. I don't want you to carry it. You'll hurt yourself." He picked it up and went angrily on with it, she trotting over the ice at his side and urging him to let her have it.

Then they met one of their neighbours, Lew Parsons, in his car.

He stopped at the corner, called, "Hello! didn't know you folks was back! Don't you want to ride home?" They climbed in thankfully. "*Ja,* I thought mister oughtn't to carry that suit-case, but he wouldn't give it up," Emma said.

Lew Parsons said, "Well, what did they do to you up there?" August said gloomily, "*Ach,* not much of anything." "Not much of anything, hey? Well, I could have told you before you went how it would be. Them places makes a big noise, but there's some stuff right down here at the drug-store that me and the missus always takes when we got anything the matter with us, and it does the business."

They went into their house. The furnace was out. The place was ice-cold. Emma worried over anything that August did, but he was determined not to let her help him start the fire. It was a bleak home-coming.

The children came in when they found that "the folks" were at home. There wasn't much to tell them. Emma said the doctors hadn't had much to say.

But people in town gradually knew. They said that Mr. Kaetterhenry had "high blood pressure," and that they'd told him he was liable to have a stroke. One might take him off any time, and they marvelled again over what a big strong man he had always seemed to be. They said that was often the way. They had time in Richland to watch and study people, to go minutely over and over physical symptoms, to see what kind of people seemed to last and what didn't.

All that winter August sat around the house, went down occasionally for the mail. Emma was fearful. She watched him. If she didn't know where he was and what he was doing, she sent Marguerite to see. People said, "He's failed just since they come back from Rochester." They saw how slowly he walked. His feet dragged as he went past their houses to the post office. He never went out to the farm any more. He said he didn't want to go there.

They were not content with merely diet and care. They tried other things. Another brand of medicine, and then a treatment for "high blood pressure," regardless of cause, that a doctor in "Wapsie" gave. They thought at first that it might be helping. Then they couldn't tell whether it did or not. Mrs. Cooley, who, people whispered, was "kind of a Christian Scientist or some such thing," told Emma about a man over at Wellington who claimed to give people mental healing. She wanted Emma to take August over there and have him try that. Emma was quite worked up over all the wonders of which Mrs. Cooley had told her, but August refused to go. Although, in medical matters, he was quite ready to believe in magic, it must be connected with something that he could see, a bottle or a knife. He said that this was "nothing but some more Christian Science," and that he had always considered almost equal in wickedness to Catholicism.

In the summer he seemed to be a little better. Perhaps it was because he could get out more. He mowed the lawn, although Emma didn't like to have him do it. He went downtown and stood about with the other men. The anxiety that had been hanging over them lightened a little. But there was always the fear of that day he might do a little too much.

The day came. There was a sale of stock out in the country, and August secretly took the car and drove out there. All of a sudden he had got tired of hanging around, and had broken loose. It happened to be one of the very hottest days of the whole summer. Emma did not know that August had gone, but she knew what it meant when she saw Carl driving up the street in their sedan. He and Dr. Brady were bringing August home.

That evening everyone in town knew of it.

"Have you heard about Mr. Kaetterhenry's stroke? *Ja,* he had a stroke this afternoon out at Gorensen's sale; ain't expected to live. Well, I guess they been kind of expecting it a long time."

The children were summoned. They drove in from the country. It had been a severe stroke. Their father might not live through the night. In all their hearts was the hope that he would not "live to be like grandma."

Several times they thought that he was dying. They went into the bedroom where he lay unconscious. But he was a vigorous man, and it took the thing a long time to kill him. He lived for three days. The children had to go back to their farms, and only Roy and Elva were there when he had another stroke and died.

"August Kaetterhenry's dead! He died at three o'clock." That was what everyone in Richland was saying now. He had never regained consciousness. They all said again how strange it seemed. What a strong man he had seemed to be when he first moved to town—had looked as if he would live for years! They remembered how he had helped to build his new house. They said what a pity that he had lived so few years to enjoy it. Now everyone was wondering where and when the funeral would be. The Kaetterhenrys were such Methodists, probably it would be in the church.

Funerals were still public events in Richland. This one was expected to be large. A great many people came in from the country.

Townspeople turned out, although they hadn't known August very well, to see what kind of service it would be and who was there. All the pews were filled as Tom Peters, who was studying with the local undertaker, led one family after another to their places in a creaking silence. They wanted to hear what the Methodist quartet, Dr. Brady, Herb Carter, Willie Stille, and Mr. Rush, would sing. Most of all, they wanted to see "who had come from away." They whispered, "My, he must have had a lot of relations!" "Well, some of these are hers."

The five front rows at the side were reserved for the mourners. There were all the children and the children-in-law and the grandchildren. Grandpa Stille, of course, couldn't get in, although he had wanted to come, had sighed and mourned over "the young folks going." Herman and Mollie Klaus were there. There were five families of Stilles. Those whom people really wanted to see were "his folks," who had come from Turkey Creek. Sophie Klaus and her husband, Heinie and Ferdinand Kaetterhenry and their wives. Mina had come. She was a fat, toothless old widow now. She had always cared the most for August, although he had not done much for her. She wore a little scrap of cheap black veiling on her ancient summer hat. The two brothers were heavier men than August, more like the old man Kaetterhenry.

There was a long procession of cars that went out to the cemetery. Most of them were from the country. All the children and all the relatives from Turkey Creek, and a good many of the other country people from the Richland neighbourhood. It pleased the Turkey Creek relatives to see how many. August had been the most successful brother, and Richland was more metropolitan than Turkey Creek.

They drove down the hard, brown, dusty road, slowly, stopping so that the cars wouldn't bump into one another. They went through the big iron gate of the cemetery, which was open to-day. The relatives looked around and whispered, "Oh, that's where his lot is. It's in a nice spot." August had bought the lot when he moved to town. It was over in the newer part of the cemetery, near a large evergreen.

The summer wind stirred in the unaccustomed black veils of the women as they stood about the grave. "Must be a country funeral," people driving past said when they saw all the waiting cars and the solemn, stolid group of people there.

The children had to drive home to do the chores. But August's sister Sophie and the Ferdinand Kaetterhenrys were going to spend the night with Emma, so that she and Marguerite wouldn't be alone. The Henry and the Willie Stilles came over in the evening.

They talked about August, in voices slightly hushed, but more natural now that it was all over. They said how nice the funeral had been, how many had driven in from the country. They talked about the sermon. "This good brother who has gone before us," the minister had said. That was right. They said what a good church-member, how faithful, August had always been! Ferdinand said he remembered when he and August had "gone forward" at one of the old Turkey Creek camp-meetings. August had been faithful to his pledge. The minister had said what a good citizen and good farmer August had been. They said that that was true. Sophie and Ferdinand were proud of how much August had been able to accumulate when they remembered the old days in the cabin down on Turkey Creek. They said he had worked hard for all he had got. He had deserved it. The only pity was that he hadn't lived to get more enjoyment out of it.

Then they talked over the details of his illness. They said how quickly he had seemed to fail when he once started. It didn't seem any time since he was over at Turkey Creek the last time and had helped Heinie with the haying.

Emma cried a little. It seemed to her that August had had to work so hard, and then after he moved to town he hadn't got much out of all his work. They gave her vague consolations: "Well, we don't understand why he should have been taken this way, but, then, there's some reason." But they thought as she did. It didn't seem right that Herman Klaus, for instance, was still living, as well and happy as ever, and August was gone. They had thought of that when they had looked at Herman at the funeral.

There was consolation and pride in the column of close print in the Richland *Banner* on Thursday. Emma ordered extra copies.

"ESTEEMED RESIDENT PASSES"

And below, in smaller type:

"Retired Farmer Answers Summons."

August's life seemed different to her, more important, as she read it there, as if she had been reading about a stranger.

"On Sunday last the grim Reaper called from our midst an esteemed citizen, Mr. August Kaetterhenry. August Ernst Kaetterhenry was born on a farm near Turkey Creek, Iowa, on September 10, 1859. He was the fifth son of Casper and Luisa Kaetterhenry, who were natives of Pommern, Germany."

She read, as if she had never known it before, how August had had "such education as the schools of that day afforded," how he had "left his native township and come to Richland Township to seek his fortune, working for a time on the farm of the late Henry Baumgartner, well-known Richland Township farmer." Then how "he was united in marriage with Emma Stille, daughter of Wilhelm, now known as Grandpa Stille, and to them six children were born, all of whom survive." How he had acquired the farm, how he had made it into one of the best improved farms in Richland Township, "where the deceased's son, Carl Kaetterhenry, is now operating the farm on the principles taught him by his father. . . . Mr. Kaetterhenry was known to all his neighbours as a conscientious farmer and an honest, upright man. He united with the Methodist denomination when a young man, and was all his life one of its most faithful members and one whose loss will be felt by the church and community. . . . Mr. Kaetterhenry is survived by his sorrowing widow, Mrs. Emma Kaetterhenry, and by his children Frank, Mrs. Joe Fields, Mrs. Roy Robbins, Carl, John, and Marguerite and by numerous grandchildren. Also by his sisters Mrs. Ed Klaus and Mrs. Mina Nisson and brothers Henry and Ferdinand Kaetterhenry, all of Turkey Creek."

She had never seen all their names in print before. "Esteemed resident," "retired farmer"—it sounded like someone else than August.

Emma cut these columns out from several papers and folded the strips in the old "doctor-book" that lay on the doily on the bottom shelf of the bookcase behind the glass door.

III: THE ESTATE

THEN THERE was all the settling-up of the estate to be done.

August had never let Emma know anything of business affairs. Of late years he had permitted her to do a small amount of the buying, but he had never thought of letting her handle anything that was not directly connected with the household. He had bought the meat, subscribed for the papers, planned the garden, managed everything. Now, suddenly, she had to see to all these things.

It worried her at first. Even a little thing like sending the "card of thanks" that must be inserted in the next issue of the *Banner:*

"We, the undersigned, wish to thank our friends and neighbours for their kindness to us during the illness and death of our husband and father and for the beautiful flowers.

"(Signed) Mrs. Emma Kaetterhenry.
"The Children."

There was one of these cards in every issue of the *Banner,* and Emma always read them conscientiously, but still she did not know how to go about it to have her own put there. She made Johnnie write it for her and take it down to the *Banner* office.

She hadn't been used to getting the mail. She didn't know whether to keep on subscribing for the farm journal or not. She "hated to let it go," since August had taken it so long. She could not conceive of subscribing instead for a household magazine for herself. That seemed too audacious. She had scarcely been inside the bank. She had no idea how to make out a cheque, and was afraid of her cheque-book. She employed devices for getting out of going to the bank, such as making out a cheque to Johnnie under his directions and having him cash it, and keeping the money that came in to her from this and that. Although Johnnie explained the cheque-book to her, she said that she would never know from that how much money she had, not unless her money was somewhere where she could see it and "keep track of it." She was afraid to draw a cent. She liked to keep silver and odd change in an old tea-pot in the cupboard, as she had kept the egg money. There was the worry over what to do with the car. She would never use it. She hated to have it "sitting in the garage." Some of these auto thieves might steal it.

There were all the little worries, too, that immediately followed August's death. For a time she was "pestered" by catalogues and visits from monument men from Dubuque and Rapids City. One of the salesmen, a slick young fellow with bright grey eyes set too close together, upset her dreadfully by wanting her to order a large monument and two markers with "Father" and "Mother," promising her a reduction if she would get all three. Emma said, "It would make me think I was dead a'ready." The children said that she needn't order the things, but Emma told them that she didn't see how else she was ever going to get rid of that fellow. She even got a sample copy of the old-fashioned black memorial cards with a verse and the name in gold, "Mr. August Kaetterhenry." She wondered how those people had known that August was dead, and how they had got his name. She remembered that they had had cards like that when her oldest sister Bertha had died, but they were so "gloomy-looking" that she was glad the children didn't want her to get them now.

People were interested to hear whether August had left a will. There would be a muddle if he hadn't. Emma said, *"Ach,* I don't think pa ever made a will." But he had made one, it seemed, when he had moved into town, although he hadn't told them anything about it. The lawyer, E. P. Bland, read it to all of them. Emma had never known before "what they had." She did not understand very well now. She had thought that Frank owned the farm where he lived, but it seemed that August had still been the owner of it. Now both the farms were hers. She was to have some rent from both of them. There was the stock in the bank, which was divided among the family, and a little piece of land in Montana that no one had known that August had, and that went to the children. Emma had the house and lot in town. She was "pretty well fixed." August had accumulated more than Emma had thought; not so much as certain people in town had predicted, who always said of other people, "Aw, he's got more tucked away than anybody knows about." Of course Emma would have the taxes and insurance and repairs, things she had never thought of before.

The children wanted to sell that Montana land at once and get what they could out of it. They had always been a little afraid of their father. Even after he had left the farm and moved to town, the thought of him had checked them. Now they began to blossom out a little, to get things, to think of themselves as really adult.

Frank wouldn't do much differently than he had been doing. He was a settled young-old farmer, short and small and very quiet, a good steady worker, but one who was not likely to get ahead very far. He and Lottie had a horde of children, and they were one of those families who are always having accidents, sickness, and doctor's bills. Frank was caught in the gasolene engine and just missed being killed or mangled. Lottie, big sturdy woman that she was, had had several operations performed by her brother-in-law, a doctor in Bishop. There was one thing after another the matter with the children. Their farm was an untidy place, much like their uncle Herman's.

Carl would do better. He was going to make as good a farmer as his father. Better, some people thought. While he might not be able to keep at it quite so doggedly, might not be quite so saving, he was more ready to try things, less stubborn and set in his ways. He was just as particular about the buildings and machinery as August had been. His wife, Clara, was a hustler. She had nearly a thousand chickens, and was making money with them. Her canned goods took prizes at the Farmers' Institute in the armoury building in "Wapsie." Carl and Clara worked hard, but they "went," too. They were going to have some fun as they went along. They had no fear of poverty in their old age.

The farm looked very different now. Carl had had the house "pebble-dashed." August's name was gone from the barn now, which was painted a new shining white.

Mary, in a way, scarcely belonged to the family any more; she and Joe lived so far away, or it seemed far away. They were part of the Adams Grove neighbourhood now, and did their trading in Bishop. Joe's farm was in the timber country there. There were some limestone cliffs and a little glen on the edge of their own land. The whole country was different from that around Richland. Not just like the Turkey Creek country, but hilly and backwoodsy and queer.

Mary and Joe seemed to be happy together. Mary had never had much but hard work out of life, except for those few years when she had been a mysterious invalid. She had two children of her own besides the other four. There was no more time for books now than she had ever had, but she found an outlet in the neighbourhood church, where she taught a large Sunday-school class and worked with the young people. She went with them to Epworth League conventions, and she was famed for having the best papers in the missionary society. Sunday school was the only glimpse of anything besides "practical work" that Mary had ever known.

Elva and Roy were talking now of moving to Oklahoma. Roy had a cousin who had an interest in some oil-wells out there, and Roy was wild to go, "quit this farming."

Johnnie was turning out better now. He bought out the Beal brothers in the garage, and he took the little house near his mother's where Nannie Frost had lived. The garage was on a highway and did a good business. But it worried Emma that it kept Johnnie so busy all the time. He was up until all hours of the night. He was a good mechanic. The fact that he was dealing with things that would go, his sight of passing travel, eased his restlessness. He was less nervous now. But he had never been the same boy since the war. It seemed to have affected Johnnie and Carl in opposite ways.

Johnnie was tremendously fond of Junior, but otherwise he was not very happy at home. He had no illusions about Bernice. He knew that she was a fool. She was shiftless, and there were frequent ructions with his mother-in-law. He seemed to enjoy being near his mother, although he seldom went in and talked to her. He brought home the mail for her and cashed cheques and saw about the insurance. She was better satisfied when she thought of him now; but it worried her that Johnnie seemed to care nothing for the church. She tried, timidly and anxiously, to get him to go. He usually said that he couldn't get away from the garage, but once he told her, "No, mamma, I'm all through with that. It don't meant anything to me." She thought that perhaps it came from having a business that ran on Sunday, and that grandpa had been right: this Sunday travel was going to ruin the country. That wild streak in Johnnie that had troubled them for a while seemed to be wearing off, but there was a kind of bitterness that she couldn't understand. She thought Johnnie looked older than Carl. He was so thin! And his sunburned skin, his fair hair, his oil-stained khaki overalls seemed all of a colour—the colour of the dust on the highway that followed the wheels of the cars going endlessly past the garage.

Marguerite had finished the high school now. Emma would have liked to have her stay at home for company, but Marguerite wanted to go and take a business course in Rapids City. Half the youth of Richland were going to business college now, either in Rapids City or Dubuque, and Marguerite had to go, too. She wanted to earn money of her own, so that she could buy the kind of clothes she liked. She wanted to be in a larger town.

All of the children lived better than their parents had done, unless it was Mary. They came into town often, and they thought nothing of driving to Dubuque for a day. They had all given elaborate names to their children, which sounded absurd with the old German surnames: Maxine, Velda, Delight, Gwendolyn, Eugene, Dwayne.

Not long after August's death, Emma went out to Mollie's to see her father. Carl took her out and was to call for her. She hadn't been there for months. Grandpa Stille was over ninety now. Who could tell how much longer he might be there?

It was a sunny September day. The willows along the edge of Herman's farm sprinkled narrow, shiny, yellow leaves over the drive where they turned in, which had a patch of smooth, leathery, brownish-black mud, with cracks across it. The dingy house and the scraggly grove had a kind of beauty to-day in the sunshine and the burning blue sky.

She found grandpa in his room on the west of the house, the window looking out on the willow grove. Mollie took her in to him, went up, and shouted:

"Pa, *sieh wer hier ist!*"

He peered forward.

"Ach, ja, ja, ja—Emma ist's? Ja, so!" He put out a hand that trembled slightly.

He was thinner, bonier than ever, his hair only a few long silver wisps under an old skull-cap, his mouth sunken in under his beard. His deep-set brown eyes still had life in them. Despite the age and the dinginess, those dark quilts that she knew so well on the billowing feather-bed, the bare floor painted a dark red, there was a beauty that she felt in the old room to-day, with the September sunlight slanting in through the window and a rustling sound from the willow grove.

Mollie and Herman had told her that the old man seldom talked to them now. He seemed to be somewhere in a place of his own. Yet his mind, when he did talk, was as clear as ever. Now that the dreadful war was over, he had gone back to his dreams. He came back with an effort, repeated her name, sighed over the death of August *so jung,* but declared that there was no great sorrow in dying; roused to ask her why *die kleine Marguerite* never came out to see her old grandpa. They talked in German. He answered her when she told him where Marguerite was now and what the boys were doing, of August's death. He was kind, and held her hand as she talked, looked at her with affection in his thin old face, told her that she was a good girl. He mourned that she should have lost her husband. But when she left him he seemed to go back at once into that reverie in which he lived now, broken only by occasional mutterings, as in the old days. But they were peaceful mutterings now.

She stayed awhile with Mollie. They talked about their father. Emma said:

"Grandpa seems to be real content."

"*Ach, ja,*" Mollie said easily, "he's always happy."

"*Ja,* but what does he do in there alone all day? I should think he'd get awful' lonesome."

"No, he don't get lonesome. *Ach,* I don't know what he does. He always seems to have plenty to think about. He used to read, but that he can't do any more."

"I hate to see him sit alone like that."

"*Ach,* he's all right."

What was he doing, thinking? Mollie said that sometimes they heard him singing old German hymns, so old that she didn't know them. He wanted nothing but his tobacco, his meals, wood for his stove in winter.

Mollie had gone to the kitchen for some eggs that she was going to give Emma to take home. Emma heard the old man, in his room, praying. She had forgotten how he used to do that, so that it startled her for a moment. The German words, guttural, rich, with long pauses between, had a sound that was unearthly and yet fitting in the still, sunlit country air. She looked into his room. He sat in the old wooden rocker. His deep eyes had a withdrawn, mystic look. He did not notice her. Mollie said:

"*Ja,* we often hear him doing that."

Emma thought about it as Carl was driving her home between the September fields of dusty gold in the late afternoon. She could still hear those faint, far-apart, devout German words. August had always said that if her father had been more of a farmer and less of a preacher, he'd be better off to-day. August had despised him in a dispassionate way. But the old man had had something, she hardly knew what, that had lasted him when his work was over.

"He's got something to think about," she thought.

It was that something, she could not name it, which she had missed all her married life.

She remembered the pathos of August, coming in from the farm and saying bitterly that everything had to go Carl's way now; of him sitting about the house, trying to look at the farm journal, not knowing what to do with himself. Her father, what a frail man he had been when he had first come to live with them years ago! And here he was living still, contented with the little that he had, and well, and August was the one who was gone.

IV: MRS. EMMA KAETTERHENRY

Retired farmers, widows, spinsters—these made up most of the little town of Richland. Emma was one of the widows now—widows living alone on small independent incomes, on the rents from farms, or helped by their children.

Marguerite was in Rapids City now. Women in Richland said disapprovingly that she ought to have stayed with her mother, but they were appeased by hearing that Marguerite was making twenty-two dollars a week as a stenographer. And they heard that she was engaged to that young fellow who sometimes came home with her, although she didn't seem to be marrying him.

She came home over Sunday sometimes. She brought her "friend," a slim, glossy-haired young man who was employed in an office in Rapids City, and who had bought a second-hand car in which they drove to Richland. They drove down on Sunday morning, and after dinner they either sat talking in low, meaning voices while Emma dozed—"You didn't? Oh, you did, too. How do *I* know? Sure I know!" —or drove out to Carl's. Emma told Marguerite that she ought to stop and see grandpa; but when they came back, and she asked them about it, Marguerite said, "Oh, we didn't get over there this time." Emma did not know whether these two were engaged or not.

Marguerite had converted herself into a very urban young lady. Her chief business in staying in Rapids City was to watch the proper length of skirts and waists and to have everything right. She was tall, still thin, and wore her clothes well. The only thing about her looks that really worried her was that her hair was too fuzzy to take a wave well. She and another girl were doing their own cooking in light-housekeeping rooms, and what she saved on food she spent on clothes. Emma thought it was dreadful when she saw what Marguerite was wearing out to Carl's, "just out in the country"—those sheer dresses and light, high-heeled slippers and silk stockings. But she did nothing more than murmur:

"Is that what you're going to wear out there? Won't you spoil it?"

Marguerite was a real Kaetterhenry, however. At home she had done none of the work, but now that she had a job, although the interest of her life was in clothes, she did her work well and disdained the slipshod ways of other stenographers. She was cool, hard, scrupulous, level-headed, a good worker. She seemed to be a nice, capable girl, people in Richland had decided, although she wasn't much comfort to her mother.

Even if she was alone, there were still claims upon Emma. There was the Aid Society, of which she was now one of the chief supports. She still worked in the kitchen at church suppers. She was sent for when there was sickness in the country. She was often called upon to keep the grandchildren while Carl and Clara, or Elva and Roy, drove to Dubuque. Some of the little ones stayed with her while the others were sick with measles or whooping-cough or scarlet fever. She often had Junior with her. Bernice was "always on the go," or fancied that she had something the matter with her. "Ma"—"grandma" they were beginning to call her—was still the stand-by of all the children, and "grandma's house" was the place where they all expected to go when they went to town.

But in a way she was knowing leisure for the first time in her life. She did not feel the responsibility that she had felt when things were dependent upon her alone. She always had plenty of time to herself. She was doing what she pleased in ways that she had never done before. She had friends outside her home, elderly ladies like herself, with whom she spent pleasant, gossipy afternoons, as she hadn't done while August was living. Her personality, smothered and silent for many years, was blossoming out, very faintly and timidly, but a little, enough to shed a kind of light of content and freedom over this quiet end of life. She might be lonely later on, but she was not now. She was a Stille, not a Kaetterhenry. That showed now. She could be happy pottering about on her own devices. The children said ma got along better alone than they'd been afraid she would.

She had gradually got used to the fact that money was her own, that there was no one but herself to say what she should spend and what she shouldn't. She did not say much about it, but not even her children realized what a wonder and pleasure it was to her to have a little money in her own hands. She still felt timid and out of place when she went into the bank. She made the boys do it for her. She was still very cautious about what she spent, could not overcome the lifelong habit of hoarding and thinking about the future. It seemed wicked to her to spend more than a very little on herself, she had had the self-effacement of mother and wife so ground into her. But when she admired a piece of goods in the store window, she could think, "Well, I can have it if I want it." She needn't ask anybody.

She could enjoy buying small presents for the grandchildren, getting cloth to make up for them, sending dollar bills in letters to Marguerite so that she could get herself something she wanted. She gave generously when she was solicited for the church, and people said, "I guess it was him that was the close one more than she. She gives real freely." She no longer had to turn away agents who came to the house selling things that she didn't want, something that had always given her tender and sentimental heart a guilty feeling. She said "they might need it; you could never be sure." She'd rather take the chance and not send anyone away. She had never subscribed for the household magazine that she wanted, thinking three dollars a year almost too sinful a waste for reading-matter; but she had a little magazine at which she never looked, having given her subscription to a young Armenian—"a young foreigner," she called him—who had asked her to "vote for him" by giving him a subscription. The youth who got the most of these "votes" would be elected by the magazine company for a year at college. She never heard whether her young foreigner had been elected.

Emma even talked of taking a trip some time out to Nebraska to see her brother Ed. But just as soon as the children began to press her to go, she would begin to make excuses. She did not quite have the courage to make a trip, or decide on one, by herself. If they had gone while pa was still alive, then that would have been different.

The children could hardly believe their Aunt Mollie when she told them that as a girl their mother had "liked to go." Now it was hard for them to get ma even to drive to Dubuque with them. She only told them mildly, *ach,* she had forgotten how, she'd stayed at home so much. It was something that she had looked forward to when they were working so hard on the farm, that when they "once had something" and "got to town," she could go again as much as she pleased. She did not tell the children now how timid she felt about starting out anywhere, how she "seemed better off at home."

They could not believe, either, that she had been a giggler, as Mollie said. There was a picture of Emma and Mollie in the album, taken in the same dresses and hats that they had worn to the Richland Grove Fourth of July celebration, the first place where Emma had gone with August. The children laughed over Aunt Mollie's spit-curls, and said that she needn't talk; and their mother's hat with a ridiculous feather, the attitude of the two girls sitting there displaying their finery. The children said, "Don't you talk to us!" But they couldn't really believe that their quiet, shy mother had been as she looked in that photograph.

But she did go a little, more than she had been doing. She never missed church, of course. She went to the "aids" and the missionary-meetings. She got Mrs. Henry Stille to stop for her and went to the Social Circle Club. She didn't mind going to places so much if she had someone to go with her. She enjoyed entertaining the club more now than when she had felt that it was bothering August. He had grumbled about "What do all those women want to sit around and talk for? Better go home and look after their houses." She felt more free to serve what refreshments she pleased.

She looked better than she had for years, a plump, shapeless elderly woman, with grey hair a little curling; spectacles—good ones now, with light, narrow shell rims; she had got them "up at Rochester"—and mild, soft, faded brown eyes. She was dowdy and countrified, but wore clothes of lasting materials, always having one good silk dress, and letting Marguerite persuade her to buy a new spring hat instead of wearing her old one again.

She still got up early every morning. Not so early as when August was living, however. Then they were awake at four, as they had been in the country. Now she lay abed sometimes until after six o'clock. That gave her a scared, delicious, audacious feeling. She liked to work in the garden in the early morning. She enjoyed having time for flowers. She had always had a few on the farm, but couldn't take care of them. They were food for her sense of beauty. Now she chose the seeds herself. She planted moss roses near the house and had Johnnie put up a trellis, shocked that he did it on Sunday. She liked to be out there planting in the spring. She put on an ancient black calico wrapper, a sunbonnet, a black, padded, sleeveless jacket, and some old shoes of August's, and went out in the yard. It was silent and sunny, no sound but an occasional car on the road, a rooster crowing, sometimes the noise of Junior's little kiddy-car on the cement walk. She liked the feel of the cool spring earth, sun-warmed on the surface, black and moist and chill underneath, as she patted it over the tiny dry seeds. She talked to Junior, said, "Dig over there in the corner, Junie, if you have to dig too, then"; but her mind was far away from him, in some wordless place of mysterious content.

She ate most of her meals alone at the little table in the kitchen. That was what she minded most of living alone—the meals. Carl and Clara had made her promise that she would cook herself real meals and not just take to lunching, as many women did when they had no men to cook for. She obeyed them pretty well, although sometimes she said, "*Ach,* just for myself!" She took great pains with her housework, although she worked slowly since there was no reason to hurry. There was a kind of mystery and contentment, too, in moving about the quiet, bright house as she worked. She wanted to keep the floors as shining as when the house was new. It worried her, although she did not say so, to have the grandchildren "get things around." After they had gone, she went about picking things up after them. She had never had time for that on the farm.

In the afternoon she often had to take care of Junior for Bernice. He was her favourite, although she would not say so, of all the grandchildren, just as Johnnie had secretly been her favourite of the children. Junior didn't seem to have suffered from the shortcomings of his mother. He was one of the sturdiest babies in town, one of whom women said lovingly, "That dear little Junior Kaetterhenry!" and men, "Ain't he a buster, though!" His fat, white cheeks and his brown eyes and his engaging smile, the fact that he had won second place in the baby-show in "Wapsie," consoled his grandmother for the fact that Johnnie had made a poor marriage, and that he didn't go to church or "believe." It seemed that the Lord must not be angry with Johnnie, since he had given him Junior. She baked cookies so that she would have some for Junior—"gran'ma's cookies," he called them—and had bought some little celluloid animals at the ten-cent store in Dubuque. He followed her about the house and asked questions, and shrieked "Daddy!" when any man went past in an automobile. And yet she felt it a kind of strain to have him there. She loved him, but she felt a kind of relief when Bernice came flouncing in to get him and take him home.

She did more fancy work now. She liked to make little clothes for the grandchildren, and tried to be very impartial with them. Marguerite picked out "cute patterns" for her in Rapids City. These little youngest Kaetterhenrys dressed very differently than her children had done. She made little bright-coloured chambray frocks, with apples and morning-glories in appliqué.

She had to care for the lot in the cemetery. She got Johnnie to drive her out there. She said that she didn't mind walking back, and usually there was someone coming along in a car who would take her as far as town. The monument was up now, a large, square, polished grey stone, with "KAETTERHENRY" carved upon it; below that:

"August Ernst
1859–1922"

and below that a space. But she had not bought her own marker. Johnnie had got rid of the monument man for her. She had had a photograph taken of the lot when the stone was put up, and she cherished that.

She kept a vase on August's grave, which she filled with flowers in the summer, although the bunches of sweet-peas and cosmos frequently withered before she could get out with a fresh bouquet. She had had a small bridal-wreath bush set out in a corner of the lot. This summer she was going to have a border of that little pink love-in-a-mist around the grave. She wanted her lot to look as well as any in the cemetery.

The Richland cemetery was in a high, sunny spot. She was not unhappy as she went about there, filling the vase, moving slowly down the narrow path through the thick grass to the small iron gate.

She told the children that she did not lack for company. Another elderly widow who had been a farmer's wife, Mrs. Wall, lived on the next street in a large, square house painted pale blue. Emma called for Mrs. Wall, and they went to the prayer-meeting and the evening church-service together, and to the missionary-meeting and the "aid." It "made it nice for both of them," people said.

Mrs. Wall came over sometimes in the evening. They sat together, sometimes in the front room, or "just out in the kitchen." Mrs. Wall knew more of what was going on than Emma did, although she said that she didn't hear so much now that she didn't have a man coming home from town. They talked over illnesses and approaching weddings and of those whom they had seen going past their houses that day. Emma told Mrs. Wall about her operation, and Mrs. Wall told her about those of sisters and sisters-in-law and brothers. They talked about the birth of children and grandchildren. Each one found a consolation in detailing to the other the last illness and death of her husband—all the symptoms from week to week, the death, the laying-out, the funeral, in hushed, confiding voices, shaking their heads and murmuring, "Yes, oh, it must have been terrible. I know what that is." They sat in the twilight together, sympathizing and condoling and narrating. Emma said it helped her to have someone to tell these things to. She would not have told them to the children.

The two women talked of religion together, of what they thought heaven was going to be like, of the way that they thought God looked at things. Emma had no such mystic fervour as her old father, but the hymns, the prayers, the familiar words, were an emotional satisfaction. They comforted her.

They talked of their troubles, said of them that such things were hard to bear; they didn't always see why they must be—Johnnie's getting such a poor wife and turning away from the church, Grandma Stille's helplessness, Mr. Wall's sufferings from cancer. These women had both worked hard. Now they were getting old, and many things had not turned out as they had thought they would.

Mrs. Wall sometimes said:

"Well, we've all had our troubles. All had things to go through. Well, I say we ought to be thankful that we've got good homes, and children to look after us if we need it; that we don't have to be sent to the poorhouse like that poor old woman in Bishop the other day. Did you hear about that?"

Emma said:

"*Ja,* that's true, too."

THE THREE READERS

Section III: Selected by Carl Van Doren

Introductory Remarks

It is chiefly by accident that all these selections are from American writers. That was not, at first, my conscious aim. But when the work was nearly done I noticed that the Americans were much in the majority and decided to let them have the field to themselves. Beyond this there is no general comment I can make on the pieces here included except that I delighted in every one of them at first reading, still enjoy them, and would like to share my pleasure with other readers.

The Jefferson letter to Maria Cosway I had not read till a few weeks ago, when I was sent to it by a remark of Gerald Johnson in a book review. Then I did not read more than a paragraph before I was set on putting it in this Reader, and half afraid to go on for fear it might turn out disappointing. It did not. The many-sided mind that had so much more to say about almost everything else than about love, here wrote about love like a philosopher, like a man. When Jefferson wrote it, he was forty-three years old, four years a widower, and United States minister to France. Among his close friends in Paris were Richard and Maria Cecilia Louisa Cosway, both of them English painters. When in October 1786 they returned to England, Jefferson felt the desolation, tempered by philosophy, which appears in the letter he sent after the lady. I do not know whether he had ever told her any of the things he wrote or whether she had been aware of his feelings. She sent back a note of four lines from Antwerp which seemed to make it plain that she had only a friendly interest in him. Their friendship survived the episode, and they could still exchange letters of affectionate regard thirty-four years later.

My familiarity with George Ade's "Fables in Slang" goes back more than forty years, when the earliest appeared, but I do not remember reading the one I here include till 1923 when I read them all for a critical essay I was writing. This Fable belongs with half a dozen that have stuck in my memory like burs ever since. There were three I found it hard to decide among. But one I had already chosen for an anthology, and another is a favorite of Sinclair Lewis, who has a kind of rediscoverer's claim to it. What was left to me is one of the shortest of the Fables, and one of the sharpest.

In midsummer 1941 I gave a lecture at a town on the Susquehanna. Afterwards somebody from the audience told me he had been sorry to learn that my friend Sinclair Lewis was dead. Then it turned out that Mr. Lewis, whom I had seen a few days before, had reported his imaginary funeral, with me present among the mourners, in a magazine which somebody else hurried out and bought for me. I thought and still think that Mr. Lewis has never packed more meat and more fun into so few words as there are in "The Death of Arrowsmith." Hoax and skit, it is also a treasure, like Franklin's imaginary epitaph on himself.

In 1922 I read, at almost the same time, George Santayana's "Preface" to his selected *Poems* of that year and the terse note by A. E. Housman in his *Last Poems,* also published in 1922, on the "continuous excitement" in which he wrote *A Shropshire Lad* during the early months of 1895, not far from the months when George Santayana was writing his Sonnets. Most of the Shropshire lyrics and many of the Sonnets I knew by heart, and it excited me to think of them as so nearly contemporary though there was an Atlantic between the poets when they wrote. Reading the Santayana "Preface" last night, I found myself stirred as much as when I read it twenty years ago by his acute and beautiful description of his poems and of their place in the making of his philosophy.

When I encountered John Bainbridge's Profile of Hu Shih's Musketeer in *The New Yorker,* I had not heard of Daniel Arnstein and did not know he had gone to organize traffic on the Burma Road. Now, though the Road has been temporarily lost to the enemy, I shall not forget either the name of the man or his achievement, and I should like as many people as possible to remember how this American served China, where he will live in history as a hero to the nation.

Two days after Thoreau died, Emerson, at the funeral in the First Church in Concord, delivered a eulogy which he later wrote out at greater length for the *Atlantic.* The two men had been close friends for years, Thoreau at first something of a disciple, later a living example of a kind of thinker and doer that Emerson greatly admired. There may have been younger persons who had spent more hours with Thoreau than Emerson had, but nobody understands Thoreau better, and nobody could explain him so well. With the warmth of a friend, Emerson united the strength of a sage. In all that has since then been written about Thoreau this first account of him has never been surpassed—or, I think, equalled—in penetration or felicity. It sums up a man as few writers in any literature have known how to do.

If stories of guerrilla warfare were not so much in the news, I might not have thought of William Gilmore Simms's fine ballad "The Swamp Fox," celebrating the partisan warfare between the pro-British Tories and the pro-American Whigs in South Carolina during the Revolution, which in that state was a fierce civil war. The Swamp Fox was the name given to Francis Marion, leader of the Whig or patriot forces when the state was over-run with the enemy.

After Marjorie Kinnan Rawlings's "The Pelican's Shadow," published in *The New Yorker,* was reprinted in a volume of short stories, I happened to speak of it to two or three friends, and found that each of us had intended to write to her when it originally appeared and again when it was republished, to tell her of our delight in her sketch in caustic of a complete pedant. None of us had done it, but I then did, and got from her a conditional promise to write other stories some day in the same manner. She should be held to her promise.

Reading Herman Melville's *Mardi* during the First World War, and feeling lost in that wilderness of allegorical adventures, I came upon—and still remember coming upon—two chapters, one called "Dedicated to the College of Physicians and Surgeons" and the other called "Dreams," which seemed to me like happy islands in a bewildering ocean. If the book as a whole is a gigantic cipher, "Dreams" is Melville's signature candidly exposed in the narrative.

Because my brother Mark Van Doren and I have severely avoided writing about each other for the public, I make no general comment on *A Winter Diary,* and say only that it is for me personally the most satisfying of all country poems. It is the poetic record of an actual winter he spent with his wife and two young sons on their farm in Connecticut.

Though plays written for radio production are only slowly coming to be thought of as a form of art, I include Norman Corwin's "Daybreak," which I heard on the air and which I find thrilling when read. Even without the music and the sound effects which are so important a part of a radio production, the mere words of the narrative and dialogue come nearer to presenting the whole story than the dialogue of a stage play does. The reader of a stage play misses the visible action. A radio play has no visible action to miss. The story is in the words. I have chosen "Daybreak," not only because it seems to me Mr. Corwin's best radio play, but also because its vast panorama displays the whole earth in what would now be called a global vision.

From this latest kind of American drama I turn, again for contrast, to the earliest. Writing my life of Benjamin Franklin, in 1937 I had to study the treaty between the Province of Pennsylvania and the Ohio Indians, at Carlisle in 1753, to which Franklin went as one of the Pennsylvania commissioners on the first diplomatic mission of his career. At that time I had never read the text of any Indian treaty, and as I read this I could not believe my eyes. For it was an amazing historical drama which was both truth and literature. All over the United States, I reflected, students of American literature and history annually read pages of eighteenth-century writing, but persistently overlook the great Indian treaties which are, outside of Franklin and some theological and more political discourses, the American century's masterpieces—and more than that. For they are world masterpieces in the long record of relations between civilized and savage races.

My innocent discovery was independent, but I soon learned that a few collectors already knew and valued the written minutes of these treaties and that Lawrence Wroth had been influentially talking and writing about them for ten years or so. For that matter, Franklin as printer for Pennsylvania had printed thirteen of the Pennsylvania treaties in stately pamphlets now rare and worth many times their weight in gold or any metal. I could never hope to own one, even if I could find one for sale. But there are ways and ways of getting what you want. I hinted to Julian Boyd, of the Historical Society of Pennsylvania, that the Society could do a good turn to history and literature by reproducing some of the treaties in facsimile. Within a few months he had got a patron in E. E. Brownell, collateral descendant of Franklin's only known teacher, and had reproduced all the Franklin Indian treaties in a folio about the splendor of which President Roosevelt and H. L. Mencken were—for once—in agreement.

So far, the Indian treaties have been read, since their own day, chiefly by the studious and the curious. I now offer one of them to the largest public it has ever had a chance to have, in the confidence that it will at last take the place it deserves among the permanent treasures of the American past.

CARL VAN DOREN

Thomas Jefferson to Maria Cosway

LOVE LETTER OF A PHILOSOPHER

Paris, October 12, 1786

My Dear Madam,—Having performed the last sad office of handing you into your carriage, at the pavillon de St. Denis, and seen the wheels get actually into motion, I turned on my heel and walked, more dead than alive, to the opposite door, where my own was awaiting me. Mr. Danquerville was missing. He was sought for, found, and dragged down stairs. We were crammed into the carriage, like recruits for the Bastile, and not having soul enough to give orders to the coachman, he presumed Paris our destination, and drove off. After a considerable interval, silence was broke, with a *"Je suis vraiment affligé du départ de ces bons gens."* This was a signal for a mutual confession of distress. We began immediately to talk of Mr. and Mrs. Cosway, of their goodness, their talents, their amiability; and, though we spoke of nothing else, we seemed hardly to have entered into the matter, when the coachman announced the rue St. Denis, and that we were opposite Mr. Danquerville's. He insisted on descending there, and traversing a short passage to his lodgings. I was carried home. Seated by my fireside, solitary and sad, the following dialogue took place between my Head and my Heart.

Head. Well, friend, you seem to be in a pretty trim.

Heart. I am indeed the most wretched of all earthly beings. Overwhelmed with grief, every fibre of my frame distended beyond its natural powers to bear, I would willingly meet whatever catastrophe should leave me no more to feel, or to fear.

Head. These are the eternal consequences of your warmth and precipitation. This is one of the scrapes into which you are ever leading us. You confess your follies, indeed; but still you hug and cherish them; and no reformation can be hoped where there is no repentance.

Heart. Oh, my friend! this is no moment to upbraid my foibles. I am rent into fragments by the force of my grief! If you have any balm, pour it into my wounds; if none, do not harrow them by new torments. Spare me in this awful moment! At any other, I will attend with patience to your admonitions.

Head. On the contrary, I never found that the moment of triumph, with you, was the moment of attention to my admonitions. While suffering under your follies, you may perhaps be made sensible of them, but the paroxysm over, you fancy it can never return. Harsh, therefore, as the medicine may be, it is my office to administer it. You will be pleased to remember, that when our friend Trumbull used to be telling us of the merits and talents of these good people, I never ceased whispering to you that we had no occasion for new acquaintances; that the greater their merits and talents, the more dangerous their friendship to our tranquillity, because the regret at parting would be greater.

Heart. Accordingly, Sir, this acquaintance was not the consequence of my doings. It was one of your projects, which threw us in the way of it. It was you, remember, and not I, who desired the meeting at Legrand and Motinos. I never trouble myself with domes nor arches. The Halle aux Bleds might have rotted down, before I should have gone to see it. But you, forsooth, who are eternally getting us to sleep with your diagrams and crotchets, must go and examine this wonderful piece of architecture; and when you had seen it, oh! it was the most superb thing on earth! What you had seen there was worth all you had yet seen in Paris! I thought so, too. But I meant it of the lady and gentleman to whom we had been presented; and not of a parcel of sticks and chips put together in pens. You, then, Sir, and not I, have been the cause of the present distress.

Head. It would have been happy for you if my diagrams and crotchets had gotten you to sleep on that day, as you are pleased to say they eternally do. My visit to Legrand and Motinos had public utility for its object. A market is to be built in Richmond. What a commodious plan is that of Legrand and Motinos; especially, if we put on it the noble dome of the Halle aux Bleds. If such a bridge as they showed us can be thrown across the Schuylkill, at Philadelphia, the floating bridges taken up, and the navigation of that river opened, what a copious resource will be added, of wood and provisions, to warm and feed the poor of that city? While I was occupied with these objects, you were dilating with your new acquaintances, and contriving how to prevent a separation from them. Every soul of you had an engagement for the day. Yet all these were to be sacrificed, that you might dine together. Lying messengers were to be despatched into every quarter of the city, with apologies for your breach of engagement. You, particularly, had the effrontery to send word to the Duchess Danville, that on the moment we were setting out to dine with her, despatches came to hand, which required immediate attention. You wanted me to invent a more ingenious excuse; but I knew you were getting into a scrape, and I would have nothing to do with it. Well; after dinner to St. Cloud, from St. Cloud to Ruggieri's, from Ruggieri's to Krumfoltz; and if the day had been as long as a Lapland summer day, you would still have contrived means among you to have filled it.

Heart. Oh! my dear friend, how you have revived me by recalling to my mind the transactions of that day! How well I remember them all, and that, when I came home at night, and looked back to the morning, it seemed to have been a month agone. Go on, then, like a kind comforter, and paint to me the day we went to St. Germains. How beautiful was every object! the Port de Reuilly, the hills along the Seine, the rainbows of the machine of Marly, the terrace of St. Germains, the chateaux, the gardens, the statues of Marly, the pavillon of Lucienne. Recollect, too, Madrid, Bagatelle, the King's garden, the Dessert. How grand the idea excited by the remains of such a column. The spiral staircase, too, was beautiful. Every moment was filled with something agreeable. The wheels of time moved on with a rapidity, of which those of our carriage gave but a faint idea. And yet, in the evening, when one took a retrospect of the day, what a mass of happiness had we travelled over! Retrace all those scenes to me, my good companion, and I will forgive the unkindness with which you were chiding me. The day we went to St. Germains was a little too warm, I think; was it not?

Head. Thou art the most incorrigible of all the beings that ever sinned! I reminded you of the follies of the first day, intending to deduce from thence some useful lessons for you; but instead of listening to them, you kindle at the recollection, you retrace the whole series with a fondness, which shows you want nothing, but the opportunity, to act it over again. I often told you, during its course, that you were imprudently engaging your affections, under circumstances that must have cost you a great deal of pain; that the persons, indeed, were of the greatest merit, possessing good sense, good humor, honest hearts, honest manners, and eminence in a lovely art; that the lady had, moreover, qualities and accomplishments belonging to her sex, which might form a chapter apart for her; such as music, modesty, beauty, and that softness of disposition, which is the ornament of her sex and charm of ours; but that all these considerations would increase the pang of separation; that their stay here was to be short; that you rack our whole system when you are parted from those you love, complaining that such a separation is worse than death, inasmuch as this ends our sufferings, whereas that only begins them; and that the separation would, in this instance, be the more severe, as you would probably never see them again.

Heart. But they told me they would come back again, the next year.

Head. But, in the meantime, see what you suffer; and their return, too, depends on so many circumstances, that if you had a grain of prudence, you would not count upon it. Upon the whole, it is improbable, and therefore you should abandon the idea of ever seeing them again.

Heart. May heaven abandon me if I do!

Head. Very well. Suppose, then, they come back. They are to stay two months, and, when these are expired, what is to follow? Perhaps you flatter yourself they may come to America?

Heart. God only knows what is to happen. I see nothing impossible in that supposition; and I see things wonderfully contrived sometimes, to make us happy. Where could they find such objects as in America, for the exercise of their enchanting art? especially the lady, who paints landscapes so inimitably. She wants only subjects worthy of immortality, to render her pencil immortal. The Falling Spring, the Cascade of Niagara, the passage of the Potomac through the Blue Mountains, the Natural Bridge; it is worth a voyage across the Atlantic to see these objects; much more to paint, and make them, and thereby ourselves, known to all ages. And our own dear Monticello; where has nature spread so rich a mantle under the eye? mountains, forests, rocks, rivers. With what majesty do we there ride above the storms! How sublime to look down into the workhouse of nature, to see her clouds, hail, snow, rain, thunder, all fabricated at our feet! and the glorious sun, when rising as if out of a distant water, just gilding the tops of the mountains, and giving life to all nature! I hope in God, no circumstance may ever make either seek an asylum from grief! With what sincere sympathy I would open every cell of my composition, to receive the effusion of their woes! I would pour my tears into their wounds; and if a drop of balm could be found on the top of the Cordilleras, or at the remotest sources of the Missouri, I would go thither myself to seek and to bring it. Deeply practised in the school of affliction, the human heart knows no joy which I have not lost, no sorrow of which I have not drunk! Fortune can present no grief of unknown form to me! Who, then, can so softly bind up the wound of another, as he who has felt the same wound himself? But heaven forbid they should ever know a sorrow! Let us turn over another leaf, for this has distracted me.

Head. Well. Let us put this possibility to trial then, on another point. When you consider the character which is given of our country, by the lying newspapers of London, and their credulous copiers in other countries; when you reflect that all Europe is made to believe we are a lawless banditti, in a state of absolute anarchy, cutting one another's throats, and plundering without distinction, how could you expect that any reasonable creature would venture among us?

Heart. But you and I know that all this is false: that there is not a country on earth, where there is greater tranquillity; where the laws are milder, or better obeyed; where every one is more attentive to his own business, or meddles less with that of others; where strangers are better received, more hospitably treated, and with a more sacred respect.

Head. True, you and I know this, but your friends do not know it.

Heart. But they are sensible people, who think for themselves. They will ask of impartial foreigners, who have been among us, whether they saw or heard on the spot, any instance of anarchy. They will judge, too, that a people, occupied as we are, in opening rivers, digging navigable canals, making roads, building public schools, establishing academies, erecting busts and statues to our great men, protecting religious freedom, abolishing sanguinary punishments, reforming and improving our laws in general; they will judge, I say, for themselves, whether these are not the occupations of a people at their ease; whether this is not better evidence of our true state, than a London newspaper, hired to lie, and from which no truth can ever be extracted but by reversing everything it says.

Head. I did not begin this lecture, my friend, with a view to learn from you what America is doing. Let us return, then, to our point. I wish to make you sensible how imprudent it is to place your affections, without reserve, on objects you must so soon lose, and whose loss, when it comes, must cost you such severe pangs. Remember the last night. You knew your friends were to leave Paris to-day. This was enough to throw you into agonies. All night you tossed us from one side of the bed to the other; no sleep, no rest. The poor crippled wrist, too, never left one moment in the same position; now up, now down, now here, now there; was it to be wondered at, if its pains returned? The surgeon then was to be called, and to be rated as an ignoramus, because he could not divine the cause of this extraordinary change. In fine, my friend, you must mend your manners. This is not a world to live at random in, as you do. To avoid those eternal distresses, to which you are forever exposing us, you must learn to look forward, before you take a step which may interest our peace. Everything in this world is matter of calculation. Advance then with caution, the balance in your hand. Put into one scale the pleasures which any object may offer; but put fairly into the other, the pains which are to follow, and see which preponderates. The making an acquaintance, is not a matter of indifference. When a new one is proposed to you, view it all round. Consider what advantages it presents, and to what inconveniences it may expose you. Do not bite at the bait of pleasure, till you know there is no hook beneath it. The art of life is the art of avoiding pain; and he is the best pilot, who steers clearest of the rocks and shoals with which it is beset. Pleasure is always before us; but misfortune is at our side: while running after that, this arrests us. The most effectual means of being secure against pain, is to retire within ourselves, and to suffice for our own happiness. Those which depend on ourselves, are the only pleasures a wise man will count on: for nothing is ours, which another may deprive us of. Hence the inestimable value of intellectual pleasures. Ever in our power, always leading us to something new, never cloying, we ride serene and sublime above the concerns of this mortal world, contemplating truth and nature, matter and motion, the laws which bind up their existence, and that Eternal Being who made and bound them up by those laws. Let this be our employ. Leave the bustle and tumult of society to those who have not talents to occupy themselves without them. Friendship is but another name for an alliance with the follies and the misfortunes of others. Our own share of miseries is sufficient: why enter then as volunteers into those of another? Is there so little gall poured into our cup, that we must need help to drink that of our neighbor? A friend dies, or leaves us: we feel as if a limb was cut off. He is sick: we must watch over him, and participate of his pains. His fortune is shipwrecked: ours must be laid under contribution. He loses a child, a parent, or a partner: we must mourn the loss as if it were our own.

Heart. And what more sublime delight than to mingle tears with one whom the hand of heaven hath smitten! to watch over the bed of sickness, and to beguile its tedious and its painful moments! to share our bread with one to whom misfortune has left none! This world abounds indeed with misery; to lighten its burthen, we must divide it with one another. But let us now try the virtue of your mathematical balance, and as you have put into one scale the burthens of friendship, let me put its comforts into the other. When languishing then under disease, how grateful is the solace of our friends! how are we penetrated with their assiduities and attentions! how much are we supported by their encouragements and kind offices! When heaven has taken from us some object of our love, how sweet is it to have a bosom whereon to recline our heads, and into which we may pour the torrent of our tears! Grief, with such a comfort, is almost a luxury! In a life, where we are perpetually exposed to want and accident, yours is a wonderful proposition, to insulate ourselves, to retire from all aid, and to wrap ourselves in the mantle of self-sufficiency! For, assuredly, nobody will care for him who cares for nobody. But friendship is precious, not only in the shade, but in the sunshine of life; and thanks to a benevolent arrangement of things, the greater part of life is sunshine. I will recur for proof to the days we have lately passed. On these, indeed, the sun shone brightly. How gay did the face of nature appear! Hills, valleys, chateaux, gardens, rivers, every object wore its liveliest hue! Whence did they borrow it? From the presence of our charming companion. They were pleasing, because she seemed pleased. Alone, the scene would have been dull and insipid: the participation of it with her gave it relish. Let the gloomy monk, sequestered from the world, seek unsocial pleasures in the bottom of his cell! Let the sublimated philosopher grasp visionary happiness, while pursuing phantoms dressed in the garb of truth! Their supreme wisdom is supreme folly; and they mistake for happiness the mere absence of pain. Had they ever felt the solid pleasure of one generous spasm of the heart, they would exchange for it all the frigid speculations of their lives, which you have been vaunting in such elevated terms. Believe me, then, my friend, that that is a miserable arithmetic which could estimate friendship at nothing, or at less than nothing. Respect for you has induced me to enter into this discussion, and to hear principles uttered which I detest and abjure. Respect for myself now obliges me to recall you into the proper limits of your office. When nature assigned us the same habitation, she gave us over it a divided empire. To you, she allotted the field of science; to me, that of morals. When the circle is to be squared, or the orbit of a comet to be traced; when the arch of greatest strength, or the solid of least resistance, is to be investigated, take up the problem; it is yours; nature has given me no cognizance of it. In like manner, in denying to you the feelings of sympathy, of benevolence, of gratitude, of justice, of love, of friendship, she has excluded you from their control. To these, she has adapted the mechanism of the heart. Morals were too essential to the happiness of man, to be risked on the uncertain combinations of the head. She laid their foundation, therefore, in sentiment, not in science. That she gave to all, as necessary to all; this to a few only, as sufficing with a few. I know, indeed, that you pretend authority to the sovereign control of our conduct, in all its parts; and a respect for your grave saws and maxims, a desire to do what is right, has sometimes induced me to conform to your counsels. A few facts, however, which I can readily recall to your memory, will suffice to prove to you, that nature has not organized you for our moral direction. When the poor, wearied soldier whom we overtook at Chickahominy, with his pack on his back, begged us to let him get up behind our chariot, you began to calculate that the road was full of soldiers, and that if all should be taken up, our horses would fail in their journey. We drove on therefore. But, soon becoming sensible you had made me do wrong, that, though we cannot relieve all the distressed, we should relieve as many as we can, I turned about to take up the soldier; but he had entered a bye-path, and was no more to be found; and from that moment to this, I could never find him out, to ask his forgiveness. Again, when the poor woman came to ask a charity in Philadelphia, you whispered that she looked like a drunkard, and that half a dollar was enough to give her for the ale-house. Those who want the dispositions to give, easily find reasons why they ought not to give. When I sought her out afterwards, and did what I should have done at first, you know that she employed the money immediately towards placing her child at school. If our country, when pressed with wrongs at the point of the bayonet, had been governed by its heads instead of its hearts, where should we have been now? Hanging on a gallows as high as Haman's. You began to calculate, and to compare wealth and numbers: we threw up a few pulsations of our blood; we supplied enthusiasm against wealth and numbers; we put our existence to the hazard, when the hazard seemed against us, and we saved our country: justifying, at the same time, the ways of Providence, whose precept is, to do always what is right, and leave the issue to Him. In short, my friend, as far as my recollection serves me, I do not know that I ever did a good thing on your suggestion, or a dirty one without it. I do forever, then, disclaim your interference in my province. Fill paper as you please with triangles and squares: try how many ways you can hang and combine them together. I shall never envy nor control your sublime delights. But leave me to decide, when and where friendships are to be contracted. You say, I contract them at random. So you said the woman at Philadelphia was a drunkard. I receive none into my esteem, till I know they are worthy of it. Wealth, title, office, are no recommendations to my friendship. On the contrary, great good qualities are requisite to make amends for their having wealth, title, and office. You confess, that, in the present case, I could not have made a worthier choice. You only object, that I was so soon to lose them. We are not immortal ourselves, my friend; how can we expect our enjoyments to be so? We have no rose without its thorn; no pleasure without alloy. It is the law of our existence; and we must acquiesce. It is the condition annexed to all our pleasures, not by us who receive, but by him who gives them. True, this condition is pressing cruelly on me at this moment. I feel more fit for death than life. But, when I look back on the pleasures of which it is the consequence, I am conscious they were worth the price I am paying. Notwithstanding your endeavors, too, to damp my hopes, I comfort myself with expectations of their promised return. Hope is sweeter than despair; and they were too good to mean to deceive me. "In the summer," said the gentleman; but "in the spring," said the lady; and I should love her forever, were it only for that! Know, then, my friend, that I have taken these good people into my bosom; that I have lodged them in the warmest cell I could find; that I love them, and will continue to love them through life; that if fortune should dispose them on one side the globe, and me on the other, my affections shall pervade its whole mass to reach them. Knowing then my determination, attempt not to disturb it. If you can, at any time, furnish matter for their amusement, it will be the office of a good neighbor to do it. I will, in like manner, seize any occasion which may offer, to do the like good turn for you with Condorcet, Rittenhouse, Madison, La Cretelle, or any other of those worthy sons of science, whom you so justly prize.

I thought this a favorable proposition whereon to rest the issue of the dialogue. So I put an end to it by calling for my nightcap. Methinks, I hear you wish to heaven I had called a little sooner, and so spared you the ennui of such a sermon. I did not interrupt them sooner, because I was in a mood for hearing sermons. You too were the subject; and on such a thesis, I never think the theme long; not even if I am to write it, and that slowly and awkwardly, as now, with the left hand. But, that you may not be discouraged from a correspondence which begins so formidably, I will promise you, on my honor, that my future letters shall be of a reasonable length. I will even agree to express but half my esteem for you, for fear of cloying you with too full a dose. But, on your part, no curtailing. If your letters are as long as the Bible, they will appear short to me. Only let them be brimful of affection. I shall read them with the dispositions with which Arlequin, in *Les deux billets,* spelt the words *"je t'aime,"* and wished that the whole alphabet had entered into their composition.

We have had incessant rains since your departure. These make me fear for your health, as well as that you had an uncomfortable journey. The same cause has prevented me from being able to give you any account of your friends here. This voyage to Fontainebleau will probably send the Count de Moutier and the Marquis de Brehan, to America. Danquerville promised to visit me, but has not done it as yet. De la Tude comes sometimes to take family soup with me, and entertains me with anecdotes of his five and thirty years' imprisonment. How fertile is the mind of man, which can make the Bastile and dungeon of Vincennes yield interesting anecdotes! You know this was for making four verses on Madame de Pompadour. But I think you told me you did not know the verses. They were these: *"Sans esprit, sans sentiment, Sans etre belle, ni neuve, En France on peut avoir le premier amant: Pompadour en est l'épreuve."* I have read the memoir of his three escapes. As to myself, my health is good, except my wrist which mends slowly, and my mind which mends not at all, but broods constantly over your departure. The lateness of the season obliges me to decline my journey into the south of France. Present me in the most friendly terms to Mr. Cosway, and receive me into your own recollection with a partiality and warmth, proportioned not to my own poor merit, but to the sentiments of sincere affection and esteem, with which I have the honor to be, my dear Madam, your most obedient humble servant.

The Fable of the Foozle & The Successful Approach

BY GEORGE ADE

EVERY YEAR a lot of Americans went over to London to rub up against the Aristocracy, if possible. One year two Men went over. They intended to hang around and look Wistful until the Nobility and Landed Gentry would take some Notice of them.

Each had a Scheme for securing Recognition.

The first chased himself to Regent Street and bought an entire Outfit of British Clothes. He began to use the sound of A as in Father and say Mean Things about the Boers. He held his Hat in his Hand whenever he approached a Title. He went out of his Way to run down the vulgar Americans. Consequently he was walked upon and despised as a Toady.

The other Man allowed his Hair to grow down over his Collar. He wore a Buck Taylor Hat with a Leather Strap around it and kept it at an Angle of 45 degrees. He refused the B. and S. and demanded Cocktails. When he met an Englishman he called him Pard and held out his Flipper and said he'd be catawampously Jiggered if he wasn't all-fired Proud to meet him. He plucked the Tail Feathers from the gullorious Bird of Freedom and waved them defiantly at the Lion and the Unicorn. He said that the British Isles were merely a Breakwater for the Continent and wouldn't make a Patch on the Land of Liberty.

He was invited to all the Drawing-Rooms because it was a Pleasure to meet such a breezy and Typical American.

MORAL: *When you are in Rome do as the Romans expect you to do.*

The Death of Arrowsmith
An auto-obituary

BY SINCLAIR LEWIS

SINCLAIR LEWIS, who died peacefully in his sleep yesterday afternoon, at his small country-place in northwestern Connecticut, has, at the age of eighty-six, been rather generally forgotten. For the past ten or fifteen years he has indulged in so secluded a life, devoting himself, apparently, only to his cats, his gardens, and brief essays on such little-read novelists as Mark Twain, that to many persons it may have been a surprise to find that he was still living. Yet at one time he was a figure of considerable notoriety, because of his jeering yet essentially kindly shafts at the pomposity and inefficiency of contemporary politicians and industrialists.

Although now they are almost unread, a few of his novels, particularly *Main Street, Arrowsmith, Babbitt, Elmer Gantry,* and the ponderous four-volume chronicle of an American family, *The Tintayres,* which Mr. Lewis began in 1944 and completed in 1950, are familiar to all sociologists and literary historians for their picture of the priggish and naive first half of this century. That this picture was well rounded or unprejudiced, no one will maintain.

Mr. Lewis seems essentially to have been a cheerful pathologist, exposing the clichés and sentimentalities of his day—the hearty falseness of senators and what were once known as "business boosters," the smirking attitudes toward women in his times, the personal ambitiousness of the clergy, the artists, and the professional men, and the brazen mawkishness of patriotism.

To the discerning reader of later years, it is evident that Mr. Lewis smote—or tried to smite—sentimentality because he knew himself to be, at heart, a sentimentalist to whom green hills and barricade-jumping soldiers and smiling girls and winter storms were as childishly exciting as they were to any popular female novelist. It also was evident that he mocked the cruder manifestations of Yankee imperialism because he was, at heart, a fanatic American, who never really liked the condescensions of the English people among whom he often lived—including two solid years in Derbyshire in 1951–52.

The "style" of Mr. Lewis' rather long-winded pictures of Americana seems, on recent study, to indicate a descent from extraordinarily discrepant literary ancestors. From a perusal of his books, together with his own admissions, one may find him astonishingly deriving from both Dickens and Swinburne, H. G. Wells and A. E. Housman, Thomas Hardy and H. L. Mencken and Hamlin Garland. On the other hand, he seems to have left no literary descendants. Unlike his celebrated contemporaries, Theodore Dreiser (1871–1952) and Colonel Ernest Hemingway, who was so dramatically killed while leading his mixed Filipino and Chinese troops in the storming of Tokio in 1949, Mr. Lewis seems to have affected but little the work of younger writers of fiction. Whether this is a basic criticism of his pretensions to power and originality, or whether, like another contemporary, Miss Willa Cather, he was an inevitably lone and insulated figure, we have not as yet the perspective to see.

For a good many years, Mr. Lewis was an extensive and, it would almost seem, a foolishly experimental wanderer. He began his work with years on newspapers and in magazine and publishing offices; he traveled through every state in the union; he knew most of Europe and, after the end of World War II, in 1944, most of Asia. He even—possibly in unconscious imitation of his idol, Dickens—dabbled with acting, over three or four years, appearing in various professional companies, with no especial credit or discredit either.

But on his return from England in 1952, he settled immovably in the rural Connecticut to which he had many ties. Though Mr. Lewis himself was born (in 1885) in a Minnesota prairie hamlet, where his father was a typical country physician, that father and his ancestors for eight or nine generations were born in Connecticut, along the Housatonic River, near which Mr. Lewis himself has lived these past twenty years. He attended Yale, and did his first newspaper work on the New Haven *Journal and Courier*. It was natural then that he should have settled in Connecticut, being weary of travel and of what he himself once called (in his brief travel book, *Tea for One-and-one-half,* Random House, 1945), "the chronic wanderer's discovery that he is everywhere such an Outsider that no one will listen to him even when he kicks about the taxes and the beer."

Lewis was tall, lean, awkward, with a rough complexion and, in his later years, a skull completely bald, save for a fringe of still rusty hair. Had he sported a tousled wig and a chin whisker, he would almost comically have been taken for an impersonation of Uncle Sam, and a large share of the yearly dwindling number of interviewers and librarians who made a pilgrimage to his home (a pilgrimage invariably ruined by the old man's derisive frivolity about all artistic poses) have noted that with advancing years he became more and more the Last Surviving Connecticut Yankee. Even his voice assumed a Yankee twang now forgotten save in bad plays.

His neighbors tell, as their liveliest recollection of him, that when Dr. Sir Wilfred Willoughby Westfrisket, Eisenbein Professor of American Literature at Oxford, waited for him at his home one entire afternoon, Mr. Lewis was at a local garage, playing pinochle with the village constable-undertaker.

Although Lewis seems to have had no "school" of imitators whatever, it is to be surmised that his influence on our literature has been healthful in his derision of dullness and formalism. His use of American lingo and humorous exaggeration intermingled with the more nearly scholastic manner that was an inheritance from his college days, is at least the equal in dignity and romantic charm of any prince, any labor-leader with 10,000,000 followers—or any novelist!

His only surviving near relatives are his elder son, Wells, who was, it will be remembered, a captain in the A. E. F. of 1942, and who is probably a more distinguished, certainly a far more subtle and fastidious novelist than his father; his younger son, Michael, president of the Afro-China Airways; and his nephew, Freeman Lewis, the publisher.

The funeral, which was at the Millerton Cremation Sanctuary, was, by Mr. Lewis' dying request, attended only by the three servants (or, as he eccentrically called them, the "helpers") on his estate, together with the venerable Dr. Carl Van Doren, president emeritus of Columbia University and formerly ambassador to France. The only music was the playing of Beethoven's *Seventh Symphony,* in records, and the only oratory, Dr. Van Doren's sole observation, "This was a good workman and a good friend, who could still laugh in days when the world had almost worried itself out of the power of laughter."

A Preface to My Poems

BY GEORGE SANTAYANA

New editions of books are a venture for publishers rather than authors. The author has committed his rash act once for all at the beginning and he can hardly retract or repeat it. Nevertheless if I had not connived and collaborated at this selection of verses written (almost all of them) in my younger days, they probably would not have reappeared. I therefore owe an apology to my best critics and friends, who have always warned me that I am no poet; all the more since, in the sense in which they mean the word, I heartily agree with them. Of impassioned tenderness or Dionysiac frenzy I have nothing, nor even of that magic and pregnancy of phrase—really the creation of a fresh idiom—which marks the high lights of poetry. Even if my temperament had been naturally warmer, the fact that the English language (and I can write no other with assurance) was not my mother-tongue would of itself preclude any inspired use of it on my part; its roots do not quite reach to my centre. I never drank in in childhood the homely cadences and ditties which in pure spontaneous poetry set the essential key. I know no words redolent of the wonder-world, the fairy-tale, or the cradle. Moreover, I am city-bred, and that companionship with nature, those rural notes, which for English poets are almost inseparable from poetic feeling, fail me altogether. Landscape to me is only a background for fable or a symbol for fate, as it was to the ancients; and the human scene itself is but a theme for reflection. Nor have I been tempted into the by-ways even of towns, or fascinated by the aspect and humours of all sorts and conditions of men. My approach to language is literary, my images are only metaphors, and sometimes it seems to me that I resemble my countryman Don Quixote, when in his airy flights he was merely perched on a high horse and a wooden Pegasus; and I ask myself if I ever had anything to say in verse that might not have been said better in prose.

And yet, in reality, there was no such alternative. What I felt when

I composed those verses could not have been rendered in any other form. Their sincerity is absolute, not only in respect to the thought which might be abstracted from them and expressed in prose, but also in respect to the aura of literary and religious associations which envelops them. If their prosody is worn and traditional, like a liturgy, it is because they represent the initiation of a mind into a world older and larger than itself; not the chance experiences of a stray individual, but his submission to what is not his chance experience; to the truth of nature and the moral heritage of mankind. Here is the uncertain hand of an apprentice, but of an apprentice in a great school. Verse is one of the traditions of literature. Like the orders of Greek architecture, the sonnet or the couplet or the quatrain are better than anything else that has been devised to serve the same function; and the innate freedom of poets to hazard new forms does not abolish the freedom of all men to adopt the old ones. It is almost inevitable that a man of letters, if his mind is cultivated and capable of moral concentration, should versify occasionally, or should have versified. He need not on that account pose as a poetic genius, and yet his verses (like those of Michael Angelo, for instance) may form a part, even if a subordinate part, of the expression of his mind. Poetry was made for man, not man for poetry, and there are really as many kinds of it as there are poets, or even verses. Is Hamlet's Soliloquy poetry? Would it have conveyed its meaning better if not reined in by the metre, and made to prance and turn to the cadences of blank verse? Whether better or worse, it would certainly not be itself without that movement. Versification is like a pulsing accompaniment, somehow sustaining and exalting the clear logic of the words. The accompaniment may be orchestral, but it is not necessarily worse for being thrummed on a mandolin or a guitar. So the couplets of Pope or Dryden need not be called poetry, but they could not have been prose. They frame in a picture, balanced like the dance. There is an elevation, too, in poetic diction, just because it is consecrated and archaic; a pomp as of a religious procession, without which certain intuitions would lose all their grace and dignity. Borrowed plumes would not even seem an ornament if they were not in themselves beautiful. To say that what was good once is good no longer is to give too much importance to chronology. Aesthetic fashions may change, losing as much beauty at one end as they gain at the other, but innate taste continues to recognise its affinities, however remote, and need never change. Mask and buskin are often requisite in order to transport what is great in human experience out of its embosoming littleness. They are inseparable from finality, from perception of the ultimate. Perhaps it is just this tragic finality that English poets do not have and do not relish: they feel it to be rhetorical. But verse after all is a form of rhetoric, as is all speech and even thought; a means of pouring experience into a mould which fluid experience cannot supply, and of transmuting emotion into ideas, by making it articulate.

In one sense I think that my verses, mental and thin as their texture may be, represent a true inspiration, a true docility. A Muse—not exactly an English Muse—actually visited me in my isolation; the same, or a ghost of the same, that visited Boethius or Alfred de Musset or Leopardi. It was literally impossible for me then not to re-echo her eloquence. When that compulsion ceased, I ceased to write verses. My emotion—for there was genuine emotion—faded into a sense that my lesson was learned and my troth plighted; there was no longer any occasion for this sort of breathlessness and unction. I think the discerning reader will probably prefer the later prose versions of my philosophy; I prefer them myself, as being more broadly based, saner, more humorous. Yet if he is curious in the matter he may find the same thing here nearer to its fountain-head, in its accidental early setting, and with its most authentic personal note.

For as to the subject of these poems, it is simply my philosophy in the making. I should not give the title of philosopher to every logician or psychologist who, in his official and studious moments, may weigh argument against argument or may devise expedients for solving theoretical puzzles. I see no reason why a philosopher should be puzzled. What he sees he sees; of the rest he is ignorant; and his sense of this vast ignorance (which is his natural and inevitable condition) is a chief part of his knowledge and of his emotion. Philosophy is not an optional theme that may occupy him on occasion. It is his only possible life, his daily response to everything. He lives by thinking, and his one perpetual emotion is that this world, with himself in it, should be the strange world which it is. Everything he thinks or utters will accordingly be an integral part of his philosophy, whether it be called poetry or science or criticism. The verses of a philosopher will be essentially epigrams, like those which the Greek sages composed; they will moralise the spectacle, whether it be some personal passion or some larger aspect of nature.

My own moral philosophy, especially as expressed in this more sentimental form, may not seem very robust or joyous. Its fortitude and happiness are those of but one type of soul. The owl hooting from his wintry bough cannot be chanticleer crowing in the barnyard, yet he is sacred to Minerva; and the universal poet, who can sing the humours of winter no less lustily than those of spring, may even speak of his "merry note," worthy to mingle with the other pleasant accidents of the somberer season,

> When icicles hang by the wall,
> . . . .
> And coughing drowns the parson's saw.

But whether the note seem merry or sad, musical or uncouth, it is itself a note of nature; and it may at least be commended, seeing it conveys a philosophy, for not conveying it by argument, but frankly making confession of an actual spiritual experience, addressed only to those whose ear it may strike sympathetically and who, crossing the same dark wood on their own errands, may pause for a moment to listen gladly.

Hu Shih's Musketeer

BY JOHN BAINBRIDGE

ONE DAY early last spring [1941], Harry Hopkins called up Daniel Arnstein, the New York trucking man and president of the Terminal taxicab company, and asked him if he'd mind taking a little trip to China. The Chinese, Hopkins said, were in a traffic jam. The Burma Road was all clogged up and only a trickle of war supplies was going over it to the front. The United States was preparing to ship about a billion dollars' worth of lend-lease material to China, but before it was sent the administration wanted somebody who knew the trucking business to go over there, find out what was the matter, and get things moving. "Deal me in, Harry," said Arnstein, who had met Hopkins a few years before and discovered they shared an interest in poker, whiskey, and horses. Three months later, Arnstein, whose only contact with the Far East up to then consisted of a few evenings spent at Ruby Foo's, was on his way across the Pacific as a dollar-a-year man. In Chicago, where he started his professional career driving a taxi, in San Francisco, in Honolulu, and in Manila, he assured newspaper reporters and anybody else who would listen that the Burma Road could be made to work like U.S. No. 1. "It's as simple as A B C," he told a reporter in San Francisco three weeks before he landed in China. The farther west he got, the more explicit he grew. "The idea is to go over and install American methods of moving freight," he announced in Honolulu. "Those American methods are the best in the world. They work here and they'll work in Burma."

Arnstein's spirit was willing but his geography was weak. Although the Burma Road begins about a hundred miles inside the Burmese border, most of it lies in China. To reach the road, supplies headed for China are landed at Rangoon, the Indian Ocean port on the southern coast of Burma. From Rangoon they are shipped north by railroad to the Burmese town of Lashio. There the railway ends and the Burma Road begins. Stretching northeast from Lashio over some of the most formidable mountain country in the world, the road winds up at Kunming, a distance of seven hundred and twenty-six miles. At Kunming it joins another highway, which leads to Chungking, capital of Free China and final destination of supplies. With the exception of food and the domestically manufactured rifles and bullets, every ounce of war material that China needs must find its tortuous way over the Burma Road. It is an incredible journey. At one point the highway dives from a height of seventy-two hundred feet to twenty-five hundred feet and climbs again to seventy-five hundred feet within the space of forty miles, less than the distance from New York to Norwalk. In spots the road is as wide as Fifth Avenue, but for over half the way its width is only nine feet. Nowhere over its twisting course can a driver see more than an eighth of a mile straight ahead. The top speed for safe driving (or what passes for safety on the Burma Road) is fifteen miles an hour. The road is unpaved and is without a single fence or guardrail. During the five months of the rainy season, from May through September, the roadbed dissolves into a mass of mud. The rest of the time it is an endless cloud of dust and thick with mosquitoes; there are also landslides and air raids, and cholera, typhoid, and malaria flourish along the route. In the early stages of its construction four out of five workers on the road died of malaria.

Like the Great Wall of China, the Chinese portion of the Burma Road was built by hand. With a government appropriation of less than $2,000,000, construction began, after the outbreak of war in eastern China, in August, 1937, at which time the British also went to work on the Burmese side. Chinese men, women, and children were recruited from villages along the route of the new road. Supplying their own food, shelter, and tools, they set to work, for three or four cents a day, chipping at the mountainsides with adzes. A few compressed-air drills for drilling holes in which to plant dynamite charges were their only modern equipment. Stone rollers were used to smooth the road. They were chiselled out of the rock by hand and drawn along by bullocks. To make fills, earth was dug out of the cliffsides and carried in baskets wherever it was needed. In December of 1938 the Burma Road was opened to traffic. During the sixteen months which had elapsed a quarter of a million Chinese had hacked out a road over seven hundred miles long and built some two thousand culverts and almost three hundred bridges, including two important suspension bridges where the highway crosses the Mekong and Salween Rivers. Japanese aviators have been trying for months to bomb out these two bridges. They have scored several hits, none of them critical. But even if one of the bridges were destroyed, traffic would not be halted for long; the Chinese have devised temporary expedients of one sort and another to keep trucks moving across the rivers. The Chinese are philosophical about bombs and air raids. "It cost Japanese a thousand dollars for bomb to make hole," one interpreter explained brightly to Arnstein, "and it cost Chinese eight cents to fill it up."

For several months after the completion of the Burma Road it was not an important route for goods entering China. Throughout 1939 and the first part of 1940, the bulk of China's supplies still entered at Shanghai, Hangchow, Canton, and other coastal ports, which were later occupied by the Japanese. In addition, close to forty thousand tons a month were being shipped by railway and road through French Indo-China. When France fell, the Japanese inveigled Indo-China into refusing to allow goods headed for China to cross her territory. The Burma Road was now the only route of consequence from the outside world into Free China. Then Britain, also acceding to Japanese pressure, closed the Burma border to all traffic and for three gloomy months China was completely blockaded. In October, 1940, the border was reopened and trucks began moving over the road again. The results were disappointing. Although more than a hundred thousand tons of vital materials were piled up in Burma awaiting delivery, an average of only about four thousand tons a month was reaching Kunming. This was scarcely enough for an army of three million men. During 1940, two commissions, one British and one American, were dispatched to China to unclog the lifeline. Both got bogged down in Chinese politics and nothing happened. In February of last year [1941], Lauchlin Currie, lend-lease administrator for China, returned from Chungking with this and other disheartening information. He made his report to the White House. Late the following month, Harry Hopkins got in touch with Arnstein, who was on a fishing trip off Key Largo, in Florida. He left for Washington the next day to talk with Hopkins, Currie, and T. V. Soong, the Chinese Foreign Minister. The more Arnstein heard about the job to be done the more certain he became that he was the only man in the country who could handle it. "I began to get the American angle in all that Far Eastern stuff," he says, "so I decided to go over and do the goddam job myself."

To help him on the mission, Arnstein picked a couple of his friends, Harold C. Davis, vice-president of Consolidated Motor Lines, the largest trucking company in New England, and Marco Hellman, a transportation expert associated with Lehman Brothers.

Davis, a burly, hardheaded, good-natured ex-truck driver who, like Arnstein, came up the hard way, took along a movie camera and two other cameras and conscientiously kept a day-by-day diary of the trip. Hellman, who is small, quiet, and a Harvard man, had the title of financial adviser and doubled as diplomatic expert. Whenever Arnstein would profanely bawl out a Chinese official, Hellman would smilingly explain that all American businessmen talked like that. Arnstein's function is explained by an entry Davis made in his diary shortly before the mission's departure. "Dan seems to have the whole expedition departmentalized," he noted. "Whenever any problem arises, he says, 'Harold, that's your department' or 'Mickey [Hellman's nickname], that's your department.' When we asked what *he* was going to do, Dan said, 'Hell, I can't be tied down to a department. I'm going to do all the thinking on this trip.' " Before Arnstein and his colleagues left, they had inoculations for smallpox, cholera, and typhoid. Arnstein, who likes to get things done fast, took his cholera and typhoid shots together. Afterward he felt a trifle chilly, so he downed a few double Scotches. The combination left him physically dishevelled and he set out for China with a curious typhoid-cholera-whiskey hangover.

At eight o'clock on the morning of July 12th, the American mission arrived in Chungking, and at five o'clock that afternoon they were received by Generalissimo and Mme. Chiang Kai-shek. Arnstein was surprised by the simplicity of the Generalissimo's living quarters, a small frame structure with fewer rooms than his own house on Beekman Place. Through an interpreter, the Generalissimo made a nice little speech thanking the Americans for the personal and financial sacrifices they were making in coming to help China. Arnstein, a man of many words, made a long speech in reply. In the midst of his declamation he put his foot on a low table, apparently under the impression that it was a running board, and knocked a vase of flowers into Hellman's lap, leaving him very moist. "Dan paid no attention," Davis wrote in his diary. "He just speeded up the conversation." At a fast clip, Arnstein informed Chiang Kai-shek that he had served in the first World War and that he figured he ought to be doing something for his country again, even though he was, at fifty, too old to carry a gun. When all this had been relayed to the Generalissimo, he smiled and replied, "The service you will render here will be much greater than any single soldier with a gun." He added that he was going to send a message to his troops telling them how Mr. Arnstein had left his business to come and work for China at a salary of a dollar a year.

After paying his compliments to Generalissimo and Mme. Chiang, Arnstein was eager to get started on his inspection trip over the Burma Road, but the Chinese seemed to be in no great hurry. For ten days he and his party lingered in Chungking, where they were unceasingly entertained by Chinese officials. One of the biggest functions was a dinner party for eighteen at the home of General Ho Ying-Chin, the Minister of War. The affair, as Davis observed in his diary, was a brilliant social triumph for Arnstein, who sat at the General's right. "After our glasses had been filled with rice wine," the entry reads, "Danny started right off the bat calling for a toast to General Ho's health. This seemed to startle our hosts a bit, as they generally ease into it, but it broke the ice, which up to then had made the party rather stiff. We had some more rice wine, and General Ho called for a toast to Danny's health. After dinner we killed a bottle of Russian brandy and polished off with some Five-Star Hennessy." The General's enthusiasm died sometime before dawn, but Arnstein was still in high gear.

Finally setting out, Arnstein and his colleagues flew to Kunming, where a convoy of four new Dodge sedans and a truck to carry baggage was waiting for them. Besides the Americans, the expedition included five Chinese chauffeurs, two interpreters, T. C. Chen, a government official who had something to do with supervising traffic on the road, a pair of soldiers, and a cook. The cook, as it turned out, just went along for the ride, since the supply of G. Washington coffee, baked beans, and other canned goods which Arnstein had brought all the way from San Francisco was inadvertently left behind in Chungking. They stayed overnight in whatever accommodations they could find and picked up their meals at the homes of minor provincial officials along the route. Most of the time they slept, when not kept awake by rats, on straw mats. One night they put up at a temple. "It was the best place in town," Arnstein says, "but it was full of those goddam idols." He and his colleagues made the trip from Kunming to Lashio in five days, driving until late at night and stopping during the day to inspect trucks, look over the meagre service facilities, talk to truck drivers they encountered on the way, and make exhaustive notes on their observations.

To truckers who had managed some of the biggest motor freight lines in the United States, the situation on the Burma Road was fantastic. Sixteen separate governmental agencies had a hand in running it. None of them kept any records of the amount or kind of cargo moved or how long it took trucks to make their runs. Each agency was running an independent business with its own fleet of trucks and repair stations. One employed thirty mechanics to take care of fifty trucks while another had fifteen men to service a fleet of a hundred and fifty. In the village of Hsiakwan, Arnstein found a dozen trucks belonging to one government agency laid up for lack of spare parts. Across the road in a garage owned by another agency were all the spare parts needed. Apparently nobody had figured out how to get them to the other side of the road.

Arnstein also discovered that more than half the traffic on the Burma Road was made up of private trucks hauling commercial cargo instead of war materials. Between Lashio and Kunming, these trucks had to check in and out of eleven customs houses and provincial toll stations. When private trucks were held up at these stations, government trucks were also often delayed, sometimes for days, since the road at many points is too narrow to permit passing. As a result, government trucks were taking from ten to thirty days to make the 726-mile run. Arnstein learned of one instance in which twenty government trucks carrying paper currency for the Central Bank of China were held up en route for a total of eleven days. Some of the toll stations were collecting legitimate taxes. In one case, however, Arnstein found an enterprising provincial official who had set up a little toll booth on his own and was halting trucks to collect what he vaguely referred to as school taxes. At Wanting, a town on the Burmese border, drivers had to struggle past eight desks before getting on their way. Arnstein's own convoy was held up at Wanting for six hours because two hundred and fifty trucks, lined up three abreast, blocked the road. To add to the delays, officials at the toll stations were operating on a business-as-usual basis; they opened at eight and closed at six, regardless of the number of trucks waiting to clear. At one station, Arnstein noticed an official sitting in his office in the middle of the day reading a magazine while trucks outside were lined up for a quarter of a mile. "The son of a bitch was sitting there with a smile on his puss reading *True Confessions,*" Arnstein says, still furious.

Of the scores of trucks which Arnstein inspected on his trip over the Burma Road, not one showed any sign of having been greased. The Chinese drivers, it turned out, had never heard about greasing, and consequently their trucks stood up for only about a dozen round trips. Out of 2,887 government trucks, 1,480 were in working order; the rest were laid up, mainly because of lack of lubrication. Whenever machines broke down, the Chinese abandoned them at the roadside. In a field near Kunming, Arnstein counted a hundred and sixty trucks which had been left to rust, and at Lecfong a hundred and eighty more, many of them with good tires. "To think," said Dan, who kept lecturing his Chinese companions en route, "that the U. S. A. sent over fifty thousand tires, and then I come along and find a situation like this. What's the idea?" On the journey, Arnstein carried on an endless monologue about lubrication. Stopping a truck on the road and finding the shackles, springs, and steering knuckles dry and caked with mud, Arnstein would haul the driver out of his cab and give him a lacing in English. Not understanding what all the racket was for, the driver would scramble around under the truck with Arnstein, nodding and smiling politely, and then get back in his truck and wave a cheery good-bye. Arnstein felt frustrated.

Changing a tire on the Burma Road, Arnstein found, was a major operation taking about half a day. Having no jacks or tire irons and no tools except a pair of pliers, a screwdriver, and a hammer, a driver, when he got a flat, had to round up four or five coolies and a barrel. Using a stout pole as a lever, all hands hoisted the axle and rolled the barrel underneath. If no barrel was handy, the coolies hauled over a boulder. Since even the simplest tools were scarce, Arnstein was surprised to discover an elaborate and expensive mechanism known as a power tester in a ramshackle repair shed deep in the interior. Nobody could explain how a power tester, which is a sort of stethoscope to test motors and is usually found only in the best-equipped garages in this country, had wound up on the Burma Road. The Chinese regarded it with wonderment and admiration. "The more we go into the problems here," Davis observed midway in the trip, "the nuttier they seem. We have to take time out occasionally and play a couple of games of cards to relax our brains."

Their brains grew tense when they discovered that several of the trucking agencies had a rule requiring drivers to wash their own trucks several times a month. They saw many drivers, with their trucks loaded for the road, working on them with a bucket of water as late as ten in the morning. In the repair shops they found mechanics spending all their time trying to fix up the government's oldest trucks while new ones were being allowed to run as long as they would without attention. Government trucks on the road were moving in convoys of between fifteen and twenty vehicles, a practice which provided an unduly attractive target for Japanese bombers and also limited the progress of the entire procession to the speed of the slowest truck. If one of the trucks broke down, the rest of the convoy would hang around until the repairs had been made, even if it took six or eight hours. Inspecting and adjusting carburetors to conserve gasoline was as unfamiliar a practice as greasing; Arnstein estimated that the Chinese were wasting from twenty-five to forty per cent of their gas. Loading was haphazard. The Chinese stacked the heaviest freight in the front of the trucks, and front springs were snapping constantly. In addition, one-and-a-half-ton trucks were being loaded as heavily as a four-ton truck should be. This was not entirely the fault of the Chinese. Arnstein found that some of the American companies selling trucks to China had been painting "4 ton" on every one-and-a-half-ton vehicle before it left the assembly plants in Rangoon. Since the Chinese were paying for large trucks, they figured they were getting them and loaded them up accordingly. Each truck had to carry, in addition to its regular cargo, enough gas —five large drums—to make the round trip. Often something went wrong, and trucks got stranded for lack of fuel. In Chungking, Arnstein saw seventy trucks in good condition which had been laid up for three weeks because they had no gas for the return trip. To complicate the overloading problem, government drivers were in the habit of illegally carrying commercial freight, which they called "pidgin cargo," and passengers, known as "yellow fish." Arnstein stopped one small truck to inspect its cargo and see how it was loaded. He lifted the tarpaulin at the back and "yellow fish" started tumbling out. Altogether, eleven passengers, along with a sizable legitimate cargo, were packed into the truck.

By American standards of professional ethics, Chinese drivers were no great shakes. They were being paid two hundred and fifty Chinese dollars a month (about $10 U.S.), but some were picking up from $1,000 to $1,500 (Chinese) a month in graft, which is more than a Chinese government minister's salary. Meeting a private truck in trouble, government drivers would stop and agreeably remove from their own trucks whatever parts were needed, sell them at a good price, and enjoy themselves for a few days with mah-jongg, wine, and the local girls. Although theoretically under strict military discipline, drivers were apt to mix business with pleasure on a grand scale. After a night of carousing they would get out on the road about noon with a rice-wine hangover. To save gas, which they could sell at forty Chinese dollars a gallon along the way, they had a dangerous habit of coasting down the twisting, spiralling grades, the ignition off, one foot on the clutch, the other on the brake. Since the road opened, thirteen hundred trucks have disappeared over the side.

Arnstein and his assistants reached the end of the road on July 26th. Three days later they flew to Rangoon, where they put up at the Strand Hotel, and, after spending their first evening at the Silver Grill, the only night club in town, they began work on their report to Chiang Kai-shek. Dictating in relays to a pair of Burmese girl stenographers, they turned out a hundred and forty double-spaced typewritten pages of irate observations, sizzling complaints, and sweeping but simple recommendations. By August 5th, these had been condensed under Hellman's direction into a final draft of thirty-five pages and Arnstein had returned to Chung-king and delivered a copy to Chiang Kai-shek. The report was written in Arnstein's own kind of diplomatic language. The fanciest and most tactful word in it is "intolerable;" it is also the most frequent. "The main reason that practically no tonnage is moving the full length of the Burma Road," the report begins, "is due to an entire lack of knowledge of the fundamentals of motor transportation by the men now in charge. The present governmental agencies that are trying to operate trucks on the road are overloaded with executives and office personnel. No one gets right down into the actual operating end of the business." The report goes on to prescribe a remedy for every ailment.

Eighteen hours after receiving the report and having it translated, Chiang Kai-shek acted on one of its strongest recommendations, ordering the customs houses and toll stations on the road to stay open twenty-four hours a day. He also gave orders that instead of eleven toll and customs houses scattered along the route, one central office to transact all this business be opened at a place where ample parking space was available. He directed that any delay of a government truck of more than half an hour be reported directly to him. Another recommendation was to disband the sixteen government agencies and to appoint an experienced trucking man, preferably an American, to have authority over all operations on the road. The Generalissimo agreed, and this post has been filled by Lieutenant Colonel James Wilson, a West Point graduate who has had seven years' experience in the trucking business. Following Arnstein's blueprint and reporting to Chiang Kai-shek, Wilson is now installing a truck-dispatching system modelled on American lines. Six terminals are being set up along the road at intervals of a day's run. Besides mechanics and equipment for greasing and repairing trucks, each terminal will include comfortable overnight accommodations for drivers. When the terminals are completed, drivers will be required to check out of one in the morning and into the next that night. The convoy system has been abandoned, so each driver will be on his own. Before taking to the road, trucks will be rigidly inspected, to make sure they will not break down in transit. To man the terminals, six managers, a maintenance supervisor, and eighteen dispatchers and mechanics, all Americans hand-picked by Arnstein and Davis, arrived in China about six weeks ago. Within the last few days, Arnstein has received word that a second group, consisting of forty-six American managers and mechanics, who were stranded at Manila when war was declared, are now on their way to Rangoon and will presently be at work in China. Acting as teachers, the technicians from the United States will train the Chinese in American methods of greasing, repairing, and loading trucks.

Taking another of Arnstein's recommendations, Chiang Kai-shek ordered that all private trucks arriving in Rangoon from America be required to carry government freight and gasoline on three out of every four trips over the road. This proposal alone has been responsible for getting at least a thousand additional tons of freight to Chungking every month. Construction of a gasoline pipeline into the interior is under way, and filling stations are being set up along the road from Lashio about halfway to Kunming. Forty-five hundred new heavy-duty American trucks are now rolling over the road, and more are on the way. A start has been made on a project to pave certain sections of the highway with American asphalt, ten thousand tons of which have already arrived. Schools have been opened to teach Chinese drivers the fundamentals of handling their machines; the instructors are Americans employed by the truck manufacturers. Government trucks are now permitted to carry two paying passengers apiece; half the money collected goes to the driver, the other half to the government. To enforce this rule and to keep drivers from hauling contraband freight, coasting down grades, and selling parts of their trucks, prowl cars have been ordered to carry on a constant patrol of the highway. The road police, Arnstein says, will have their hands full, since they will have to protect the drivers not only from themselves but also from the outside interference of highway robbers, who flourish in considerable force along the Burma Road. You can't change a nation overnight, he points out, and in frontier country you have to expect a certain amount of Wild West stuff. What is more important, in his view, is that the road is being kept open and that so long as supplies keep moving over it in increasing quantity China can continue to defend herself and ultimately take the offensive. Arnstein is confident that this vital freight will keep moving. Practically all lend-lease material for China has been shipped by way of South Africa, so even if Singapore should fall, he thinks, supply ships could still reach Rangoon. At least a hundred American flyers, all of whom resigned from the United States Army or Navy to aid China, are now assigned to defending the Burma

Road from air attack. They have so far been notably successful. "There's been some squawking in the papers lately about conditions on the road," Arnstein says. "God knows it's no Boston Post Road, but at least the stuff is moving now." Specifically, the amount of freight moved over the Burma Road since Arnstein went to work has increased between four and five hundred per cent.

Chiang Kai-shek, pleased as he was with Arnstein's work on the Burma Road, was even more delighted with his diplomatic coup in getting Great Britain to remove the Burmese transit tax on lend-lease supplies. Before Arnstein arrived, China had been required to pay the government of Burma a tax of one per cent of the value of these supplies. The levy did not apply to British goods headed for China. Frequently the Chinese did not have the cash to pay the tax, and badly needed lend-lease material was piling up on the border. When Arnstein heard about this, he began calling on Burmese officials, starting with the Defense Minister and winding up with U Saw, the Premier of Burma, and Sir Reginald Dorman-Smith, the Governor General. He told them all caustically and a bit profanely he thought it was not only unjust but shortsighted to make it difficult for China to get supplies to fight an aggressor that might someday be attacking Burma itself. Sir Reginald and the other officials gave him tea and a polite brushoff. When Arnstein got back to Chungking, he called in newspaper correspondents and raged about the tax. "I'm no politician," Arnstein exclaimed, "I'm just a truckman. But I say this tax has got to go and, believe you me, it's going. Wait till this story busts wide open in the United States." Three weeks later the British Embassy in Chungking announced that the transit duty had been abolished, thus saving China several million dollars a year.

The night before they left Chungking to return to the United States, Arnstein, Davis, and Hellman were invited to dinner by Generalissimo and Mme. Chiang Kai-shek. Chiang Kai-shek made a speech effusively praising the report and proposing that the three men take control not only of the Burma Road but of all the roads in China. They could name their own salary, he said. When they turned down the proposition, the Generalissimo suggested that at least one of them remain. Finally, he proposed that Arnstein and his colleagues form a commercial company, backed by Chinese government funds, to take over the Burma Road and operate it as a private concession. Arnstein declined in a speech that nevertheless pleased the Generalissimo. "I don't see why we should make money out of the war when the Chinese themselves can do the job," he said. "This system will work. If it doesn't, I'll be back in three months to fix it. If it does, I'll be back in six months to get a pat on the back." Chiang Kai-shek seemed cheered, and replied in English, "Good, good, good." As they were leaving, he presented each of the Americans with an autographed picture of himself. Three weeks later they were back in New York. Arnstein was met at the airport by his wife and daughter and escorted home by a fleet of fifteen Terminal cabs, the windows of which were plastered with stickers reading, "Welcome Home, Dan."

Since his return, Arnstein has found it difficult to settle down to routine business. He worries a lot about the Burma Road and flies down to Washington frequently to talk with Harry Hopkins and Lauchlin Currie, the lend-lease administrator, and get reports on how things are going over there. "Danny's heart," one of his friends said recently, "belongs to China." A few weeks ago about sixty of Arnstein's friends gave him a belated home-coming party. Among the guests were Dr. Hu Shih, the Chinese Ambassador, and Dr. C. L. Shia, the president of the Chinese News Service. After Davis had shown the pictures he took in China and Arnstein had made a long talk, the Chinese guests spoke about the guest of honor. "I prophesy," said Dr. Shia, winding up his address, "that Mr. Arnstein's name will be recorded not alone in the history of China but as well in the history of the world." After comparing Arnstein with Porthos, the strong man of the Three Musketeers, Dr. Hu Shih, too, put him down as a likely candidate for the history books. He was more specific. "As for the others," said Dr. Hu, "I cannot say. But when I write my history of China, Mr. Arnstein's name will be there." Since Dr. Hu Shih is considered by some people to be the greatest Chinese scholar since Confucius, the tribute was impressive. When the party was over, Arnstein walked down the street with a few friends to the Copacabana. He danced a couple of sambas, and then, in a warm glow of Scotch-and-water, he fell to musing on his position as a historical character. "Imagine," he said, "a goddam hoodlum like me going down in history."

Thoreau

BY RALPH WALDO EMERSON

HENRY DAVID THOREAU was the last male descendant of a French ancestor who came to this country from the Isle of Guernsey. His character exhibited occasional traits drawn from this blood in singular combination with a very strong Saxon genius.

He was born in Concord, Massachusetts, on the 12th of July, 1817. He was graduated at Harvard College in 1837, but without any literary distinction. An iconoclast in literature, he seldom thanked colleges for their service to him, holding them in small esteem, whilst yet his debt to them was important. After leaving the University, he joined his brother in teaching a private school, which he soon renounced. His father was a manufacturer of lead-pencils, and Henry applied himself for a time to this craft, believing he could make a better pencil than was then in use. After completing his experiments, he exhibited his work to chemists and artists in Boston, and having obtained their certificates to its excellence and to its equality with the best London manufacture, he returned home contented. His friends congratulated him that he had now opened his way to fortune. But he replied, that he should never make another pencil. "Why should I? I would not do again what I have done once." He resumed his endless walks and miscellaneous studies, making every day some new acquaintance with Nature, though as yet never speaking of zoölogy or botany, since, though very studious of natural facts, he was incurious of technical and textual science.

At this time, a strong, healthy youth, fresh from college, whilst all his companions were choosing their profession, or eager to begin some lucrative employment, it was inevitable that his thoughts should be exercised on the same question, and it required rare decision to refuse all the accustomed paths, and keep his solitary freedom at the cost of disappointing the natural expectations of his family and friends: all the more difficult that he had a perfect probity, was exact in securing his own independence, and in holding every man to the like duty. But Thoreau never faltered. He was a born protestant. He declined to give up his large ambition of knowledge and action for any narrow craft or profession, aiming at a much more comprehensive calling, the art of living well. If he slighted and defied the opinions of others, it was only that he was more intent to reconcile his practice with his own belief. Never idle or self-indulgent, he preferred, when he wanted money, earning it by some piece of manual labor agreeable to him, as building a boat or a fence, planting, drafting, surveying, or other short work, to any long engagements. With his hardy habits and few wants, his skill in wood-craft, and his powerful arithmetic, he was very competent to live in any part of the world. It would cost him less time to supply his wants than another. He was therefore secure of his leisure.

A natural skill for mensuration, growing out of his mathematical knowledge, and his habit of ascertaining the measures and distances of objects which interested him, the size of trees, the depth and extent of ponds and rivers, the height of mountains, and the air-line distance of his favorite summits,—this, and his intimate knowledge of the territory about Concord, made him drift into the profession of land-surveyor. It had the advantage for him that it led him continually into new and secluded grounds, and helped his studies of Nature. His accuracy and skill in this work were readily appreciated, and he found all the employment he wanted.

He could easily solve the problems of the surveyor, but he was daily beset with graver questions, which he manfully confronted. He interrogated every custom, and wished to settle all his practice on an ideal foundation. He was a protestant *à outrance,* and few lives contain so many renunciations. He was bred to no profession; he never married; he lived alone; he never went to church; he never voted; he refused to pay a tax to the State; he ate no flesh, he drank no wine, he never knew the use of tobacco; and, though a naturalist, he used neither trap nor gun. He chose, wisely, no doubt, for himself, to be the bachelor of thought and Nature. He had no talent for wealth, and knew how to be poor without the least hint of squalor or inelegance. Perhaps he fell into his way of living without forecasting it much, but approved it with later wisdom. "I am often reminded," he wrote in his journal, "that, if I had bestowed on me the wealth of Crœsus, my aims must be still the same, and my means essentially the same." He had no temptations to fight against,—no appetites, no passions, no taste for elegant trifles. A fine house, dress, the manners and talk of highly cultivated people were all thrown away on him. He much preferred a good Indian, and considered these refinements as impediments to conversation, wishing to meet his companion on the simplest terms. He declined invitations to dinner-parties, because there each was in every one's way, and he could not meet the individuals to any purpose. "They make their pride," he said, "in making their dinner cost much; I make my pride in making my dinner cost little." When asked at table what dish he preferred, he answered, "The nearest." He did not like the taste of wine, and never had a vice in his life. He said,—"I have a faint recollection of pleasure derived from smoking dried lily-stems, before I was a man. I had commonly a supply of these. I have never smoked anything more noxious."

He chose to be rich by making his wants few, and supplying them himself. In his travels, he used the railroad only to get over so much country as was unimportant to the present purpose, walking hundreds of miles, avoiding taverns, buying a lodging in farmers' and fishermen's houses, as cheaper, and more agreeable to him, and because there he could better find the men and the information he wanted.

There was somewhat military in his nature not to be subdued, always manly and able, but rarely tender, as if he did not feel himself except in opposition. He wanted a fallacy to expose, a blunder to pillory, I may say required a little sense of victory, a roll of the drum, to call his powers into full exercise. It cost him nothing to say No; indeed, he found it much easier than to say Yes. It seemed as if his first instinct on hearing a proposition was to controvert it, so impatient was he of the limitations of our daily thought. This habit, of course, is a little chilling to the social affections; and though the companion would in the end acquit him of any malice or untruth, yet it mars conversation. Hence, no equal companion stood in affectionate relations with one so pure and guileless. "I love Henry," said one of his friends, "but I cannot like him; and as for taking his arm, I should as soon think of taking the arm of an elm-tree."

Yet, hermit and stoic as he was, he was really fond of sympathy, and threw himself heartily and childlike into the company of young people whom he loved, and whom he delighted to entertain, as he only could, with the varied and endless anecdotes of his experiences by field and river. And he was always ready to lead a huckleberry party or a search for chestnuts or grapes. Talking, one day, of a public discourse, Henry remarked, that whatever succeeded with the audience was bad. I said, "Who would not like to write something which all can read, like 'Robinson Crusoe'? and who does not see with regret that his page is not solid with a right materialistic treatment, which delights everybody?" Henry objected, of course, and vaunted the better lectures which reached only a few persons. But, at supper, a young girl, understanding that he was to lecture at the Lyceum, sharply asked him, "whether his lecture would be a nice, interesting story, such as she wished to hear, or whether it was one of those old philosophical things that she did not care about." Henry turned to her, and bethought himself, and, I saw, was trying to believe that he had matter that might fit her and her brother, who were to sit up and go to the lecture, if it was a good one for them.

He was a speaker and actor of the truth,—born such,—and was ever running into dramatic situations from this cause. In any circumstance, it interested all bystanders to know what part Henry would take, and what he would say; and he did not disappoint expectation, but used an original judgment on each emergency. In 1845 he built himself a small framed house on the shores of Walden Pond, and lived there two years alone, a life of labor and study. This action was quite native and fit for him. No one who knew him would tax him with affectation. He was more unlike his neighbors in his thought than in his action. As soon as he had exhausted the advantages of that solitude, he abandoned it. In 1847, not approving some uses to which the public expenditure was applied, he refused to pay his town tax, and was put in jail. A friend paid the tax for him, and he was released. The like annoyance was threatened the next year. But, as his friends paid the tax, notwithstanding his protest, I believe he ceased to resist. No opposition or ridicule had any weight with him. He coldly and fully stated his opinion without affecting to believe that it was the opinion of the company. It was of no consequence, if every one present held the opposite opinion. On one occasion he went to the University Library to procure some books. The librarian refused to lend them. Mr. Thoreau repaired to the President, who stated to him the rules and usages, which permitted the loan of books to resident graduates, to clergymen who were alumni, and to some others resident within a circle of ten miles' radius from the College. Mr. Thoreau explained to the President that the railroad had destroyed the old scale of distances,—that the library was useless, yes, and President and College, useless, on the terms of his rules,—that the one benefit he owed to the College was its library,—that, at this moment, not only his want of books was imperative, but he wanted a large number of books, and assured him that he, Thoreau, and not the librarian, was the proper custodian of these. In short, the President found the petitioner so formidable, and the rules getting to look so ridiculous, that he ended by giving him a privilege which in his hands proved unlimited thereafter.

No truer American existed than Thoreau. His preference of his country and condition was genuine, and his aversation from English and European manners and tastes almost reached contempt. He listened impatiently to news or *bon mots* gleaned from London circles; and though he tried to be civil, these anecdotes fatigued him. The men were all imitating each other, and on a small mould. Why can they not live as far apart as possible, and each be a man by himself? What he sought was the most energetic nature; and he wished to go to Oregon, not to London. "In every part of Great Britain," he wrote in his diary, "are discovered traces of the Romans, their funereal urns, their camps, their roads, their dwellings. But New England, at least, is not based on any Roman ruins. We have not to lay the foundations of our houses on the ashes of a former civilization."

But, idealist as he was, standing for abolition of slavery, abolition of tariffs, almost for abolition of government, it is needless to say he found himself not only unrepresented in actual politics, but almost equally opposed to every class of reformers. Yet he paid the tribute of his uniform respect to the Anti-Slavery Party. One man, whose personal acquaintance he had formed, he honored with exceptional regard. Before the first friendly word had been spoken for Captain John Brown, after the arrest, he sent notices to most houses in Concord, that he would speak in a public hall on the condition and character of John Brown, on Sunday evening, and invited all people to come. The Republican Committee, the Abolitionist Committee, sent him word that it was premature and not advisable. He replied,—"I did not send to you for advice, but to announce that I am to speak." The hall was filled at an early hour by people of all parties, and his earnest eulogy of the hero was heard by all respectfully, by many with a sympathy that surprised themselves.

It was said of Plotinus that he was ashamed of his body, and 'tis very likely he had good reason for it,—that his body was a bad servant, and he had not skill in dealing with the material world, as happens often to men of abstract intellect. But Mr. Thoreau was equipped with a most adapted and serviceable body. He was of short stature, firmly built, of light complexion, with strong, serious blue eyes, and a grave aspect,—his face covered in the late years with a becoming beard. His senses were acute, his frame well-knit and hardy, his hands strong and skilful in the use of tools. And there was a wonderful fitness of body and mind. He could pace sixteen rods more accurately than another man could measure them with rod and chain. He could find his path in the woods at night, he said, better by his feet than his eyes. He could estimate the measure of a tree very well by his eyes; he could estimate the weight of a calf or a pig, like a dealer. From a box containing a bushel or more of loose pencils, he could take up with his hands fast enough just a dozen pencils at every grasp. He was a good swimmer, runner, skater, boatman, and would probably outwalk most countrymen in a day's journey. And the relation of body to mind was still finer than we have indicated. He said he wanted every stride his legs made. The length of his walk uniformly made the length of his writing. If shut up in the house, he did not write at all.

He had a strong common sense, like that which Rose Flammock, the weaver's daughter, in Scott's romance, commends in her father, as resembling a yardstick, which, whilst it measures dowlas and diaper, can equally well measure tapestry and cloth of gold. He had always a new resource. When I was planting forest-trees, and had procured half a peck of acorns, he said that only a small portion of them would be sound, and proceeded to examine them, and select the sound ones. But finding this took time, he said, "I think, if you put them all into water, the good ones will sink"; which experiment we tried with success. He could plan a garden, or a house, or a barn; would have been competent to lead a "Pacific Exploring Expedition"; could give judicious counsel in the gravest private or public affairs.

He lived for the day, not cumbered and mortified by his memory. If he brought you yesterday a new proposition, he would bring you to-day another not less revolutionary. A very industrious man, and setting, like all highly organized men, a high value on his time, he seemed the only man of leisure in town, always ready for any excursion that promised well, or for conversation prolonged into late hours. His trenchant sense was never stopped by his rules of daily prudence, but was always up to the new occasion. He liked and used the simplest food, yet, when some one urged a vegetable diet, Thoreau thought all diets a very small matter, saying that "the man who shoots the buffalo lives better than the man who boards at the Graham House." He said,—"You can sleep near the railroad, and never be disturbed: Nature knows very well what sounds are worth attending to, and has made up her mind not to hear the railroad-whistle. But things respect the devout mind, and a mental ecstasy was never interrupted." He noted, what repeatedly befell him, that, after receiving from a distance a rare plant, he would presently find the same in his own haunts. And those pieces of luck which happen only to good players happened to him. One day, walking with a stranger, who inquired where Indian arrow-heads could be found, he replied,

"Everywhere," and, stooping forward, picked one on the instant from the ground. At Mount Washington, in Tuckerman's Ravine, Thoreau had a bad fall, and sprained his foot. As he was in the act of getting up from his fall, he saw for the first time the leaves of the *Arnica mollis*.

His robust common sense, armed with stout hands, keen perceptions, and strong will, cannot yet account for the superiority which shone in his simple and hidden life. I must add the cardinal fact, that there was an excellent wisdom in him, proper to a rare class of men, which showed him the material world as a means and symbol. This discovery, which sometimes yields to poets a certain casual and interrupted light, serving for the ornament of their writing, was in him an unsleeping insight; and whatever faults or obstructions of temperament might cloud it, he was not disobedient to the heavenly vision. In his youth, he said, one day, "The other world is all my art: my pencils will draw no other; my jack-knife will cut nothing else; I do not use it as a means." This was the muse and genius that ruled his opinions, conversation, studies, work, and course of life. This made him a searching judge of men. At first glance he measured his companion, and, though insensible to some fine traits of culture, could very well report his weight and calibre. And this made the impression of genius which his conversation often gave.

He understood the matter in hand at a glance, and saw the limitations and poverty of those he talked with, so that nothing seemed concealed from such terrible eyes. I have repeatedly known young men of sensibility converted in a moment to the belief that this was the man they were in search of, the man of men, who could tell them all they should do. His own dealing with them was never affectionate, but superior, didactic,—scorning their petty ways,—very slowly conceding, or not conceding at all, the promise of his society at their houses, or even at his own. "Would he not walk with them?" "He did not know. There was nothing so important to him as his walk; he had no walks to throw away on company." Visits were offered him from respectful parties, but he declined them. Admiring friends offered to carry him at their own cost to the Yellow-Stone River,—to the West Indies,—to South America. But though nothing could be more grave or considered than his refusals, they remind one in quite new relations of that fop Brummel's reply to the gentleman who offered him his carriage in a shower, "But where will *you* ride, then?"—and what accusing silences, and what searching and irresistible speeches, battering down all defences, his companions can remember!

Mr. Thoreau dedicated his genius with such entire love to the fields, hills, and waters of his native town, that he made them known and interesting to all reading Americans, and to people over the sea. The river on whose banks he was born and died he knew from its springs to its confluence with the Merrimack. He had made summer and winter observations on it for many years, and at every hour of the day and the night. The result of the recent survey of the Water Commissioners appointed by the State of Massachusetts he had reached by his private experiments, several years earlier. Every fact which occurs in the bed, on the banks, or in the air over it; the fishes, and their spawning and nests, their manners, their food; the shad-flies which fill the air on a certain evening once a year, and which are snapped at by the fishes so ravenously that many of these die of repletion; the conical heaps of small stones on the river-shallows, one of which heaps will sometimes overfill a cart,—these heaps the huge nests of small fishes; the birds which frequent the stream, heron, duck, sheldrake, loon, osprey; the snake, musk-rat, otter, woodchuck, and fox, on the banks; the turtle, frog, hyla, and cricket, which make the banks vocal,—were all known to him, and, as it were, townsmen and fellow-creatures; so that he felt an absurdity or violence in any narrative of one of these by itself apart, and still more of its dimensions on an inch-rule, or in the exhibition of its skeleton, or the specimen of a squirrel or a bird in brandy. He liked to speak of the manners of the river, as itself a lawful creature, yet with exactness, and always to an observed fact. As he knew the river, so the ponds in this region.

One of the weapons he used, more important than microscope or alcohol-receiver to other investigators, was a whim which grew on him by indulgence, yet appeared in gravest statement, namely, of extolling his own town and neighborhood as the most favored centre for natural observation. He remarked that the Flora of Massachusetts embraced almost all the important plants of America,—most of the oaks, most of the willows, the best pines, the ash, the maple, the beech, the nuts. He returned Kane's "Arctic Voyage" to a friend of whom he had borrowed it, with the remark, that "most of the phenomena noted might be observed in Concord." He seemed a little envious of the Pole, for the coincident sunrise and sunset, of five minutes' day after six months: a splendid fact, which Annursnuc had never afforded him. He found red snow in one of his walks, and told me that he expected to find yet the *Victoria regia* in Concord. He was the attorney of the indigenous plants, and owned to a preference of the weeds to the imported plants, as of the Indian to the civilized man,—and noticed, with pleasure, that the willow bean-poles of his neighbor had grown more than his beans. "See these weeds," he said, "which have been hoed at by a million farmers all spring and summer, and yet have prevailed, and just now come out triumphant over all lanes, pastures, fields, and gardens, such is their vigor. We have insulted them with low names, too,—as Pigweed, Wormwood, Chickweed, Shad-Blossom." He says, "They have brave names, too,—Ambrosia, Stellaria, Amelanchia, Amaranth, etc."

I think his fancy for referring everything to the meridian of Concord did not grow out of any ignorance or depreciation of other longitudes or latitudes, but was rather a playful expression of his conviction of the indifferency of all places, and that the best place for each is where he stands. He expressed it once in this wise:—"I think nothing is to be hoped from you, if this bit of mould under your feet is not sweeter to you to eat than any other in this world, or in any world."

The other weapon with which he conquered all obstacles in science was patience. He knew how to sit immovable, a part of the rock he rested on, until the bird, the reptile, the fish, which had retired from him, should come back, and resume its habits, nay, moved by curiosity, should come to him and watch him.

It was a pleasure and a privilege to walk with him. He knew the country like a fox or a bird, and passed through it as freely by paths of his own. He knew every track in the snow or on the ground, and what creature had taken this path before him. One must submit abjectly to such a guide, and the reward was great. Under his arm he carried an old music-book to press plants; in his pocket, his diary and pencil, a spy-glass for birds, microscope, jack-knife, and twine. He wore straw hat, stout shoes, strong gray trousers, to brave shrub-oaks and smilax, and to climb a tree for a hawk's or a squirrel's nest. He waded into the pool for the water-plants, and his strong legs were no insignificant part of his armor. On the day I speak of he looked for the Menyanthes, detected it across the wide pool, and, on examination of the florets, decided that it had been in flower five days. He drew out of his breast-pocket his diary, and read the names of all the plants that should bloom on this day, whereof he kept account as a banker when his notes fall due. The Cypripedium not due till tomorrow. He thought, that, if waked up from a trance, in this swamp, he could tell by the plants what time of the year it was within two days. The redstart was flying about, and presently the fine grosbeaks, whose brilliant scarlet makes the rash gazer wipe his eye, and whose fine clear note Thoreau compared to that of a tanager which has got rid of its hoarseness. Presently he heard a note which he called that of the night-warbler, a bird he had never identified, had been in search of twelve years, which always, when he saw it, was in the act of diving down into a tree or bush, and which it was vain to seek; the only bird that sings indifferently by night and by day. I told him he must beware of finding and booking it, lest life should have nothing more to show him. He said, "What you seek in vain for, half your life, one day you come full upon all the family at dinner. You seek it like a dream, and as soon as you find it you become its prey."

His interest in the flower or the bird lay very deep in his mind, was connected with Nature,—and the meaning of Nature was never attempted to be defined by him. He would not offer a memoir of his observations to the Natural History Society. "Why should I? To detach the description from its connections in my mind would make it no longer true or valuable to me: and they do not wish what belongs to it." His power of observation seemed to indicate additional senses. He saw as with microscope, heard as with ear-trumpet, and his memory was a photographic register of all he saw and heard. And yet none knew better than he that it is not the fact that imports, but the impression or effect of the fact on your mind. Every fact lay in glory in his mind, a type of the order and beauty of the whole.

His determination on Natural History was organic. He confessed that he sometimes felt like a hound or a panther, and, if born among Indians, would have been a fell hunter. But, restrained by his Massachusetts culture, he played out the game in this mild form of botany and ichthyology. His intimacy with animals suggested what Thomas Fuller records of Butler the apiologist, that "either he had told the bees things or the bees had told him." Snakes coiled round his leg; the fishes swam into his hand, and he took them out of the water; he pulled the woodchuck out of its hole by the tail, and took the foxes under his protection from the hunters. Our naturalist had perfect magnanimity; he had no secrets: he would carry you to the heron's haunt, or even to his most prized botanical swamp,—possibly knowing that you could never find it again, yet willing to take his risks.

No college ever offered him a diploma, or a professor's chair; no academy made him its corresponding secretary, its discoverer, or even its member. Perhaps these learned bodies feared the satire of his presence. Yet so much knowledge of Nature's secret and genius few others possessed, none in a more large and religious synthesis. For not a particle of respect had he to the opinions of any man or body of men, but homage solely to the truth itself; and as he discovered everywhere among doctors some leaning of courtesy, it discredited them. He grew to be revered and admired by his townsmen, who had at first known him only as an oddity. The farmers who employed him as a surveyor soon discovered his rare accuracy and skill, his knowledge of their lands, of trees, of birds, of Indian remains, and the like, which enabled him to tell every farmer more than he knew before of his own farm; so that he began to feel as if Mr. Thoreau had better rights in his land than he. They felt, too, the superiority of character which addressed all men with a native authority.

Indian relics abound in Concord,—arrow-heads, stone chisels, pestles, and fragments of pottery; and on the river-bank, large heaps of clam-shells and ashes mark spots which the savages frequented. These, and every circumstance touching the Indian, were important in his eyes. His visits to Maine were chiefly for love of the Indian. He had the satisfaction of seeing the manufacture of the bark-canoe, as well as of trying his hand in its management on the rapids. He was inquisitive about the making of the stone arrow-head, and in his last days charged a youth setting out for the Rocky Mountains to find an Indian who could tell him that: "It was well worth a visit to California to learn it." Occasionally, a small party of Penobscot Indians would visit Concord, and pitch their tents for a few weeks in summer on the river-bank. He failed not to make acquaintance with the best of them; though he well knew that asking questions of Indians is like catechizing beavers and rabbits. In his last visit to Maine he had great satisfaction from Joseph Polis, an intelligent Indian of Oldtown, who was his guide for some weeks.

He was equally interested in every natural fact. The depth of his perception found likeness of law throughout Nature, and I know not any genius who so swiftly inferred universal law from the single fact. He was no pedant of a department. His eye was open to beauty, and his ear to music. He found these, not in rare conditions, but wheresoever he went. He thought the best of music was in single strains; and he found poetic suggestion in the humming of the telegraph-wire.

His poetry might be bad or good; he no doubt wanted a lyric facility and technical skill; but he had the source of poetry in his spiritual perception. He was a good reader and critic, and his judgment on poetry was to the ground of it. He could not be deceived as to the presence or absence of the poetic element in any composition, and his thirst for this made him negligent and perhaps scornful of superficial graces. He would pass by many delicate rhythms, but he would have detected every live stanza or line in a volume, and knew very well where to find an equal poetic charm in prose. He was so enamored of the spiritual beauty that he held all actual written poems in very light esteem in the comparison. He admired Æschylus and Pindar; but, when some one was commending them, he said that "Æschylus and the Greeks, in describing Apollo and Orpheus, had given no song, or no good one. They ought not to have moved trees, but to have chanted to the gods such a hymn as would have sung all their old ideas out of their heads, and new ones in." His own verses are often rude and defective. The gold does not yet run pure, is drossy and crude. The thyme and marjoram are not yet honey. But if he want lyric fineness and technical merits, if he have not the poetic temperament, he never lacks the causal thought, showing that his genius was better than his talent. He knew the worth of the Imagination for the uplifting and consolation of human life, and liked to throw every thought into a symbol. The fact that you tell is of no value, but only the impression. For this reason his presence was poetic, always piqued the curiosity to know more deeply the secrets of his mind. He had many reserves, an unwillingness to exhibit to profane eyes what was still sacred in his own, and knew well how to throw a poetic veil over his experience. All readers of "Walden" will remember his mythical record of his disappointments:—

"I long ago lost a hound, a bay horse, and a turtle-dove, and am still on their trail. Many are the travellers I have spoken to concerning them, describing their tracks, and what calls they answer to. I have met one or two who had heard the hound, and the tramp of the horse, and even seen the dove disappear behind a cloud; and they seemed as anxious to recover them as if they had lost them themselves."

His riddles were worth the reading, and I confide, that, if at any time I do not understand the expression, it is yet just. Such was the wealth of his truth that it was not worth his while to use words in vain. His poem entitled "Sympathy" reveals the tenderness under that triple steel of stoicism, and the intellectual subtilty it could animate. His classic poem on "Smoke" suggests Simonides, but is better than any poem of Simonides. His biography is in his verses. His habitual thought makes all his poetry a hymn to the Cause of causes, the Spirit which vivifies and controls his own.

> "I hearing get, who had but ears,
> And sight, who had but eyes before;
> I moments live, who lived but years,
> And truth discern, who knew but learning's lore."

And still more in these religious lines:—

> "Now chiefly is my natal hour,
> And only now my prime of life;
> I will not doubt the love untold,
> Which not my worth or want hath bought,
> Which wooed me young, and wooes me old,
> And to this evening hath me brought."

Whilst he used in his writings a certain petulance of remark in reference to churches or churchmen, he was a person of a rare, tender, and absolute religion, a person incapable of any profanation, by act or by thought. Of course, the same isolation which belonged to his original thinking and living detached him from the social religious forms. This is neither to be censured nor regretted. Aristotle long ago explained it, when he said, "One who surpasses his fellow-citizens in virtue is no longer a part of the city. Their law is not for him, since he is a law to himself."

Thoreau was sincerity itself, and might fortify the convictions of prophets in the ethical laws by his holy living. It was an affirmative experience which refused to be set aside. A truth-speaker he, capable of the most deep and strict conversation; a physician to the wounds of any soul; a friend, knowing not only the secret of friendship, but almost worshipped by those few persons who resorted to him as their confessor and prophet, and knew the deep value of his mind and great heart. He thought that without religion or devotion of some kind nothing great was ever accomplished: and he thought that the bigoted sectarian had better bear this in mind.

His virtues, of course, sometimes ran into extremes. It was easy to trace to the inexorable demand on all for exact truth that austerity which made this willing hermit more solitary even than he wished. Himself of a perfect probity, he required not less of others. He had a disgust at crime, and no worldly success could cover it. He detected paltering as readily in dignified and prosperous persons as in beggars, and with equal scorn. Such dangerous frankness was in his dealing that his admirers called him "that terrible Thoreau," as if he spoke when silent, and was still present when he had departed. I think the severity of his ideal interfered to deprive him of a healthy sufficiency of human society.

The habit of a realist to find things the reverse of their appearance inclined him to put every statement in a paradox. A certain habit of antagonism defaced his earlier writings,—a trick of rhetoric not quite outgrown in his later, of substituting for the obvious word and thought its diametrical opposite. He praised wild mountains and winter forests for their domestic air, in snow and ice he would find sultriness, and commended the wilderness for resembling Rome and Paris. "It was so dry, that you might call it wet."

The tendency to magnify the moment, to read all the laws of Nature in the one object or one combination under your eye, is of course comic to those who do not share the philosopher's perception of identity. To him there was no such thing as size. The pond was a small ocean; the Atlantic, a large Walden Pond. He referred every minute fact to cosmical laws. Though he meant to be just, he seemed haunted by a certain chronic assumption that the science of the day pretended completeness, and he had just found out that the *savans* had neglected to discriminate a particular botanical variety, had failed to describe the seeds or count the sepals. "That is to say," we replied, "the blockheads were not born in Concord; but who said they were? It was their unspeakable misfortune to be born in London, or Paris, or Rome; but, poor fellows, they did what they could, considering that they never saw Bateman's Pond, or Nine-Acre Corner, or Becky-Stow's Swamp. Besides, what were you sent into the world for, but to add this observation?"

Had his genius been only contemplative, he had been fitted to his life, but with his energy and practical ability he seemed born for great enterprise and for command; and I so much regret the loss of his rare powers of action, that I cannot help counting it a fault in him that he had no ambition. Wanting this, instead of engineering for all America, he was the captain of a huckleberry party. Pounding beans is good to the end of pounding empires one of these days; but if at the end of years, it is still only beans!

But these foibles, real or apparent, were fast vanishing in the incessant growth of a spirit so robust and wise, and which effaced its defeats with new triumphs. His study of Nature was a perpetual ornament to him, and inspired his friends with curiosity to see the world through his eyes, and to hear his adventures. They possessed every kind of interest.

He had many elegances of his own, whilst he scoffed at conventional elegance. Thus, he could not bear to hear the sound of his own steps, the grit of gravel; and therefore never willingly walked in the road, but in the grass, on mountains and in woods. His senses were acute, and he remarked that by night every dwelling-house gives out bad air, like a slaughter-house. He liked the pure fragrance of melilot. He honored certain plants with special regard, and, over all, the pond-lily,—then, the gentian, and the *Mikania scandens,* and "life-everlasting," and a bass-tree which he visited every year when it bloomed, in the middle of July. He thought the scent a more oracular inquisition than the sight,—more oracular and trustworthy. The scent, of course, reveals what is concealed from the other senses. By it he detected earthiness. He delighted in echoes, and said they were almost the only kind of kindred voices that he heard. He loved Nature so well, was so happy in her solitude, that he became very jealous of cities, and the sad work which their refinements and artifices made with man and his dwelling. The axe was always destroying his forest. "Thank God," he said, "they cannot cut down the clouds!" "All kinds of figures are drawn on the blue ground with this fibrous white paint."

I subjoin a few sentences taken from his unpublished manuscripts, not only as records of his thought and feeling, but for their power of description and literary excellence.

"Some circumstantial evidence is very strong, as when you find a trout in the milk."

"The chub is a soft fish, and tastes like boiled brown paper salted."

"The youth gets together his materials to build a bridge to the moon, or, perchance, a palace or temple on the earth, and at length the middle-aged man concludes to build a wood-shed with them."

"The locust z-ing."

"Devil's-needles zigzagging along the Nut-Meadow brook."

"Sugar is not so sweet to the palate as sound to the healthy ear."

"I put on some hemlock-boughs, and the rich salt crackling of their leaves was like mustard to the ear, the crackling of uncountable regiments. Dead trees love the fire."

"The bluebird carries the sky on his back."

"The tanager flies through the green foliage as if it would ignite the leaves."

"If I wish for a horse-hair for my compass-sight, I must go to the stable; but the hair-bird, with her sharp eyes, goes to the road."

"Immortal water, alive even to the superficies."

"Fire is the most tolerable third party."

"Nature made ferns for pure leaves, to show what she could do in that line."

"No tree has so fair a bole and so handsome an instep as the beech."

"How did these beautiful rainbow-tints get into the shell of the fresh-water clam, buried in the mud at the bottom of our dark river?"

"Hard are the times when the infant's shoes are second-foot."

"We are strictly confined to our men to whom we give liberty."

"Nothing is so much to be feared as fear. Atheism may comparatively be popular with God himself."

"Of what significance the things you can forget? A little thought is sexton to all the world."

"How can we expect a harvest of thought who have not had a seed-time of character?"

"Only he can be trusted with gifts who can present a face of bronze to expectations."

"I ask to be melted. You can only ask of the metals that they be tender to the fire that melts them. To nought else can they be tender."

There is a flower known to botanists, one of the same genus with our summer plant called "Life-Everlasting," a *Gnaphalium* like that which grows on the most inaccessible cliffs of the Tyrolese mountains, where the chamois dare hardly venture, and which the hunter, tempted by its beauty, and by his love (for it is immensely valued by the Swiss maidens), climbs the cliffs to gather, and is sometimes found dead at the foot, with the flower in his hand. It is called by botanists the *Gnaphalium leontopodium,* but by the Swiss *Edelweisse,* which signifies *Noble Purity.* Thoreau seemed to me living in the hope to gather this plant, which belonged to him of right. The scale on which his studies proceeded was so large as to require longevity, and we were the less prepared for his sudden disappearance. The country knows not yet, or in the least part, how great a son it has lost. It seems an injury that he should leave in the midst his broken task, which none else can finish,—a kind of indignity to so noble a soul, that it should depart out of Nature before yet he has been really shown to his peers for what he is. But he, at least, is content. His soul was made for the noblest society; he had in a short life exhausted the capabilities of this world; wherever there is knowledge, wherever there is virtue, wherever there is beauty, he will find a home.

The Swamp Fox

BY WILLIAM GILMORE SIMMS

We follow where the Swamp Fox guides,
His friends and merry men are we;
And when the troop of Tarleton rides,
We burrow in the cypress-tree.
The turfy hummock is our bed,
Our home is in the red deer's den,
Our roof, the tree-top overhead,
For we are wild and hunted men.

We fly by day and shun its light,
But, prompt to strike the sudden blow,
We mount and start with early night,
And through the forest track our foe.
And soon he hears our chargers leap,
The flashing sabre blinds his eyes,
And ere he drives away his sleep,
And rushes from his camp, he dies.

Free bridle-bit, good gallant steed,
That will but ask a kind caress
To swim the Santee at our need,
When on his heels the foemen press,—
The true heart and the ready hand,
The spirit stubborn to be free,
The twisted bore, the smiting brand,—
And we are Marion's men, you see.

Now light the fire and cook the meal,
The last perhaps that we shall taste;
I hear the Swamp Fox round us steal.
And that's a sign we move in haste.

He whistles to the scouts, and hark!
You hear his order calm and low.
Come, wave your torch across the dark,
And let us see the boys that go.

We may not see their forms again,
God help 'em, should they find the strife!
For they are strong and fearless men,
And make no coward terms for life.
They'll fight as long as Marion bids,
And when he speaks the word to shy,
Then, not till then, they turn their steeds,
Through thickening shade and swamp to fly.

Now stir the fire and lie at ease,—
The scouts are gone, and on the brush
I see the Colonel bend his knee,
To take his slumbers too. But hush!
He's praying, comrades; 'tis not strange;
The man that's fighting day by day
May well, when night comes, take a change,
And down upon his knees to pray.

Break up that hoe-cake, boys, and hand
The sly and silent jug that's there;
I love not it should idly stand
When Marion's men have need of cheer.
'Tis seldom that our luck affords
A stuff like this we just have quaffed,
And dry potatoes on our boards
May always call for such a draft.

Now pile the brush and roll the log;
Hard pillow, but a soldier's head
That's half the time in brake and bog
Must never think of softer bed.
The owl is hooting to the night,
The cooter crawling o'er the bank,
And in that pond the flashing light
Tells where the alligator sank.

What! 'tis the signal! start so soon,
And through the Santee swamp so deep,

Without the aid of friendly moon,
And we, Heaven help us! half asleep!
But courage, comrades, Marion leads.
The Swamp Fox takes us out tonight;
So clear your swords and spur your steeds,
There's goodly chance, I think, of fight.

We follow where the Swamp Fox guides,
We leave the swamp and cypress-tree,
Our spurs are in our coursers' sides,
And ready for the strife are we.
The Tory camp is now in sight,
And there he cowers within his den.
He hears our shouts, he dreads the fight,
He fears, and flies from Marion's men.

The Pelican's Shadow

BY MARJORIE KINNAN RAWLINGS

THE LEMON-COLORED awning over the terrace swelled in the southeasterly breeze from the ocean. Dr. Tifton had chosen lemon so that when the hungry Florida sun had fed on the canvas the color would still be approximately the same.

"Being practical on one's honeymoon," he had said to Elsa, "stabilizes one's future."

At the moment she had thought it would have been nicer to say "our" honeymoon and "our" future, but she had dismissed it as another indication of her gift for critical analysis, which her husband considered unfortunate.

"I am the scientist of the family, my mouse," he said often. "Let me do the analyzing. I want you to develop all your latent femininity."

Being called "my mouse" was probably part of the development. It had seemed quite sweet at the beginning, but repetition had made the mouse feel somehow as though the fur were being worn off in patches.

Elsa leaned back in the long beach chair and let the magazine containing her husband's new article drop to the rough coquina paving of the terrace. Howard did express himself with an exquisite precision. The article was a gem, just scientific enough, just humorous, just human enough to give the impression of a choice mind back of it. It was his semi-scientific writings that had brought them together.

Fresh from college, she had tumbled, butter side up, into a job as assistant to the feature editor of *Home Life*. Because of her enthusiasm for the Tifton series of articles, she had been allowed to handle the magazine's correspondence with him. He had written her, on her letter of acceptance of "Algae and Their Human Brothers":

MY DEAR MISS WHITTINGTON:

Fancy a woman's editor being appealed to by my algae! Will you have tea with me, so that my eyes, accustomed to the microscope, may feast themselves on a *femme du monde* who recognizes not only that science is important but that in the proper hands it may be made important even to those little fire-lit circles of domesticity for which your publication is the *raison d'être!*

She had had tea with him, and he had proved as distinguished as his articles. He was not handsome. He was, in fact, definitely tubby. His hair was steel-gray and he wore gray tweed suits, so that, for all his squattiness, the effect was smoothly sharp. His age, forty-odd, was a part of his distinction. He had marriage, it appeared, in the back of his mind. He informed her with engaging frankness that his wife must be young and therefore malleable. His charm, his prestige, were irresistible. The "union," as he called it, had followed quickly, and of course she had dropped her meaningless career to give a feminine backing to his endeavors, scientific and literary.

"It is not enough," he said, "to be a scientist. One must also be articulate."

He was immensely articulate. No problem, from the simple ones of a fresh matrimony to the involved matters of his studies and his writings, found him without an expression.

"Howard intellectualizes about everything," she wrote her former editor, May Morrow, from her honeymoon. She felt a vague disloyalty as she wrote it, for it did not convey his terrific humanity.

"A man is a man first," he said, "and *then* a scientist."

His science took care of itself, in his capable hands. It was his manhood that occupied her energies. Not his male potency—which again took care of itself, with no particular concern for her own needs—but all the elaborate mechanism that, to him, made up the substance of a man's life. Hollandaise sauce, for instance. He had a passion for hollandaise, and like his microscopic studies, like his essays, it must be perfect. She looked at her wristwatch. It was his wedding gift. She would have liked something delicate and diamond-studded and feminine, something suitable for "the mouse," but he had chosen a large, plain-faced gold Hamilton of railroad accuracy. It was six o'clock. It was not time for the hollandaise, but it was time to check up on Jones, the manservant and cook. Jones had a trick of boiling the vegetables too early, so that they lay limply under the hollandaise instead of standing up firm and decisive. She stirred in the beach chair and picked up the magazine. It would seem as though she were careless, indifferent to his achievements, if he found it sprawled on the coquina instead of arranged on top of the copies of *Fortune* on the red velvet fire seat.

She gave a start. A shadow passed between the terrace and the ocean. It flapped along on the sand with a reality greater than whatever cast the shadow. She looked out from under the awning. One of those obnoxious pelicans was flapping slowly down the coast. She felt an unreasonable irritation at sight of the thick, hunched shoulders, the out-of-proportion wings, the peculiar contour of the head, lifting at the back to something of a peak. She could not understand why she so disliked the birds. They were hungry, they searched out their food, they moved and mated like every living thing. They were basically drab, like most human beings, but all that was no reason for giving a slight shudder when one passed over the lemon-colored awning and winged its self-satisfied way down the Florida coastline.

She rose from the beach chair, controlling her annoyance. Howard was not sensitive to her moods, for which she was grateful, but she had found that the inexplicable crossness which sometimes seized her made her unduly sensitive to his. As she feared, Jones had started the cauliflower ahead of time. It was only just in the boiling water, so she snatched it out and plunged it in ice water.

"Put the cauliflower in the boiling water at exactly six-thirty," she said to Jones.

As Howard so wisely pointed out, most of the trouble with servants lay in not giving exact orders.

"If servants knew as much as you do," he said, "they would not be working for you. Their minds are vague. That is why they are servants."

Whenever she caught herself being vague, she had a moment's unhappy feeling that she should probably have been a lady's maid. It would at least have been a preparation for matrimony. Turning now from the cauliflower, she wondered if marriage always laid these necessities for exactness on a woman. Perhaps all men were not concerned with domestic precision. She shook off the thought, with the sense of disloyalty that always stabbed her when she was critical. As Howard said, a household either ran smoothly, with the mechanism hidden, or it clanked and jangled. No one wanted clanking and jangling.

She went to her room to comb her hair and powder her face and freshen her lipstick. Howard liked her careful grooming. He was himself immaculate. His gray hair smoothed back over his scientist's head that lifted to a little peak in the back, his gray suits, even his gray pajamas were incredibly neat, as smooth and trim as feathers.

She heard the car on the shell drive and went to meet him. He had brought the mail from the adjacent city, where he had the use of a laboratory.

"A ghost from the past," he said sententiously, and handed her a letter from *Home Life*.

He kissed her with a longer clinging than usual, so that she checked the date in her mind. Two weeks ago—yes, this was his evening to make love to her. Their months of marriage were marked off into two-week periods as definitely as though the / line on the typewriter cut through them. He drew off from her with disapproval if she showed fondness between a / and a /. She went to the living room to read her letter from May Morrow.

DEAR ELSA:

Your beach house sounds altogether too idyllic. What previous incarnated suffering has licenced you to drop into an idyll? And so young in life. Well, maybe I'll get mine next time.

As you can imagine, there have been a hundred people after your job. The Collins girl that I rushed into it temporarily didn't work out at all, and I was beginning to despair when Jane Maxe, from *Woman's Outlook,* gave me a ring and said she was fed up with their politics and would come to us if the job was permanent. I assured her that it was hers until she had to be carried out on her shield. You see, I know your young type. You've burned your bridges and set out to be A Good Wife, and hell will freeze before you quit anything you tackle.

Glad the Distinguished Spouse proves as clever in daily conversation as in print. Have you had time to notice that trick writers have of saying something neat, recognizing it at once as a precious nut to be stored, then bringing it out later in the long hard winter of literary composition? You will. Drop me a line. I wonder about things sometimes.

MAY

She wanted to sit down at the portable at once, but Dr. Tifton came into the room.

"I'll have my shower later," he said, and rolled his round gray eyes with meaning.

His mouth, she noticed, made a long, thin line that gave the impression of a perpetual half-smile. She mixed the Martinis and he sipped his with appreciation. He had a smug expectancy that she recognized from her brief dealings with established authors. He was waiting for her favorable comment on his article.

"Your article was grand," she said. "If I were still an editor, I'd have grabbed it."

He lifted his eyebrows. "Of course," he said, "editors were grabbing my articles before I knew you." He added complacently, "And after."

"I mean," she said uncomfortably, "that an editor can only judge things by her own acceptance."

"An editor?" He looked sideways at her. His eye seemed to have the ability to focus backward. "And what does a wife think of my article?"

She laughed. "Oh, a wife thinks that anything you do is perfect." She added, "Isn't that what wives are for?"

She regretted the comment immediately, but he was bland.

"I really think I gave the effect I wanted," he said. "Science is of no use to the layman unless it's humanized."

They sipped the Martinis.

"I'd like to have you read it aloud," he said, studying his glass casually. "One learns things from another's reading."

She picked up the magazine gratefully. The reading would fill nicely the time between cocktails and dinner.

"It really gives the effect, doesn't it?" he said when she had finished. "I think anyone would get the connection, of which I am always conscious, between the lower forms of life and the human."

"It's a swell job," she said.

Dinner began successfully. The donac broth was strong enough. She had gone out in her bathing suit to gather the tiny clams just before high tide. The broiled pompano was delicately brown and flaky. The cauliflower was all right, after all. The hollandaise, unfortunately, was thin. She had so frightened Jones about the heinousness of cooking it too long that he had taken it off the fire before it had quite thickened.

"My dear," Dr. Tifton said, laying down his fork, "surely it is not too much to ask of an intelligent woman to teach a servant to make a simple sauce."

She felt a little hysterical. "Maybe I'm not intelligent," she said.

"Of course you are," he said soothingly. "Don't misunderstand me. I am not questioning your intelligence. You just do not realize the importance of being exact with an inferior."

He took a large mouthful of the cauliflower and hollandaise. The flavor was beyond reproach, and he weakened.

"I know," he said, swallowing and scooping generously again, "I know that I am a perfectionist. It's a bit of a bother sometimes, but of course it is the quality that makes me a scientist. A literary—shall I say literate?—no, articulate scientist."

He helped himself to a large pat of curled butter for his roll. The salad, the pineapple mousse, the after-dinner coffee and liqueur went off acceptably. He smacked his lips ever so faintly.

"Excuse me a moment, my mouse," he said. His digestion was rapid and perfect.

Now that he was in the bathroom, it had evidently occurred to him to take his shower and get into his dressing gown. She heard the water running and the satisfied humming he emitted when all was well. She would have time, for he was meticulous with his fortnightly special toilet, to begin a letter to May Morrow. She took the portable typewriter out to a glass-covered table on the terrace. The setting sun reached benignly under the awning. She drew a deep breath. It was a little difficult to begin. May had almost sounded as though she did not put full credence in the idyll. She wanted to write enthusiastically but judiciously, so May would understand that she, Elsa, was indeed a fortunate young woman, wed irrevocably, by her own deliberate, intelligent choice, to a brilliant man—a real man, second only in scientific and literary rating to Dr. Beebe.

DEAR MAY:

It was grand to hear from you. I'm thrilled about Jane Maxe. What a scoop! I could almost be jealous of both of you if my lines hadn't fallen into such gloriously pleasant places.

I am, of course, supremely happy—

She leaned back. She was writing gushily. Married women had the damnedest way, she had always noticed, of gushing. Perhaps the true feminine nature was sloppy, after all. She deleted "gloriously," crossed out "supremely," and inserted "tremendously." She would have to copy the letter.

A shadow passed between the terrace and the ocean. She looked up. One of those beastly pelicans was flapping down the coast over the sand dunes. He had already fed, or he would be flapping, in that same sure way of finding what he wanted, over the surf. It was ridiculous to be disturbed by him. Yet somewhere she suspected there must be an association of thoughts that had its base in an unrecognized antipathy. Something about the pelican's shadow, darkening her heart and mind with that absurd desperation, must be connected with some profound and secret dread, but she could not seem to put her finger on it.

She looked out from under the lemon-colored awning. The pelican had turned and was flapping back again. She had a good look at him. He was neatly gray, objectionably neat for a creature with such greedy habits. His round head, lifted to a peak, was sunk against his heavy shoulders. His round gray eye looked down below him, a little behind him, with a cold, pleased, superior expression. His long, thin mouth was unbearably smug, with the expression of a partial smile.

"Oh, go on about your business!" she shouted at him.

Reverie of Space and Time

BY HERMAN MELVILLE

DREAMS! DREAMS! golden dreams: endless, and golden, as the flowery prairies, that stretch away from the Rio Sacramento, in whose waters Danae's shower was woven;—prairies like rounded eternities: jonquil leaves beaten out; and my dreams herd like buffaloes, browsing on to the horizon, and browsing on round the world; and among them, I dash with my lance, to spear one, ere they all flee.

Dreams! dreams! passing and repassing, like Oriental empires in history; and scepters wave thick, as Bruce's pikes at Bannockburn; and crowns are plenty as marigolds in June. And far in the background, hazy and blue, their steeps let down from the sky, loom Andes on Andes, rooted on Alps; and all round me, long rushing oceans, roll Amazons and Oronocos; waves, mounted Parthians; and, to and fro, toss the wide woodlands: all the world an elk, and the forests its antlers.

But far to the South, past my Sicily suns and my vineyards, stretches the Antarctic barrier of ice: a China wall, built up from the sea, and nodding its frosted towers in the dun, clouded sky. Do Tartary and Siberia lie beyond? Deathful, desolate dominions those; bleak and wild the ocean, beating at that barrier's base, hovering 'twixt freezing and foaming; and freighted with navies of ice-bergs,—warring worlds crossing orbits; their long icicles, projecting like spears to the charge. Wide away stream the floes of drift ice, frozen cemeteries of skeletons and bones. White bears howl as they drift from their cubs; and the grinding islands crush the skulls of the peering seals.

But beneath me, at the Equator, the earth pulses and beats like a warrior's heart; till I know not, whether it be not myself. And my soul sinks down to the depths, and soars to the skies; and comet-like reels on through such boundless expanses, that methinks all the worlds are my kin, and I invoke them to stay in their course. Yet, like a mighty three-decker, towing argosies by scores, I tremble, gasp, and strain in my flight, and fain would cast off the cables that hamper.

And like a frigate, I am full with a thousand souls; and as on, on, on, I scud before the wind, many mariners rush up from the orlop below, like miners from caves; running shouting across my decks; opposite braces are pulled; and this way and that, the great yards swing round on their axes; and boisterous speaking-trumpets are heard; and contending orders, to save the good ship from the shoals. Shoals, like nebulous vapors, shoring the white reef of the Milky Way, against which the wrecked worlds are dashed; strowing all the strand, with their Himmaleh keels and ribs.

Ay: many, many souls are in me. In my tropical calms, when my ship lies tranced on Eternity's main, speaking one at a time, then all with one voice: an orchestra of many French bugles and horns, rising, and falling, and swaying, in golden calls and responses.

Sometimes, when these Atlantics and Pacifics thus undulate round me, I lie stretched out in their midst: a land-locked Mediterranean, knowing no ebb, nor flow. Then again, I am dashed in the spray of these sounds: an eagle at the world's end, tossed skyward, on the horns of the tempest.

Yet, again, I descend, and list to the concert.

Like a grand, ground swell, Homer's old organ rolls its vast volumes under the light frothy wave-crests of Anacreon and Hafiz; and high over my ocean, sweet Shakespeare soars, like all the larks of the spring. Throned on my sea-side, like Canute, bearded Ossian smites his hoar harp, wreathed with wild-flowers, in which warble my Wallers; blind Milton sings bass to my Petrarchs and Priors, and laureates crown me with bays.

In me, many worthies recline, and converse. I list to St. Paul who argues the doubts of Montaigne; Julian the Apostate cross-questions Augustine; and Thomas-à-Kempis unrolls his old black letters for all to decipher. Zeno murmurs maxims beneath the hoarse shout of Democritus; and though Democritus laugh loud and long, and the sneer of Pyrrho be seen; yet, divine Plato, and Proclus, and Verulam are of my counsel; and Zoroaster whispered me before I was born. I walk a world that is mine; and enter many nations, as Mungo Park rested in African cots; I am served like Bajazet: Bacchus my butler, Virgil my minstrel, Philip Sidney my page. My memory is a life beyond birth; my memory, my library of the Vatican, its alcoves all endless perspectives, eve-tinted by cross-lights from Middle-Age oriels.

And as the great Mississippi musters his watery nations: Ohio, with all his leagued streams; Missouri, bringing down in torrents the clans from the highlands; Arkansas, his Tartar rivers from the plain;—so, with all the past and present pouring in me, I roll down my billow from afar.

Yet not I, but another: God is my Lord; and though many satellites revolve around me, I and all mine revolve round the great central Truth, sun-like, fixed and luminous forever in the foundationless firmament.

Fire flames on my tongue; and though of old the Bactrian prophets were stoned, yet the stoners in oblivion sleep. But whoso stones me, shall be as Erostratus, who put torch to the temple; though Genghis Khan with Cambyses combine to obliterate him, his name shall be extant in the mouth of the last man that lives. And if so be, down unto death, whence I came, will I go, like Xenophon retreating on Greece, all Persia brandishing her spears in his rear.

My cheek blanches white while I write; I start at the scratch of my pen; my own mad brood of eagles devours me; fain would I unsay this audacity; but an iron-mailed hand clenches mine in a vice, and prints down every letter in my spite. Fain would I hurl off this Dionysius that rides me; my thoughts crush me down till I groan; in far fields I hear the song of the reaper, while I slave and faint in this cell. The fever runs through me like lava; my hot brain burns like a coal; and like many a monarch, I am less to be envied, than the veriest hind in the land.

A Winter Diary

BY MARK VAN DOREN

This was not written then, when measuring time
Ran smoothly to unalterable rhyme;
When even song—but still it is unsounded—
Kept the pure tally that has been confounded.
This was not written then, when sudden spring
Not yet had threatened winter, and no thing
Stood colder than the skin of apple trees.
Now every top is bursting into bees;
Now all of them, solidified to light,
Reflect a cloudy fire, as high, as white
As any sky in summer; and at last
Sharp edges of a shadow have been cast.
Thus sudden spring, with sudden summer near,
Has made a certain winter disappear:
The winter of all winters I would keep
Had I the power to put this warmth asleep
And make the world remember what I saw.
But who has power against a season's law?
Who lives a winter over, who is proof
Against the rain of months upon his roof?
A certain winter fades that I had thought
Forever in live colors to have caught.
A certain moveless winter more than moves:
Runs backward, and oblivion's great grooves
Lie deeper in the distance, and tomorrow
Nothing will be there save mist and sorrow.
Therefore must I fix it while I may:
Feign records, and upon this single day
Tie months of time together, in pretended
Sequence till they once again are ended.

. . . So it is autumn, when the city reaches,
Pulling us home from mountains and from beaches;
Down the curved roads and from the crescent sands
To oblong streets among divided lands.
Yet not us four. It is the year we stay
And watch the town-returners pour away.
Now the last stragglers of the stream have gone;
Here now we stand upon a thinning lawn—
The shade wind-shattered, and the cut grass sleeping—
Here then we stand and to the country's keeping
Tender four faces. Not a leaf that falls
But flutters through a memory of walls;
Flutters, with more to follow, till they weave
This solitude we shall at last believe.

. . . October sunshine, and a summer's day!
Yet not the heaviness long wont to lay
Slow skies upon our heads and bind us round
With the full growth of a too fruitful ground.
The morning sun was southerly, and noon
Came swiftly, and the day was over soon:
An airy thing time tossed us for our pleasure,
Blue, and wide-blown, and rich with gold leaf-treasure.
The solid green is gone, the trees are fire:
Cool fire, and top-contained, without desire;
Not caring if it lives, for lo, all day
Wind bullied it and bore the sparks away.
October sunshine and red-ember drifts;
So the long burden of a summer lifts.

. . . November rain all night, the last of three
Dark nights and mornings. We have been to see
The brook that piles grey water down the meadows.
Grey water, and there is no sun for shadows;
No wind for bare tree-talk, no thing but spreading
Rain; no thing but rain, wherein the treading
Crow-feet leave thin tracks, and grass is drowned
With a contented and a final sound.
Safely indoors now, with a fire to dry us,
We hear a whole long year go slipping by us—

Backward to die, with nothing left ahead
Save solitude and silence, and a thread
Of days that will conduct us through the cold.
The window-panes are waterfalls that fold
Small misty visions of our valley's end.
The rain is sewing curtains that will rend
And rise another day; but shut us now
In such a world as mice have up the mow.
Thus do we know ourselves at last alone;
And laugh at both the kittens, who have grown
Till here they lie, prim figures by the fire,
Paws folded, aping age and undesire.
The boys would have them up again to play.
But they are sudden-old; it is the day
For dreaming of enclosure, and of being
All of the world time missed as he was fleeing.
They think, the furry fools, to live forever.
So then do we, the curtains lifted never.

. . . It is December, and the setting sun
Drops altogether leftward of the one
Long mountain-back we used to measure by.
The maple limbs swing upward, grey and dry,
And print the lawn, now naked for the snow,
With lines that might be nothing. But we know.
We see them there across the bitten ground,
Dark lace upon the iron, and catch the sound
Of half a world contracting under cold.
Slowly it shrinks, for it is wise and old,
And waits; and in its wisdom will be spared.
So is the frosted garden-plot prepared.
The withered tops, arustle row by row,
Fear nothing still to come; for all must go.
That is their wisdom, as it is the horse's,
Whose coat the wind already reinforces,
There in the blowing paddock past the gate.
The four of us a long day, working late,
Confined her where she grazes, building the fence
She leans on; yet she would not wander hence.

She drops her head and nibbles the brown grass,
Unmindful of a season that will pass;
Long-coated, with a rump the wind can ruffle;
Shoeless, and free; but soon the snow will muffle
All of her four black feet, that study a line
Down to the ponies' corner under the pine.
So have the field-mice, folding their startled ears,
Burrowed away from owls and flying fears.
So have the hunters ceased upon the hills;
The last shot echoes and the woodland stills;
And here, along the house, the final flower
Lets fall its rusty petals hour by hour.

. . . So, in December, we ourselves stand ready.
The season we have dared is strong and heady,
But there is many a weapon we can trust.
Five cellar shelves that were but layered dust
Are wiped to kitchen neatness, and confine
Clear jellies that will soothe us when we dine:
Crab-apple, quince, and hardly-ripened grape,
With jam from every berry, and the shape
Of cherries showing pressed against the jar;
Whole pears; and where the tall half-gallons are,
Tomatoes with their golden seeds; and blunt
Cucumbers that the early ground-worms hunt.
The highest shelf, beneath the spidery floor,
Holds pumpkins in a row, with squash before:
Dark, horny Hubbards that will slice in half
And come with pools of butter as we laugh,
Remembering the frost that laid the vines
Like blackened string: September's valentines.
Firm corn, and tapering carrots, and the blood
Of beets complete the tally of saved food;
Yet over in a corner, white and square,
Is the big bin with our potato-share.
Then seven barrels of apples standing by.
We brought them down the ladder when a high
Stiff wind was there to whip us, hand and cheek;
And wheeled them to the barn, where many a week

They filled the tightest chamber; but they found
More certain safety here below the ground:
The Baldwins to be eaten, and the Spies;
But Greenings are for betty and for pies.
A dusty cellar window, old as stone,
Lets in grey light, a slowly spreading cone
Sharp-ended here, and shining, at the shelves.
All of the other spaces wrapped themselves
In darkness long ago; and there the wood
Remembers a great sky wherein they stood:
The twenty trees I walked with Louis, marking,
Once in a mist of rain; then axes barking
Through the wet, chilly weeks, with ring of wedges
Under the blows of iron alternate sledges,
Louis's and Laurier's, of equal skill.
These were the two woodchoppers whom the still
Small faces of the boys watched day by day.
They sat among brown leaves, so far away
We barely could hear their shouting as the saw
Paused, and the great trunk trembled, and a raw
Circle of odorous wood gaped suddenly there.
Now maple and oak and cherry, and a rare
Hard chestnut piece, with hickory and birch,
Piled here in shortened lengths, await my search:
Coming with lantern and with leather gloves
To choose what provender the furnace loves.
From wall to wall a dozen resting rows:
We shall be warm, whatever winter blows.
So for the range upstairs a mound uprises,
By the back fence, of birch in sapling sizes.
Old Bailey cut them through a lonely fall—
He and his axe together, that was all:
They in a thicket, and the white poles gleaming;
Now a high frozen pile the sun is steaming.
We shall be warm, whatever north wind catches
Any of us outside the rattling latches;
Down the sloped road, or where the yard descends
To the barn's angle with its gusty ends,
Or higher, beyond the garden and the orchard—
We shall not be snow-worried or wind-tortured.

The armor we have sent for has arrived.
The great book spread its pages, and we dived
Like cormorants for prey among the rocks;
And chose, and duly ordered; and the box
Came yesterday. A winter's woolen wraps:
Thick-wristed mittens and two stocking caps;
Three fleece-lined jackets that will turn all weather,
And one cut neat for ladies out of leather;
Red sweaters, nut-brown shirts, and rubber-soled
Great workman's shoes for wading in the cold.
We shall be warm; or we can stamp indoors,
Wool failing, till the supper and the chores.

. . . So quietly it came that we could doubt it.
There was no wind from anywhere to shout it.
Simply it came, the inescapable cold,
Sliding along some world already old
And stretched already there had we perceived it.
Now by this hour the least one has believed it.
Snippy, the lesser kitten, lies entangled
Deep in the fur of Snappy, where a dangled
Feed-sack drapes a box inside the shed.
I found them with the lantern, playing dead:
Those very creatures, Snippy and her brother,
Who in the orange sunset tumbled each other,
Lithe by the stepping-stone. Through such a night
How often have they put the frost to flight;
How often, when the blackness made them bolder,
Have they confounded time, that grew no colder.
Yet not this night; they recognize the god,
As in the barn the black mare, left to nod,
Stands in her blanket, dozing. I have come
From tending her, and heard the ominous hum
Of branches that no wind moved overhead;
Only a tightness and a stealth instead.
The stiffened world turns hard upon its axis,
Laboring; but these yellow lamps relax us,
Here in the living-room at either end.
She by the south one, I by the north pretend

Forgetfulness of pavements; or remark
How very dead the sky is, and how dark—
In passing, with the air of two that pore
On things familiar, having been before.
It is our way of knowing what is near.
This is the time, this is the holy year
We planned for, casting every cable off.
That was a board-creak; that was the horse's cough;
That was no wind, we say; and looking down,
Smile at the wolf-dog, Sam, who dreams of brown
Clipped fields that he will lope in when he wakes.
He dreams, and draws his ankles up, and slakes
Imaginary thirsts at frozen pools.
He is the wolf-dog, he is the one that fools
New comers up the yard; for gentler beast
Prowled never to the pantry for a feast.
He is the boys' companion, who at dusk
Ran rings with them tonight, and worried the husk
Of daylight in his teeth, and stood his hair
Wind-upright. Now he sleeps unthinking there,
Companion of the boys, who long ago
Climbed the dark stairs to bed. So we below
Should come there too, we say; and say it again,
And laugh to hear the clock tick out the ten.
We are not sleepy; this is the holy year
Let it tick on to midnight, and for cheer
Start coffee in the kitchen, while I spread
Bright jam upon the goodness of cut bread.

. . . We were awakened by a double shout:
"Get up, you lazy people, and look out!"
There was a weight of stillness on my eyes;
But in my ears innumerable sighs
Of snowflakes settling groundward past the glass.
I stood and stared, saying for jest "Alas!
My sight fails, I can see the merest dim
Milk-whiteness!" "We must bring it up to him!"
Cried one; and both were going, when I told them:
"Dress!" So now, as breakfast waits, behold them
Marching through a mist of falling specks.

They stop and raise their faces, and it flecks
Their foreheads till they laugh; then treading on,
Leave tracks across the swiftly thickening lawn.
I let them go this morning for the milk—
The car wheels turning softly in a silk
New coverlet as wide as eyes could see.
The chimney smoke was rising, round and free,
From every ridge of shingles: even there
Where Grandmother waved and pointed at the air.
The wolf-dog running with us need not pause,
Tasting the untamed whiteness; for his jaws
Dipped as he loped along, and fiercely entered
Now the far past wherein his mind was centered.
Back at the barn the Shetland ponies wheeled,
Biting each other's manes, their little field
Grown boundless by some fantasy, and fenceless.
They romped like shaggy dogs, and were as senseless,
Fluttering at the gate, as moths, and small.
They waited for the big one in the stall.
She whinnied as we came, and only stopped
When I rose up the ladder and hay dropped.
She will have finished breakfast in an hour.
So we, and through a sudden whirling shower
Shall bring her to the ponies. Then our talk
Will come once more to sleds, and up the walk
I shall again make promises; and keep them,
Thinking of flakes and how a wind can heap them.
This wind is gentle, and the grey sheet sways.
I am no prophet if it falls and stays.

. . . All yesterday it melted, and at night
Was nothing, and the prophecy was right.
But in a play-house corner stand the sleds,
Almost as high as the excited heads
Of two that will be on them when the slopes
Glisten once more. And so the boys have hopes
While I have present pleasure; for the ground
Grows musical wherever I am bound.
The mud was gone as quickly as the snow:
An afternoon of thaw, but then a low

Crisp sunset sound of shrinking, and the crack
Of coldness like a panther coming back.
Tonight the snowless evening and the moon
Kept my late feet contented with a tune
More ancient than the meadows, where the stones
Rise ever up: unburiable bones.
The bareness of the world was like a bell
My feet, accustomed, struck; and striking well,
Let the rung sound be mingled with the dry
Primeval winter moonlight flowing by.
Alone outdoors and late, the resonant lawn
Moved with me as I lagged, and moving on
Bore all my senses fieldward to those bones
Of permanence, the unalterable stones.
There is no such intensity of lasting
Anywhere out of meadows, where the fasting
Grasses worship something in December
Older than any moist root can remember;
Older than age, drier than any drouth;
Something not to be praised by word of mouth.
I did not praise them then, nor shall henceforth;
But shall remind me, so, what change is worth:
Timothy round a rock, and daisies hiding
Something that will be there again—abiding
Longer than hope and stronger than old despair;
Something not to be dated under the air.
I looked at stones; and faces looked at me:
Sidewise, always sidewise, past a tree
Or slanting down some corner, or obliquely
Squinting where the moon fell, and as weakly.
I saw them not but knew them: the tired faces
Of those who may not leave their acred places:
Those of a time long gone that never dies.
You know it by the darkness of their eyes,
And by the way they work to comprehend
Who lives here now beyond a century's end.
Who lives and does not labor, and makes light
Of the grim gods that once were day, were night;
That carved a cheek, bent breasts, and knotted hands.
Not one of them withdraws or understands.

Not one of them but looked at me; and I,
Intruder here, seemed helpless to reply.
Not by their older choosing are we here,
Not by their doom made free of gods and fear.
Was then the better time? I said; and thought
How excellently winter moonshine taught
The shapes of winter trees. That maple there,
How shadeless, how upflowing, and how fair!
Even without their leaves the elm-limbs drooped;
The alders leaned; and birches interlooped
Their lacy, blackened fingers past the pines.
The great dead chestnut where the loud crow dines
Writhed on, its mighty arms unskilled to fall.
The evergreens were solid over all,
And hickories and tulips, few of limb,
Held what they had straight out for time to trim.
Was then the better world, I wondered—daring
Suddenly now an answer from the staring
People of old days, the accusing faces.
But none of us, tree-watching on these places,
Ever will hear a sentence from the source.
Gone is their blood, and spent their bitter force;
They only live to chafe us down the wind
And leave us ever afterward thin-skinned:
Wondering on them, the only-good,
On whom these lighter feet too long intrude.

. . . We have had company of Friday nights.
We have looked out of windows till the lights
Of cars too long in coming dipped and streamed;
Then ended by the door as time had dreamed.
Two late ones from the city, blinking here
In the warm lamplight, with the kittens near—
These have been shown their room, the spare northeast one;
Have laughed and begged a bite: even the least one,
Even a crust to pay them for the ride.
Already coffee bubbled, fit to glide,
As quickly as cups were ready, from the spout.
Already there were cookies placed about;

And soon the supper entered that would keep us
Longer awake than wise, with talk to steep us
In every winter's moment we had missed.
So we unrolled our pleasures, till the list
Grew endless, and the meaning of it fled.
So, as the boys before us, up to bed.
For all of us a lazy breakfast waited,
With coffee and tobacco, brownly mated,
Warming the day to come. We tilted chairs,
Lit pipes, and fingered forks; till unawares
Time bore us half to noon; and looking out,
We argued what the weather was about.
Some said it would be overcast till night,
Settling themselves forever; but the right
Was mostly with the walkers and the curious.
First then the barn, where the black mare was furious,
Tossing as I excused our long delay.
No answer, but the eyes among the hay
Dived languorously and said I was forgiven.
The cutter by the car could not be driven.
I found it years ago and dragged it here
To a dry floor and braced it; but the clear
Curved figure will be never swift again.
Snow or no snow, it is for living men
Another last reminder of the old
Dim people who are dead. A crimson fold
Of lining flaps and braves the window frost.
But all the rest is poor and language-lost:
No bells to shake, no orders to be going
Down a long hill where only time is snowing—
Flake by flake forgotten, till the white
Far past of it is shadowy with night.
We took the road and turned, and crossed the bridge;
Then, needing not to beg the privilege,
Crossed neighbor Allyn's meadow to his row
Of sandknolls; then, as all the cattle go,
Between the roundest couple home to tea.
So Saturday, and night, when we agree
What games shall silence evening, and what talk
Shall bring the ghost whose breast is brittle chalk.

So Sunday, with a visit to the great
Grandfather pine that guards the burial gate.
Neglected there, the town's first graveyard lies
Where once the Hurlburt roadway took the rise,
Bringing a country mourner up to pray.
But year by year the woodchucks have their way,
And higher mounds are there than used to reckon
The small well-buried length of smith or deacon.
So all the week-end over, and the pair
Departed; and a blizzard in the air.

. . . That second snow fulfilled us while it lasted.
But now for two brown weeks the fields have fasted
Under a windless, under a lukewarm sun.
Christmas Eve and New Year's Day are done,
And here we stand expectant, straining dumbly
Toward a long stretch that will not lie so comely:
Three dark, inclement months before the spring.
Or such the hope; we want no softer thing,
No disappointment deepened day by day.
That second snow, dissolving, drained away
Too much of sudden glory, and too much
Of the towered god whose mantle we must touch.
There was no blizzard in it after all.
Only a thickening sky, so slow to fall
That Monday passed, and Tuesday. Then a hush;
Then a faint flick, as if a fox's brush
Had gained the woods in safety, and the hole;
Then steadily, steadily down the winter stole.
All afternoon it hissed among some clump
Of shrubbery, and deepened round the pump;
All afternoon, till time put out the light.
Then the black rustling through the soundless night:
Dark flake on flake colliding where no gaze
Of beast or person followed. Dim the ways
Of snow in great high darkness; strange the sound
Of whiteness come invisible to ground.
And yet the lamps awhile allowed the glance
Of a stray whirl of moth wings blown to dance,
Confused, beyond the four and twenty panes.

Here once we sat and watched the autumn rains
Stitching a wall of water. Now the snow—
A frailer fall, and gentler—came to sew
New raiment for the sun-accustomed sashes.
The upstairs window that a north wind lashes,
Beating the maple on it gust by gust,
Hung silent, like a picture; but it thrust
Pure light on brilliant branches, layered well
With silver that as slowly rose and fell,
No visible lawn beneath it, and no thing,
Round or above, save blackness in a ring:
A prone, suspended skeleton creeping hither,
All knuckle joints and bare bones twigged together.
Next morning then, with Christmas five days off,
What wonder if we called this well enough?
What wonder if the two boys prematurely
Counted upon continuance, and surely
Bragged of a snowy hill for him, the guest:
The expected boy, of all their friends the best,
Due now from deep Virginia on a night;
Their own, to play a week with out of sight?
So off they hurried, pulling the sleds behind them,
To cross the nearest meadow-stretch and find them
Somewhere a perfect slope that they could pack:
The runners for the hundredth time and back
Deep-sinking through the softness, with dragged feet
To finish a rough design and leave it neat.
I watched them for a little from the road,
Then called, and she came with me to the snowed
White forest edge, and over the wall inspected
The prints of birds; or how a deer directed
Leap after leap to gain his inland thicket.
A pine branch sagged to the earth, but I could flick it,
Filling my neck with flakes as up it reared,
Snow-loosened of its many-pointed beard.
Meanwhile the cry of coasters over the hill,
With moment interruptions, clear and still,
That said the feet were staggering up again.
We came, and Sam the wolf-dog joined them then
In a loud, urgent welcome, bark and word.

For he had crossed the field to make a third,
And close-pursued them, snapping at their feet
Now up the slope, now down; then off to meet
Plump Snappy, most companionable cat,
Who, plowing the snow alone, arrived and sat
Like something stone of Egypt, not for play.
He watched us, two by two, slide swift away,
Then turned his head, encouraging the weak one,
Snippy, the little sister, the grey meek one,
Who half from home had squatted in a track;
And wailed until we saved her, walking back.
That was the day, with four days still to come,
We prophesied long whiteness; hearing the hum
Of trees contracted slowly in no wind;
Or watching the clouds a clear sun dipped and thinned.
That was the night the low moon, all but waned,
Came to me once—upstarting at the strained
Hurt sound of something strangled in the woods—
Came to me at the window, over floods
Of waveless shining silence, and I said:
There is a month of coldness dead ahead.
But Thursday of a sudden thawed it all,
And Friday, like a silly thing of fall,
An innocent late-summer thing, declared
Calm days, with every melting meadow bared.
So when they blew their horn and gained the gate—
Those weary three Virginians—only a late
Cool breath of proper evening blew to greet them.
Sam leapt out ahead of us to meet them.
Then the old rejoicing, four and three;
With talk of the north till bedtime, and the tree
We all must bring tomorrow: a picked pine
To anchor in a room with block and twine.
We found it, best of several by a swamp,
And sawed and bore it hither amid the romp
Of boys and tumbling cats, that on warm haunches
Settled to watch us trim the bristling branches;
Looping the ends with silver-studded cord
And lo, with more than patience could afford

Of cranberries and popcorn needled through:
Now red, now white, now one and one, and two.
From every room, when darkness well was down,
Came packages of mystery, in brown
Creased paper if a boy or man were giver;
But if a lady, candle-light would quiver
On multicolored tissue, gold and green.
Then silence, with a glow behind the screen
To point our way to bed, the lamps unlighted.
Then dawn, and stairs acreak, and something sighted
Even beyond the door that we had closed;
Then breakfast, and the mysteries deposed.
No more the ache of waiting; shed the power
Preeminent of any future hour.
That was the height; the rest was going down,
With random walks, or driving into town,
Or sitting after sunfall over tea.
We tidied rooms and set the spangled tree
Midway the snowless lawn, and spiked it there—
Popcorn and berries on it, and a square
Of suet tied with string to tempt the flying
Birds. But there were kittens always spying,
Ready to pounce and punish; and at last
A brief wind laid it over like a mast.
The rest was milder pleasure, suiting well
Our seven tongues that had so much to tell.
We talked. And then the final day was come.
Farewell, you three! And if the end was dumb,
Remember this: there was no charm to say
As down the hill your fenders sloped away.
So Christmas Eve and New Year's Day are done;
And still the lukewarm, still the windless sun
Possesses what it watches: hidden here,
A barn and painted house, from which appear
Four little figures scanning a clear sky.
It doubtless will be clouded by and by,
And doubtless yield each one his small desire.
Now only tracks, minute upon the mire.

. . . O welcome night-wind, crazily arriving,
You had not warned us till we heard you striving,
Here and at every corner of the house—
Now a great beast and now a nibbling mouse—
Striving in every stature to undo us;
There was no rumor of your marching to us,
No swift annunciation; or eight hands
Loud, loud had hailed you, giving you our lands,
Ourselves, and all this valley to unsettle.
We only lay and heard you; heard the rattle
Of shutters, and caught the groan as you went on
Of nails from weather-boarding all but drawn.
We only lay, pulling the covers higher,
Until at dayrise, grouping about the fire,
We greeted a hundred frost-hills on the panes;
Looked through, and saw the still wind-worried lanes
Thrash heavily; and walking out a little,
Said the snapped, hanging branches were wind-spittle.
Nor was the blowing over; still at twelve
High limbs were double-curving, like a helve,
And through the day, beneath white clouds and round ones,
All was a sea, with us the happy drowned ones—
Drifting among the layers of thin cold,
Self-separated. Some, the slow and old,
Slid lazily, floating beyond a world;
But some were childish-violent, and curled
And slapped our willing foreheads as they raced.
Layer upon clear layer built a waste
Of space for minds to work in, high and low.
Then the loud night that bade the softness go,
With iron for morning ground, and every print
Of dog or man foot stamped as in a mint:
All metal, all eternal, if this cold,
High, many-shelving universe could hold.
It held; and laid a film across the pond;
Laid more, and laying others, brought the fond
Brown wolf-dog there to slide beside the boys—
Bewildered, but enchanted by the noise
Of brittle alder-sticks and clapping hands.
So now the ice in hourly thickened bands

Is pressing tight around us, pond and lawn.
One moment, and the mighty gale was gone,
Far-whistling. Then a silence, and the fall
To nothing. Then the crisp iron over all.

. . . Slap, slap, the sound of car chains going by,
With elsewhere only stillness, under dry
Fantastic heaps of white the wind renews.
It reached us evenly, as snowfalls use;
But there were days of fury when the air,
Whirled white as flour, was powdery everywhere;
Till now the finest grains, like desert sand,
Wait upon eddies they will not withstand.
The snow-plows on the highway come and go:
Not vainly, but a devil takes the snow
Some windy times, and then the car lanes fill
Along the leeward side of fence or hill.
The boys are in the snow house we had made
Before this blowing weather overlaid
The first wet fall with something crisp as salt.
Four walls we packed without a single fault
Between a pair of solid shutter forms.
A roof, an eastern door away from storms,
Two windows at the ends—a bread knife cut them,
Neatly, but there was then no way to shut them—
A piece of crate for cushion, and a bag:
This is their windy fortress that a flag
Flies every day in front of, and that Sam
Lies guarding, less the dragon than the lamb.
There was a man with anthracite for eyes,
And pennies for his buttons; but he lies,
Forgotten, uncreated, where he fell.
There was a castle wall beyond the well
With store of snowballs piled against a siege,
And apples for the starving, lord or liege;
But now it too is levelled, and delight
Dwells only in this hovel at the right.
Below the sheds and halfway to the wall
Stands a lean ice house, windowless and tall,

Whose ancient door hung open day by day
Till the last shining cake was stowed away.
When ice was fourteen inches teams were hitched;
Saws buzzed; and like a waterland bewitched
The silver floor divided, line and angle.
Then loaded trucks, with pairs of tongs to dangle,
Teasing the helpful boys until they tried—
Slipped, fell, and were convinced. And so inside
Sleep twice a hundred pieces of the pond,
Preserved against the dog days and beyond.

. . . These are the undistinguishable days.
This is the calm dead center of the maze
Whereinto we have wandered, and in time
Shall wander forth again, and slowly climb
A wall the other side of which is change.
Now everything is like, with nothing strange
To keep our hands aware of what they do.
This is the winter's heart, that must renew
Its steady, steady beating when an embered
Joy is all we have, and thoughts remembered.
Therefore do I listen while I may,
Monotony, to what your whispers say
Of systole, diastole, and the ribbed
Sweet rituals wherein our wills are cribbed.
Therefore shall I count the doings here
Of one full day, and represent the year.
We rise at eight, but I an hour before
Have put the pipeless furnace in a roar;
Descending slow in slippers, robe, and socks
To where, as in some Southern ship that rocks,
Dry cargo-wood inhabits all the hold.
Our destination only the days unfold:
Tier on tier down-sloping to warm weather.
But many a hundred chunks lie yet together,
Snug in their odorous rows. So I inspire
Last evening's spent and barely-breathing fire;
Pull off my gloves; ascend the under-stair;
And smoke a chilly moment in a chair.

Then up again. But they are coming down,
Each head of hair in tangles at the crown;
And suddenly we smell a breakfast waiting:
Bacon and yellow eggs; or, alternating,
Buckwheat cakes with butter for anointing;
Or third-day porridge, grey and disappointing.
Prepared with steaming water and the comb,
We gather about the range—the morning home
Of kittens, too, and Sam the wolf-dog, stretched
Full length behind it while our plates are fetched.
The Irish hands that laid our dining table
Were up in early darkness, whence a fable
Of ghost or saint, night-walking, has its rise.
We listen, masked amusement in our eyes,
And finishing our fare, proceed to measure
Whether this day is planned for work or pleasure.
There is a woodshed faucet where I fill
Two water pails, and through the winter-still
Bound morning beat the music that she loves:
The restless mare whose foretop, smoothed with gloves,
Will hang with hay-stalk in it while she drinks.
She knows my coming footfall, and she thinks
To speed her slave's arrival with a neigh.
I am too proud to hurry; yet the hay
Seems due her, and the water, none the less.
So up to where last summer's grasses press
Their rustling weight on weight; and casting down
High pitchforkfuls, I stuff the slats with brown,
Stiff breakfast which the clever ponies hear.
I listen to their trotting, small and clear,
Round the curved path to where the western door
Stands open night or day, whatever roar
Of winds or pelt of snow drives ruthless in.
They are from northern islands where the din
Of winter never daunts them. Unconfined,
They wander about the paddock till the mined
Mute hayfall wakes their wisdom. Then they race,
Two blown and hairy creatures, into place.
I leave them there, slow-nibbling, eyes astare,
And go to prod the motor in his lair:

Four thousand pounds inert, and chilled so well
Some mornings I can barely solve the spell.
I have been baffled when a weakened spark
Has failed to fire the monster, and the dark
Webbed shadows of the room have missed his roar.
I have discovered drifts against the door,
And shovelled; I have watched a winter's rains
Turn ice, and been in misery with chains:
Now on, now off, now broken and now mended;
I have as often wished a year were ended.
But now the long thing moves, and backing out
Brings Sam, who disobeys my daily shout
And lopes to where the open meadows tempt him.
I could be angry, but his ears exempt him,
Waiting erect and friendly when I come.
My way was longer round; but now the strum
Of pistons will be answered by his feet,
That guide me to the milkhouse, dark, unneat,
Where the day's pail awaits me. Then the mile
Retravelled, past the cemetery stile
That leads among the six-foot frozen mounds.
There have been mornings when I heard the sounds
Of pick and frozen shovel at a grave;
But mostly snow and timeless silence—save
That cries of farmer children ring in the wood,
Where the white Hollow school long years has stood.
Some of them wave and call my distant name;
Then bells, and marching in to serious game;
While I at my own corner mount the hill
Past Bailey's house, and hers, where now a still
White shaft of smoke that bends above the brook
Declares Grandmother up. A pause; a look;
Good morning to her, cheerful at the door;
Then on to where the barn receives the roar
Of cylinders again until they cease.
Now to the restless mare, whom I release—
High stepping, in perpetual surprise—
To where the ponies shake their shaggy eyes.
All day will they be three beyond a gate,
Ground-musical, and free of their estate;

While we that own them, in and out of doors
Must labor at our self-appointed chores.
Now the grey tool house where the chisels hang,
And hammers lie, and saws with sharpened fang
Rest nightly on their nails, invites my skill.
I am no maker, but a floor can fill
With shavings from the least instructed plane.
Or there is wood to split, come snow or rain,
When the black stove grows hungry, and the dry
Deep kitchen box demands a fresh supply.
Ten times the barrow, loaded, piles its pieces
High at the woodshed end, till all the creases
Fold a fair week of darkness, and the dented
Chopping block is with cold wounds contented.
There is one root the garden still can give.
Under the snow, under the stubble, live
Our golden parsnips, planted and forgotten.
Nothing of them is altered or frost-rotten.
The blunt pick thuds in the ground, and up they heave:
A miracle for winter to believe.
I bring them in for dinner on this day;
And while the kettle, boiling their ice away,
Fills half a room with steam I take the road
Once more, to curiosity's abode:
That box where now the mail man will have been.
Arriving slow, I thrust my fingers in;
Draw letters forth, a bundle, or a card;
And out of time abstracted pace the hard
White ground again to where three wait for me.
No ancient courier with a king's decree
Rode ever up a hill and brought so much
As these chilled messages the mind can touch,
Restoring warmth, reviving every word
That yesterday with its own motion stirred.
Meanwhile the boys have had their little school:
Two pupils and a mother, mild of rule,
Who after beds were made and dinner planned,
Called them to where the home-built easels stand
And where the primer waits that one can read.
The younger mind admits a younger need:

Long blocks that tilt together till a boat
Sits sailing; or a castle with a moat;
Or dungeon towers to keep a kitten in—
The almond-eyed four-footed Saracen.
To painting then: tongues out and foreheads glowing,
With bannerets of bright vermilion flowing
Over and up and down; or blues, or blacks,
Full to the very corners past the tacks.
One thing remains: a paragraph to trace
On paper from the blackboard's printed face.
The boy leans long upon the table leaf,
Procrastinating; for the task was brief,
And both of them had still an hour to play.
But there he leans, unwilling, till the day
Brings twelve; and half-past twelve; and brings the white
Sealed letters that are now the noon's delight.
So dinner, and a nap for everyone
Where neither snow may enter nor the sun.
So then the afternoon, that still is short—
Midwinter lags behind the sky's report:
Each day a little longer, but the dark
Comes down before a coaster may remark.
While there is light we seek the genial store,
Off by the covered bridge; or wanting more,
Ride over two east ranges to the town
Of brass that bore the body of John Brown.
Here pavements like a puzzle run and spread;
And here a shop front, gold by gaudy red,
Demands immediate entrance; for a dime
Buys anything, land-born or maritime:
A ball, a wooden car, a masted boat,
An outboard motor that will never float;
A magnet's curve, completed by a bar;
A leaden blue policeman with his star.
So home across the ranges, past the edge
Of evening, till the last high-drifted hedge
Declares the clear necessity of chains.
So out to frosty spokes and windy lanes
Where the snow, blowing, whips the wrist and scatters;
Then upward, while a broken chain-link clatters;

Upward into the barn, the engine dying
Soundless; but the ponies are replying,
Huddled before the big one at the gate.
Scarcely we listen, for we estimate
Two hours this side of supper. Time for tea.
We light the lamps and sip the mystery,
Cup after shadowy cup, with toasted cheese.
There are no country moments like to these;
When afternoon is night, and night belongs
Like a dark heirloom of descended songs
To four that sit in solitude and hear them
Through the fond nothingness that nestles near them.
From the warm circle of the shaded lamp
At last I walk to where the ponies stamp
And the tall guardian mare is loud with thirst.
A boy with lighted lantern sheds the first
Long pair of scantling shadows on the snow;
While I, the water-bearer, dimly go
Through the great backward crescent drawn behind us.
There have been evenings when she would not mind us—
The lurking mare, complacent down the meadow.
But now a clear low whistle cleaves her shadow,
Precipitately arriving. So we lead her,
Plunging, past the corner post; and heed her
Sighing as she nuzzles in the pail.
The lantern from a high and rusty nail
Swings gently, casting circles on the hay.
The kittens somewhere, noiselessly at play,
Keep watch of us, and scan the waiting door.
They love a barn, but love the kitchen more;
And lessons still may linger in each mind
Of the long milkless night they sat confined.
We leave the ponies munching in their room
And blow our lantern black, resolved to come
By starlight home—Orion and the Bears
Low-shining; but aloft upon the stairs,
Bright Castor holding Pollux by the hand.
Now endless evening, like a painted band,
Starts moving, moving past us, and we seize,
Soft-reaching, all that momently can please.

There is an hour for singing, when the book
Lies open, and a rolling eye may look
For prompting at the words of Nelly Gray,
Darby and Joan, The Miller, Old Dog Tray;
Malbrouck that went to war, and Hoosen Johnny;
Or over the ocean, over the sea my bonnie.
The dominoes that once amused us well
Lie in their box and envy bagatelle,
Whose twenty balls, thrust up the tilted board,
Pause and return—click, click—a thousand scored!
With game or song the clock goes round to eight:
Past time for two to sleep, whose laggard gait
We must not hope to hurry up the landing.
Each elder then knows where a book is standing,
Tall on the crowded table; and begins
What may go on until the darkness thins:
Page after page upturned against the light.
For so it was, on such a nipping night,
That Holmes, or Doctor Thorndyke, heard the bell
And raced with lawless death to Camberwell;
Or Watson, in an alley with his master,
Felt the steel fingers as a crutch came faster:
Tapping, tapping, tapping, till the court
Blazed with a sudden pistol's blind report.
This is the hour, and this the placeless room
For smooth concocted tales of lust and doom;
This the remote, the sanctuary year
When the safe soul must fabricate a fear.
Many a milder evening passes, too,
With Royal Casino, Rummy, and a few
Swift-changing hands of High-Low-Jack-and-the-Game.
But then three weeks ago the chess men came;
Since when, no night so busy that it misses
The march of angry Queens, whose scalloped tresses,
Stiffly erected, fly to guard a King.
We are two novices, and rashly fling
Pawns, bishops, knights, and rooks into the fray;
Yet time and blood have taught us wiser play.
There was a gift at Christmas time of Tarot—
Untaught, but we can shuffle them and harrow

A loreless mind with him, the Hanging Man;
So all those numbered mysteries that plan
What future folds the player, and what past
Is carved upon the great Tower overcast,
So every wand and pentacle and sword
Lies curious, unfathomed, on the board.
We have been known, as never back in town,
To idle till the clock weights settled down,
And till the sound of ticking ceased unheard.
We have rejoiced some evenings at the word
Of neighbors driving over; when the names,
Smith, Prentice, Landeck, interrupted games
With something else of equal clear delight.
For there was talking now into the night,
With news of health, and trips away from home,
And how the kitchen beer went all to foam.
Gossip of Hautboy, Dibble, and Great Hill,
Gossip and jest and argument, until:
Goodbye, Smith, Landeck, Prentice; come again;
Goodnight. And so a day is ended then.
Each four and twenty hours, until we rise,
Go thus. And thus the holy winter flies.

. . . February flies, with little summers
Hidden in its beard: unlicensed mummers
Performing April antics for a day.
The sun from the horizon swings away;
The sky melts upward, and a windless hand
Scatters the seeds of warmth along the land.
They will not grow, for ice is underneath,
And every creature tastes it. But a wreath
Lies thrown by playful chance upon the smiling
Meadows that a season is beguiling.
Today was so, but we were not deceived;
Though what the wolf-dog and the cats believed
There is no art of knowing. They pursued
Our every venturing step and found it good:
Down the crisp meadows to the aspen grove;
Over the highway, where a salesman drove

Dry wheels on dry macadam; then the neck
Of Harrison's pasture to the Hollenbeck.
We stood, the seven walkers, on a stone
And watched the river, waveless and alone,
Go slipping, slipping under, gravelly clear.
Snippy, a mile from nowhere, crouched to peer
At nothing in the sand; then bolder sat.
Three weeks, we said, and she would be a cat
With fearsome crying kittens of her own.
Ten months with us, no more, and nearly grown!
So Snappy, arriving plump and solemn there,
Good-natured sat, the guardian of the pair.
There was a barn foundation to explore,
Ancient of fields beyond. The rotting floor
Forewarned us, and we did not enter in;
But strolled, and where tall timothy had been
Lay half an hour on stubble under the sun;
While Sam, excited by a scent, must run
Low-whining up the fences; till a voice
Recalled him, and we made the hapless choice
Of eastward marshy meadows for return.
The hummocks mired us, but a cat could learn
The causeway's secret truth; and what we lost
Came back to us at home with tea and toast.

. . . Since yesterday a hundred years have gone.
The fore-and-after season, living on,
Rouses itself and finds its bitter breath.
This wind holds on to winter as to death.
There is no end, we say, and sauntering out,
Northwestward lean till we are whirled about,
Mute neck and shoulders stinging with the snow;
Or on this Sunday morning think to go,
Foot-heavy, where the giant maples spread
Their smooth enormous branches, long since dead.
Still in this waste of wind they do not fall;
But stiffen, like old serpents sent to crawl
On dense, on layered air; until the charm
Is lifted, and descending out of harm,

They lie leaf-covered, rigid in decay
Until the last small worm has turned away.
Here in the woodland clearings they patrol,
The wind drives steadily upon its goal.
But yonder where the hemlocks lace together
There is a sudden calm, a death of weather.
The shade is black, as once in late July
When here we walked escaping yellow sky.
The shade is black and even, and the snow
Comes filtered to the open cones below:
Slowly, slowly, slowly; strange the hush,
Here in this darkened desert of the thrush.
No hermits now; yet bands of chickadees
Tread fearless of us, chirping in the trees.
The ferns of June are withered on the rocks
Midway the icy stream that bends and locks
This needled promontory where we stand.
Oh, happy time! when nothing makes demand;
When all the earth, surrendering its strength,
Regains a taller potency at length;
Sleeps on in purest might of nothing done
Till summer heaves on high the exacting sun.

. . . Ice everywhere, a comic inch of it.
Four veteran walkers of a sudden sit
Wide-sprawling; but the cat that went so sure
Waits in the shed, distrustful and demure.
On this one day the dark mare, left inside,
Stands munching while the startled ponies slide—
Their path a river, and the river frozen—
Until a barn's captivity is chosen.
Ice everywhere; but over Goshen way
Ice on the mountains: murderous display.
Down the wild road to where the lanes were dry
We crept on crunching chains; then letting fly,
Passed houses till we gained the known plateau.
Yet now no more familiar, for the glow
Of crystals, like an ocean, blinded eyes
Untutored in the way a forest dies:

Slim birch and maple, sycamore and larch
Bent low before the mysteries of March;
Bent glassy-low, or splintered to a heap
Of glittering fragments that the sunrays sweep—
The sun, ironic, heartless, come to glance
At death and beauty shivering in a dance.

. . . I have been absent through the ending days
Of March beyond the mountains, where the ways
Of all the world drive onward as before.
I have been absent from the windy door;
Have gazed on travel-mornings out of flying
Windows at a distant winter dying.
But not our own, I said; and still believe
There will be news at home of its reprieve.
Nothing of that can change. And yet the doubt
Creeps into me as I look homesick out
On farms that are reminding me of one
Not distant now, beneath the selfsame sun.
A further valley, and a further range,
And I shall see if anything be strange.
Another dozen stations, and the three
I have been absent from will run to me,
And tell me if they know. At which the tears
Come premature, and stillness stops my ears.

. . . That very Wednesday, going to Great Hill,
The ruts all melted and the road was swill;
The hub caps foundered, and a number plate
Rose out of mire to recognize the spate.
All underground was overflowing for us,
Helpless until a wakened workhorse bore us,
Backward, absurd, to dry macadam land.
So April, with a wild unwelcome hand,
Showers proof upon us here of winter gone.
Our visitors on Friday night are wan:
Town-tired, and do not know it till we tell them.
The stripling cats, until we thought to bell them,
Havocked among the juncos, dropped to feed
On what the lawn still held of husk or seed.

A hundred misty bellies and blue backs
Move unmolested northward, leaving tracks
On certain darker mornings when a flurry
Satins the ground—not deep enough to worry
Those busy bills that, helped by hopping feet,
Find out the fruit of barberries and eat.
The apple barrels, picked over, have revealed
How many Baldwins never will be peeled;
The fungus spreads, and spots of deathly white
Show where the teeth of time have been to bite.
The wolf-dog has abandoned us by day;
He is in love across the scented way.
Nothing can keep him when the wind arrives;
He chews his chain, or alternately strives
Till the round collar slips and he goes running.
The ponies' noses have as old a cunning.
There is no forage yet, but they can smell
Green tropics creeping hither, and will fell
Each night a length of fence for dumb escape;
Then stumble back at breakfast time and gape,
Wit-withered, at the breach they cannot solve.
So, as the weeks implacably revolve
Of early, windy April, come the sprays
Of wood viburnum in the pathless ways
Where rocks and bent witch-hazel boughs declare
Once more their truce, awakening to air.
So, as the world turned sunward, Snippy died.
In the dim middle of a night she cried,
Desperate upon the steps; and lived a day.
But we have laid her slenderly away.
Her young within her she was not to bear;
So Snappy sits disconsolately there,
Under the branching crabtree; faced about,
Fixed on the clods, as if to stare her out.

. . . Spring is not yet; though how can this be long:
This crush of silence, this untimely-wrong,
Wide, cruel weight of whiteness, wing-descended
Even as we declared the winter ended?

Last night it happened. Everything, unwarned,
Suffered the soundless swoop of him the Horned,
The Universal Owl, whose ruthless plumes
Settled like death, distributing our dooms;
No feather heavy, but the sum of all
Seemed ultimate: earth's sepulchre and pall.
Not a flake settled on the flimsiest twig
But stayed; until this morning all were big
With monstrous moveless worms, that in the sun
Drip swiftly; but the evil has been done.
How fair it was last evening, when our lamp
Shone out on fleecy lilacs; yet the damp,
The clammy hand of this last dying snow—
How terrible to touch, and inly know:
This is the breaking end. So now at noon,
Divided, we behold the orchard strewn
With murdered buds and down-demolished branches.
So, by the graveyard, death upon its haunches
Sits in the form of great-grandfather-pine's
Chiefest of giant limbs, whose blackened lines
Trace there a new design of death across
Bare stones for whom no novelty of loss,
No morning news of woe can tell them more
Than that another winter shuts the door.
Divided thus—admiring, yet appalled—
We watch the season, poor, unfuneralled,
Pass with no mourners on; and recognize
What most we loved here impotent to rise.
If any sight could soften us to spring,
It is this melted, this emaciate thing.

. . . So April's plumefall was the last one, leaving
Nothing behind save midmonth warmth, and heaving
Roots, rain-drenched on many a sodden day.
Now even the rain is gone, that kept us grey;
Even the rain, preserving darkness too.
After the flood dry weather, hot and blue,
Washed every stain of winter off, and brightly
Gave us this world, so changeable and sightly:

Grass upon the mountains; smokeless-green
May fire that will not languish till the lean,
Brown, bitten earth, monotonous with stone,
Hides under hotness, leafy and alone;
Shade everywhere—as here beneath the crab,
Where Snippy lies, and rumors of Queen Mab
Bring bees to set the blossoms in a roar
While marvelling children pace the petalled floor;
Shade then for her, the borrowed Tabby, lying
With three new kittens, curious and crying:
The summer's offspring, not to be confused
With those somehow more brave that March misused.
Now the sleek mare is shod again, and trots
Each day beneath her mistress, over lots
Green-rising, or along a sandy road:
Each of them glad, the bearer and the load;
But I that walk to meet them down the lawn
Remember lazy mornings lost and gone:
Remember the cold, remember the lantern, hanging
There by her nose at night, and blizzards banging
Somewhere a shabby door; and my decision
Goes to the old, the February vision.
How old it is now, only a rake and spade;
Only a wolf-dog, panting in the shade;
Only a coatless, an oblivious pair
Of boys for whom all days to come are fair;
Only her warm hand, patting down the seed
Where sunlight lingers and the frost is freed;
Only the hay-land, live again with snakes;
Only these things can say what memory aches—
Oh, vainly—to recapture; only such
Can tell of the holy time our blood will touch—
Oh, never again, and never; only June,
That sings of something over deathly soon.
Already the mind's forgetfulness has blended
Music with music; and the months are ended.

Daybreak

A Radio-Play

BY NORMAN CORWIN

Music: Prelude, continuing under:

PILOT. A day grows older only when you stand and watch it coming at you. Otherwise it is continuous. If you could keep a half degree ahead of sunup on the world's horizons, you'd see new light always breaking on some slope of ocean or some patch of land. A morning can be paced by trailing night. This we shall do: where we begin we shall return to, circling the earth meanwhile.

Music: Up full, then into Variation Number 1, continuing under:

PILOT. We are at latitude 40° north and longitude 25° west. We will come back here at the circle's end. But now beneath us there is water, nothing else: the long Atlantic, flowing to the north: cirrus clouds resembling herringbone, high up. Along the curving fringe, ten thousand miles from top to bottom of the globe, are only islands, very far apart; some atolls in the South Atlantic, icebergs off the Sandwich archipelago. The rim of light is touching now one continent alone, of all the mainlands it will overtake today: the eastern shores of Greenland. Southwest of the Cape Verde Islands there's a thunderstorm—not much: a little rain: some grumbling from a cumulus.

Fade in thunder after the words, "Cape Verde Islands."

PILOT. Through it, unruffled, plows a tramp from Capetown, headed for the Caribbean. There is a hint of day to starboard, and a smudge of night to port; thunder above. The striking of the hour is expected momentarily inside the wheelroom.

Meanwhile the course is west nor'west.

See for yourself.

Music: Out.

Fade in light wind, water, thunder M.F., and low, muffled motor of tramp steamer.

Ship's bell striking eight. Wheelhouse door open and shut—neat click of lock, and closing.

MATE. Okay, Johnnie, I'll take over now.

JOHNNIE. Hi ya.

MATE. You look as though you could use some shut-eye.

JOHNNIE. Hasn't been a bad stretch. Storm's not much.

MATE. Gimme some tobacco before you go, will you?

JOHNNIE. Sure, take the rest of this can. Have some more in the locker.

MATE. Thanks. What's the course?

JOHNNIE. Eleven point six by thirty-one point four. Course west nor'-west, two degrees. Steady as she goes.

MATE. Right. (*Yawning.*) Well—I hope the old man's in a better humor than he was on my last watch. Thought he was goin' to eat the glass right outa the binnacle lamp.

JOHNNIE (*chuckles*). Yeah, he's been on the prod for the last three days. Well, see ya later.

Door open and shut. Fade entire background effect down and out as:

Music: In; up; and behind:

PILOT. The tramp's a hundred miles behind us now—as quick as that; the thunder also. Now the sun's antennae reach another five degrees yet west of Greenwich. Nothing now but water south of Greenland, clear down past the humid zones of the equator, down the easy ground swells to the barriers of ice in the Antarctic.

Music: Segue to Variation Number 2 and quicken under:

PILOT. That dark shape coming toward us is the bulge of South America, the coastline of Brazil. Now you can smell the spices in the offshore breeze. That's Pernambuco over there; the green light 'way below us is the airport at Natal.

Now in succession come the mountain ranges, like slow-turning gears. That string of lights is Rio. The coast spreads wider, north and south, and for the first time you begin to sense this is a continent, rotating hugely toward the sun. The endless forests in the Matto Grosso, they are tipped with light; the jungle life's astir, the birds a-twitter; to the north, the great mouth of the Amazon yawns wide, the islands in it looming suddenly.

Music: Fading under:

PILOT. Yet at this very moment day is touching on the continent of North America—the shores of Newfoundland. Fog's drifting in from the Grand Banks; we cannot see the chimneys of St. John's.

Faint foghorn.

PILOT. The whole Atlantic seaboard, Eastport to Key West, is still in darkness. Further down the hemisphere, light picks its way among the Lesser Antilles, spreads out down Venezuela, down the Gran Chaco, the Pampas of the Argentine—stirs sleepers in their sleep in Buenos Aires. In the Sertao of Bahia, beyond the reach of tourists and authorities, the forbidden dance of the mecumba pauses while a priestess invokes the spirit of the dawn.

MECUMBA SINGER. *The "Xango."*

Silence for a moment after song.

PILOT. Back further in the jungle, where the Negro River cuts a swath, the tropic black is still unbroken. (*Pause.*)

Music: Variation Number 3.

PILOT. But north again, north-north, beyond the rain, the mountains, over the rooftops of Caracas, over the Indies, dawn is coming now to Hancock County, Maine. There in Penobscot Bay, a lobster fisherman rides home with light of day behind him, and a lighthouse just ahead. On his way in he meets a neighbor pulling up lobster pots.

One-cylinder putt-putt of a small fishing boat.

LEM. How they runnin', Manny?

MANNY. Only eight so far in two strings. Crabs mostly. They eat the danged bait till they ain't nothin' left for the lobsta.

LEM. Same with me. Guess the bottom's dryin' up, dang it.

MANNY. My old lady said she'd throw me outa the house if I di'n bring one home.

LEM. Well . . . (*Motor picking up.*) good luck, Manny. Hope you fill 'er to the scuppers.

MANNY. So long, Lem.

Music: Variation Number 4.

PILOT. Even as we lingered, day has trickled down the coast, past Portland, past the rocking spars of fishing boats in Gloucester, over the dam at Lawrence, and the gas tank in Lynn; and on Shore Drive at Winthrop jogs a milk-cart, going about its business on rubber tires.

Horse hooves in. Cart stops. Footsteps on stone; footsteps upstairs; bottle clinks. Downstairs; steps on stone. Cart resumes. So does:

PILOT. And this young light which makes milk bottles pink in Winthrop, and begins to lift the land-fog from Cape Cod, also at this very moment reddens the high peak of Aconcagua in the Andes of the Argentine—the highest peak in all the ranging hemisphere.

Music: Variation Number 5 begins under the words, "land-fog from Cape Cod."

PILOT. It washes over narrow Chile, too, and skips across the triple mountain ranges of Peru, to gleam at last from breakers on the long Pacific shore.

Cape Horn and Sandy Hook are tinctured now; Magellan's windy straits, Columbus' San Salvador, and Henry Hudson's river all are lighted by the same oncoming dawn. The highest mountain and the highest building meet the morning in the same hushed moment. Thirty-fourth Street in Manhattan is awash with prophecy of day. A little north by east of where the Empire State is, underground at Madison and Fifty-third, a stranger in Manhattan tries to find his way.

Slight echo in for hollow sound of empty subway at night. Footsteps descending metal-stripped stairs; train up and out of station well in background. Click of coin.

MAN (*heavy Southern accent*). Change, please.

Several coins slid along counter.

MAN. Can y'all tell me whut train Ah take for the George Washington Bridge?

ATTENDANT. Lessee. . . . Go down to the first level. Take any train. If it's an F train, get off at the next stop, Fiftieth and Sixth Avenoo . . .

MAN. Look, Mister, I want to go uptown!

ATTENDANT. Yeah, Mac, but these trains all happen to go downtown, so you hafta change. So get off at Fiftieth and Sixth Avenoo an' then cross over to the uptown side. Then take a train marked D an' get off at Columbus Soicle—Fifty-ninth Street. Then wait fer an A train on the same track, an' that'll take ya right to the bridge at 179th Street.

MAN (*rehearsing*). Change at Fiftieth and Sixth Avenue—take a train marked D to Columbus Circle—an' then what?

ATTENDANT. Then the A train to 179th.

MAN. Oh yes, A to 179th Street. Thank yuh, Mister.

ATTENDANT. Wait a minute. That's only for one of the trains. If the first one through here's an E train, take 'er down to Eighth Avenoo and Forty-second Street . . .

MAN. Yuh mean Ah hafta go downtown before Ah can go uptown?

ATTENDANT. Well, you hafta get hungry before you can eat, doncha?

MAN. Yeah, but . . .

ATTENDANT. Well, all right then; so go to Forty-second Street, cross over, an' catch the A train same as before. Only difference is, here you hafta go down farther to do it. Okay? . . .

PILOT. The morning is beyond the bridges of the Hudson now and slanting through the passes of the Appalachians. The seaboard's brightening; a wind is playing with the tide off Hatteras; Miami looks alert; street lamps are turned off in Ottawa. There's drizzle over part of Lake Ontario, but Buffalo is clear; and downstream a few honeymooners are awake to see day rising on Niagara Falls. It rises also now on two canals: the Erie in New York State, and the Panama. It's the same slip of morning to both ditches, though they lie two thousand miles apart.

Detroit lights up now, and the Smoky Mountains, and Key West. Three of the five Great Lakes have caught the fire; but just as dawn arrives in Dayton, it departs beyond the western shores of South America into the waiting sea. In northern Indiana flames are spitting from the forges of the mills at Gary. Under the stacks and sooted roofs, the night shift labors on the final stretch.

Literal machine sounds (crane, ore cars, etc.) and suggestion of power and machinery in music, but with sound standing out in relief.

PILOT. The Mississippi's winding out of darkness now from top to bottom of the land; the saints are all awake—St. Paul, St. Louis, St. Joe, St. Francisville. And down the very same meridian, cross-cut by the equator, sharp in the inclination of the fragile light, is the dry archipelago of the Galápagos.

Music: Segues into Variation Number 7.

PILOT. It's snowing now on mystic Boothia, the northernmost peninsula of North America; but morning overrides the storm. Here's the magnetic pole, which keeps all of the world's compasses aquiver. While Boothia is freezing, there's a light dew brewing west of Omaha, warm winds at Dallas, and gray-green reflections in the water at the docks of Vera Cruz.

Long-brooding Popocatepetl rears his head above a zone of nimbus clouds and looks around to see if all is punctual. Now one vast sweep of plain, a sea of flatlands tilted upward toward the still dark Rockies, quietly and calmly takes on day. Hundreds of rectangle counties, county after county, come into the fold of morning. In the town of Guthrie—Logan County, Oklahoma—on the porch of a house near the Cottonwood, a boy observes the heavens getting pale.

Music: Out.

Birds in.

BOY. Betty—ya 'sleep?

GIRL (*sleepily*). No, I'm awake.

BOY. It's getting light.

GIRL (*stirring lazily to go*). Yeah, gosh. I better get in before Mom wakes up, or I'll catch it.

BOY. Aw, gee, don't go.

GIRL. I gotta.

BOY. Your mother won't be up for two hours.

GIRL. (*Makes a sound of comfortable pleasure—a sort of chuckling noise. She is snuggling up to the Boy.*)

BOY. Know something, Betty? I never been up all night in my life before.

GIRL. Me neither.

BOY. When a feller likes a girl, he *likes* to sit up with her.

GIRL. Well, if a girl likes a feller, it's about the same thing, ain't it? I mean, in the same way, sort of?

BOY. Yeah. Gosh, it's all one and the same thing, no matter how you look at it, I guess.

GIRL. I agree with you. (*Pause.*)

BOY. Ain't the sky pretty, though?

GIRL. It's breath takingly beautiful.

BOY. Wouldn't it be nice if we could do this every night?

GIRL. It would be *divine.*

BOY (*touched*). You really mean that, Betty?

GIRL. Absolutely.

BOY. Gosh. (*Gulps.*) Thanks. I didn't expect you to say it would be *divine*. That's saying a *lot*.

GIRL. Well—I—I don't take back a word of it.

BOY. Well, gee, Betty, thanks a lot.

Music: Variation Number 8, proceeding under:

PILOT. While love awakens on a porch in Guthrie, the somber Rocky Mountains watch the stars burn out above the great plateaus. Ranges rise to block the passage of the day, but not for long.

Dawn vaults them all, these mountains with Spanish names—spreads out on the square states, rolls over into Arizona.

Idling airplane motors in.

PILOT. At Tucson's airport last night's New York plane has taken on some breakfast boxes for still sleeping passengers who will awake above the desert and drink orange juice at seven thousand feet. The charts have all been checked, the weather verified, the pilot gone up front; the stewardess has closed the door. Next stop, Los Angeles.

Twin motors start; takeoff. Cross to interior motor sounds under:

PILOT. The plane is fast, but not as fast as we, for even now we're over the Grand Canyon, riotous with reds and purples—chilling with its silence and its majesty a group of tourists watching sunup from the southern rim.

MRS. PROTHERIDGE. It certainly is all it's cracked up to be, isn't it, Mrs. Stuben?

MRS. STUBEN. It's gorgeous. I seen it once before, but it seems to be more gorgeous every time I see it. Look at *that!*

PERRY (*life of the party*). Nothing like this in Brooklyn—hey, Eddie? (*Laughs hard.*)

EDDIE. You got something there, Perry. . . . You know, if somebody painted this you wouldn't believe it.

MRS. STUBEN. That's absolutely right.

MRS. PROTHERIDGE. I don't know about *you,* but *I* wouldn't like to fall down off one of them cliffs.

EDDIE. Me neither. (*Pause.*) Ain't the silence wonderful?

PERRY. Did you know that this place can be deafening with noise sometimes?

EDDIE. Is that right?

MRS. STUBEN. It can?

PERRY. Sure—when it makes a noise like a *canyon!* (*Roars with laughter, which holds until cross-fade to music.*)

Music: Variation Number 9, continuing under:

PILOT. Death Valley comes to life. Mount Whitney yawns and stretches. Ancient redwood trees look up with boredom at another day. An owl screams in the woodlands of Yosemite. The sea fog's sitting on Los Angeles, but Palos Verdes and the top of Catalina float above the mists. Rain in Seattle, heavy in Snohomish County; routine fog in San Francisco, lifting. In a café on the Embarcadero the dregs of night still linger.

Music: Sloppy piano in after the word "Embarcadero."

NICK. Sorry, Mr. Stewart, but you willa hafta go home. We closa uppa now.

STEWART. G'wan away, li'l man, I'm greatest composer since-a days o' Yasha Masha Pasha.

Music: Piano stops.

NICK (*exasperated*). Looka—looka! Gotta close 'em up, da cops taka my license if I don'. Now be good guys, g'wan, be good guys. It's-a gettin' light already, look see.

STEWART. Jesh *one* more piece. Stacatto and fewgwee by Johann Sebastian Strauss . . .

NICK. "*One-a* more, *one-a* more"—at's-a what you said before!

STEWART. Well, thish time, I'm man o' my word, Nicky, ol' boy. I'm the man *behind* the man *behind* the man o' my word, see? Jesh one more.

Music: Playing begins anew.

NICK (*hopefully*). Wella—all right. Justa thisa one.

STEWART (*over music*). Jesh thish one, jesh thish. Now take it easy, Nick, ol' boy, you sit an' lissen . . .

Music: Piano cross-fades to Variation Number 10, under:

PILOT. The snow fields of the Yukon and the Klondike mountains lie face up, interpreting the soundless and mysterious code of the aurora borealis. The streamers, green and orange, shimmering in the black Arctic night, yield occultly to new light from behind the frozen ranges to the east.

The dawn is piqued and pinched here in Alaska; it is fuller on the endless swells of the Pacific to the south—the Pacific, flowing now in space so prodigal that only stellar seas could understand. The hemisphere is falling back. McKinley passes in the great processional; Alaska's Valley of Ten Thousand Smokes turns steaming to the sun from which its planetary fire was drawn down. The roar of Katmai, angriest volcano of them all, abates none, scorning the eruption of such placid stuffs as mornings.

Sound of volcano faded in after "angriest volcano of them all."

Roar up full, diminishing under:

PILOT. South as the crow flies—flying just about two thousand miles—is another such volcano, set about by sea—Mauna Loa, monarch of the glistening Hawaiian Islands. It stands frowning down on fields of its own lava.

These islands are romantic at night, to all romanticists, but now at dawn in Honolulu, where the trade wind stirs the cocoa palms, a practical procedure's taking place inside a hospital. Beneath the white glare of the operating lamps a surgeon meets with an emergency.

Fade in quick, efficient bustle of several people moving around. Intermittent click of surgical instruments.

ANESTHETIST. Doctor, the pressure's falling rapidly, and the pulse is becoming thready.

SURGEON. Get that transfusion set ready. Doctor Jones, you scrub for transfusion.

JONES. Right, sir.

SURGEON. Is the donor outside, and has he been cross-matched?

NURSE. Yes, sir.

SURGEON. All right, start the transfusion and give him a hypo of adrenalin. (*Pause.*) Get the large kidney clamps and the heavy ligature ready. (*Pause.*) Suction.

Sound of suction in. (*This is steady hiss of air with fairly steady gurgle of liquid being sucked up a tube.*) *Pause.*

Sound of clamp being applied. (*Clamp has ratchet-catches like a handcuff but makes a smaller, cleaner sound.*)

SURGEON. Sponge. (*Pause.*)

JONES. The pulse is becoming imperceptible . . . heart sounds very feeble.

SURGEON. Inject some coramin into the veins.

JONES. Yes, sir. (*Pause.*) Doctor, the heart sounds are not audible.

SURGEON. Massage his heart. (*Pause.*) Sponge.

ANESTHETIST. Pupils are widely dilated, Doctor.

JONES. There's no response from the heart at all.

ANESTHETIST. Doctor, the patient has ceased breathing.

SURGEON. Well . . . we did all we could.

PILOT. Northward at the moment of this dawn death, the night's pushed back entire from the face of North America. It's west of Bering Strait now, in Soviet Siberia, pursued across the stepping-stones of the Aleutian Islands. Daybreak has reached the 180th meridian, where man, in spite of all his quarreling, agrees by international accord that here his calendar divides today from yesterday. A liner headed for San Pedro crosses this imaginary line. On B deck a woman is awake to greet the moment.

Sound of water in; steady, calm sea.

WOMAN. You mean we're crossing at this very moment, officer?
OFFICER. Yes, ma'am.
WOMAN. Oh, it's so thrilling! Just think, a minute ago it was Sunday —now it's Saturday! (*Laughs.*)
OFFICER. Yes, ma'am. International date line.
WOMAN. Does that mean we are a day ahead of the rest of the world?
OFFICER (*startled*). Oh, no! Where'd you get that idea?
WOMAN. Well, that's true, isn't it?
OFFICER. No, no, it merely means that . . .
WOMAN. Well, five hours ago it was midnight *Saturday*, and so it became *Sunday*. And now it's *Saturday* again. Is that fair?
OFFICER. Well, you see, madam, it works like this . . .
WOMAN. I don't understand it very well.
OFFICER. I think I can explain it. Now, a ten-day voyage from San Francisco to Yokohama will show eleven calendar days. But on the return trip, when we cross the international date line eastbound, like we just did, we go *back* one day on the calendar, into the *old* day, so that means a ten-day trip *east*bound will show nine calendar days, whereas the *west*bound voyage shows eleven calendar days.
WOMAN (*plaintively*). But doesn't the ten-day trip ever take just ten days?
OFFICER (*patiently*). No, ma'am. (*Fading.*) Now let me begin again. I think I can explain it all right. . . . You see, ordinarily the day changes with the passing of midnight. But there are always two calendar days on the earth's surface at all times. This means that . . .

Music: Comes up, crossing with the Officer. It backs the following:

PILOT. New Zealand, now, at the antipodes, diagonally across the world from Greenwich. The east coast of Australia catches day as did the east coast of Brazil twelve hours back. The sun now gilds the gold fields; the sands of the interior are tinted too, the Great Victoria Desert curving into the dry day.

Three thousand miles up the meridian, a pilgrimage ascends the slopes of Fuji. Those winding lights below us are the lanterns of the faithful, lanterns named for those who carry them, the Japanese. And to the north, there's Vladivostok looming up with lights across the sea; and now the coast of China.

Night trails its kites across the Philippines, the Dutch East Indies, Borneo. Deeper into China, up the Yangtze, past Hankow it spreads. But wait: those flicks of flame you see far, far below are not the Chinese glowworm—those are men at war, the first such spectacle since morning joined us at the twenty-fifth meridian.

Rifle fire in; hold very briefly. Cross-fade to:

Music: Variation Number 11, under:

PILOT. All quiet on the Gobi desert to the north. Southward the night is gone from Java and Australia too. The guns of Singapore are vigilant, and scrutinize the straits. Mandalay lies under heavy rain clouds; otherwise you'd make it out. Now Everest sees the coming day before all Asia to the west. In fact, it is a tight squeeze for the morning, getting by the peak which roofs the planet.

Five hundred million people sleep in India, Afghanistan, the Union of the Soviets. Dawn comes to each of them, to each one's window, arches over each one's head. It's in the tundra in the north of Russia, also in the streets of Takhta-Bazar, and the market at Termez. At Troitsk, the workers soundly sleep.

Music: A sudden change of color to underscore:

PILOT. Now in a sweeping arc the dawn cuts through three continents: still Asia, in the Urals; Europe, where the Soviets draw a line; and Africa, at easternmost Somaliland. The same light spans the Caspian, the Persian Gulf, the wildest desert of Arabia.

Artillery up through music fragmentarily for following phase:

PILOT. Below us in the Syrian morn there's movement: men and guns afoot. (*Guns out.*) There's stealthy shipping in the foggy Bosporus. (*Medium ship whistle.*) The power plant at Dneprostroy is working through the dawn.

Dynamos in after "Dneprostroy"; out after "dawn."

PILOT. The rim moves on to Finland now, at the same time it crowns the pyramid of Cheops. In the scarlet break of day the tombs of the Egyptian kings are tipped with red lights, warning airplanes.

Warring Europe starts up from a fitful sleep. The Congo in the heart of Africa awakens tranquilly. The morning, being a celestial thing, cannot begin to comprehend. This is the bleak meridian of trouble: Norway, Poland, Germany, Russia, the Balkans, Libya.

Muted bugle call—reveille—in background.

PILOT. Great camps and barracks in each land anticipate the day. But to the fields and lakes and rivers and the partly stormy sky, it's all the same—it always is the same.

Slip down the middle length of Africa: far at the southern tip, two albatrosses circle lazily above the sparkling waters off Good Hope. Capetown looks at night across the South Atlantic —night—the very night now solid in Brazil.

Two farmers meet in Switzerland, where their adjoining pastures slope down toward the valley. They say the same thing they've been saying now for twenty-seven years of mountain mornings.

HANS. Morning, Peter.

PETER. Morning, Hans.

HANS. Nice day.

PETER. Yes, very nice.

HANS. All well?

PETER. I can't complain. And you?

HANS. Fine, fine.

PETER. Good. See you later.

HANS. See you later, Peter.

Music: Variation Number 12.

PILOT. The North Sea and the Mediterranean are both lit now, and London comes up out of cover. Greenwich gives the day a careless nod and signals it the go-ahead to climb the west meridians. In vasty hushes the fresh morning cleans the traces of the dark out of the mid-Sahara. Off the Gold Coast of deep-brooding Africa, in the wide Guinea Gulf, there is a fight between two sharks, just at the mighty intersection where longitude and latitude each reach zero. Here the equator meets the mean meridian. The green Atlantic does not know it, though. The fighting sharks don't care.

The Irish Sea, Gibraltar, and St. Helena swim up out of the Afro-European night. Lisbon and Morocco and Liberia come next; Dakar and the Canaries; and now all of both continents are in full day. It's all in the Atlantic now, this far-flung fringe of daybreak. We're moving west of Greenwich once again.

Now we are back at latitude 40° north, and longitude 25° west. And this is where we started from. Beneath us there is water, nothing else: the long Atlantic flowing to the north.

Music: Finale treatment.

Note on a Forest Drama

When Benjamin Franklin in 1753 was chosen one of three commissioners to negotiate a treaty between the Province of Pennsylvania and the Ohio Indians at Carlisle, it not only marked the beginning of his career in diplomacy but it also required him to take part in one of those native ceremonies which were memorable drama before America knew it had anything like dramatic performances or dramatic literature.*

"The Indians were not, as tradition has come to regard them, perpetual enemies in endless wars against the white settlers. For three or four decades before 1763 the Six Nations—Mohawk, Oneida, Onondaga, Cayuga, Seneca, and the newly-admitted Tuscarora—of the Iroquois Confederation labored skillfully and wisely to keep the peace. Not more than perhaps fifteen thousand persons all together, living in perhaps fifty villages in central New York, the Confederation ruled a kind of empire from the St. Lawrence to the James, from the Hudson nearly to the Mississippi. Conquered tribes paid tribute to the Iroquois, who alone claimed the right to say who should go to war, and why and when. South of the Six Nations lay the hunting grounds of the Susquehanna valley to which the Iroquois had assigned the Delawares and the Shawnee, with smaller tribes. The Oneida chief Shikellamy took up his official residence in 1728 at Shomokin (now Sunbury), at the forks of the Susquehanna, and there for twenty years acted as the Confederation's vice-regent for the district. In 1729 Conrad Weiser, a Palatine who had lived from boyhood in close friendship with the Mohawk, left New York to establish himself on a farm at Tulpehocken."

The far-sighted Indian policy of Pennsylvania owed much to the

* The quoted portions of this Note are, with the permission of the Historical Society of Pennsylvania, taken from my Introduction to the Society's *Indian Treaties Printed by Benjamin Franklin 1736–1762* (1938), edited by Julian P. Boyd.

astute and secret Shikellamy. "Through him, with Weiser as interpreter, Pennsylvania made terms with the Six Nations. Together they disposed of the Delawares and the Shawnee, rebellious tributaries of the Six Nations, uncomfortable neighbors of the Pennsylvanians. This cost the Province a Delaware-Shawnee war, but it prevented what would have been a worse war with the Iroquois. The Six Nations, after their treaty with Pennsylvania, Maryland, and Virginia at Lancaster in 1744, looked on Pennsylvania as spokesman for the English generally. Canasatego, chief of the Onandaga, at Lancaster advised the English to follow the Iroquois example. 'Our wise Forefathers established Union and Amity between the *Five Nations:* this has made us formidable; this has given us great Weight and Authority with our neighbouring Nations. We are a powerful Confederacy; and, by your observing the same Methods our wise Forefathers have taken, you will acquire such Strength and Power; therefore whatever befals you, never fall out with one another.' Though the colonies were slow in learning union from the Indians, Pennsylvania's steady alliance with the Six Nations had a large effect in preserving the friendship of the Iroquois for the English. If the Iroquois with their whole empire had gone over to the French they might have won the continent.

"The Pennsylvania treaties which maintained the alliance were diplomatic dramas in a form prescribed by Iroquois ritual and for years directed by Conrad Weiser, the Pennsylvania interpreter. 'By the Interpreter's Advice,' says the earliest treaty printed by Franklin, the chiefs of the Six Nations who had arrived at Stenton in 1736 'were first spoke to in their own Way, with three small Strings of *Wampum* in Hand, one of which was delivered on each of the following Articles,' presumably by Weiser himself. Four days later, in 'the *Great Meeting-House* at *Philadelphia*' filled to the top of the galleries with curious citizens, in the presence of Thomas Penn, James Logan, and the Council, the Seneca speaker for the chiefs, also in their own way, 'spoke as follows by *Conrad Wyser*.' They had come, he said, to warm themselves at the hospitable fire which Pennsylvania had promised to keep 'in this great City,' and they desired it would 'ever continue bright and burning to the End of the World.' They desired that the road between Philadelphia and the Six Nations might 'be kept clear and open, free from all Stops or Incumbrances.' And they desired that the chain of friendship should be preserved 'free from all Rust and Spots . . . not only between this Government and us, but between all the *English* Governments and all the *Indians*.' Business had to wait on ceremony, and the whole occasion was ceremonial.

"The forest metaphors of the Fire, the Road, the Chain run through the treaties down to that at Carlisle in 1753, when a new ceremony was added, at the request if not the demand of Scarouady, chief and orator of the Oneida. He was there in company with chiefs or deputies of tributary Delawares, Shawnee, Miami (Twightwees), and Wyandots from the Ohio, where the French were threatening. If the English wanted to keep the Ohio Indians friendly, so did the Six Nations, firmly hostile to the French. The English supplied the necessary gifts at the Carlisle treaty; the Six Nations prescribed the ritual of giving. It was an applied form of the ceremony of Condolences, used among the Iroquois when chiefs or warriors had died and delegates from other nations came to mourn the loss.

"All these Ohio tribes had lately suffered the death of notable men. Scarouady, speaking for Pennsylvania as well as for the Six Nations, told the mourners: 'As we know that your Seats at Home are bloody, we wipe away the Blood, and set your Seats in Order at your Council Fire, that you may sit and consult again in Peace and Comfort as formerly.' When a string of wampum had been given he went on: 'We suppose that the Blood is now washed off. We jointly, with our Brother *Onas* [Pennsylvania], dig a Grave for your Warriors, killed in your Country; and we bury their Bones decently; wrapping them up in these Blankets; and with these we cover their Graves.' Then the gifts, already laid out before the Indians, were given to them. Scarouady ended: 'We wipe your Tears from your Eyes, that you may see the Sun, and that every Thing may become clear and pleasant to your Sight; and we desire you would mourn no more.'

"The ceremony of Condolences became as customary in treaties as the metaphorical Fire, Road, Chain. The forms grew familiar to the English, and they expert in the practice of them, but the forms were Iroquois. The governor or the commissioners of Pennsylvania would open a treaty council with a speech of several articles, presenting with each of them a string of wampum which was for the Indians an essential part of the record. Usually the Indians would put off their answer to the next day, to have time to confer among themselves. Then one of them, speaker for them all, would take up each article, repeating it from a memory as accurate as written minutes, and replying to it again with formal wampum. Though there might be hundreds of Indians and white men present at a treaty gathering, and all sorts of caucuses offstage, the actual councils were grave and punctilious, as orderly as a trial before a high court of law, as straightforward in action as a good play. . . .

"The Iroquois statesmen were perfectly aware that only by remaining neutral could they hold the balance of power, and that only so long as they held the balance of power could they hope to survive at all in the face of immensely superior numbers and wealth. So, at treaty after treaty, they schemed for English support of the Confederation, made concessions only when they had to, looked out for the interests of the Indian trade, and exacted or coaxed whatever they could in the way of goods and munitions given as peace-making presents by the English. While their advantage lasted, a league of ragged villages held off two great empires, inflexibly and proudly forcing the empires to treat with them in the village language. . . .

"The Indian treaty was a form of literature which had no single author. Shikellamy and Scarouady may have suggested the metaphors and rites to be used, but they had to be adapted by Weiser as impresario, and then be accepted by the government of Pennsylvania. The secretaries who kept the minutes never dreamed they were making literature, nor need Franklin have guessed that he was printing it in his folios. These were simply the records of public events. The events, being based on ritual, had their own form, and they fixed the form of the record. Accuracy in such cases was art. Now and then the secretaries left out speeches or parts of speeches uttered by the hard tongues of the Indians, but there was not too much expurgation, and there was no literary self-consciousness. Here for once life seems to have made itself almost unaided into literature.

"Nothing quite like the Indian treaties exists anywhere else in the literature of the world. Vercingetorix is only a character in Caesar's narrative, presented as Caesar liked. But Canasatego and Scarouady . . . with many minor chieftains live on in the actual words they spoke face to face with their conquerors, in a breathing-spell before the conquest. For a time savage ritual had power over civilized men, who were obliged to listen. Years later white story-tellers were to lend romantic color to the vanished race. Their invented stories could not equal the treaties, even as romance. The plain facts, as the treaties set them forth, are alive with poetry no less than truth, with humor and drama, and with the fresh wisdom of simple experience."

. . . . .

The text here given follows the rare original folio printed by Franklin and Hall at Philadelphia in 1753, with no changes except that the modern *s* is substituted for the long *s* (*ſ*) then used. Such spellings as *Mohock* for Mohawk or *Oneido* for Oneida will mislead nobody, and the following are not very difficult: *Canawa* (Kanawha), *Cheepaways* (Chippewa), *Mohongely, Mohongialo* (Monongahela), *Outawas* (Ottawa), *Owendaets* (Wyandot), *Scarrooyady* (Scarouady), *Shawonese* (Shawnee), *Weningo* (Venango).

A

TREATY

HELD WITH THE

OHIO INDIANS,

AT

CARLISLE,

In OCTOBER, 1753.

PHILADELPHIA:
Printed and Sold by B. FRANKLIN, and D. HALL, at the
New-Printing-Office, near the Market. MDCCLIII.

A

TREATY, &c.

To the Honourable JAMES HAMILTON, *Esq; Lieutenant-Governor, and Commander in Chief, of the Province of* Pennsylvania, *and Counties of* New-Castle, Kent *and* Sussex, *upon* Delaware,

The REPORT of RICHARD PETERS, ISAAC NORRIS, *and* BENJAMIN FRANKLIN, *Esquires, Commissioners appointed to treat with some Chiefs of the* Ohio Indians, *at* Carlisle, *in the County of* Cumberland, *by a Commission, bearing Date the* 22*d Day of* September, 1753.

May it please the GOVERNOR,

NOT knowing but the *Indians* might be waiting at *Carlisle*, we made all the Dispatch possible, as soon as we had received our Commission, and arrived there on the Twenty-sixth, but were agreeably surprized to find that they came there only that Day.

IMMEDIATELY on our Arrival we conferred with *Andrew Montour*, and *George Croghan*, in order to know from them what had occasioned the present coming of the *Indians*, that we might, by their Intelligence, regulate our first Intercourse with them; and were informed, that tho' their principal Design, when they left *Ohio*, was to hold a Treaty with the Government of *Virginia*, at *Winchester*, where they had accordingly been; yet they intended a Visit to this Province, to which they had been frequently encouraged by *Andrew Montour*, who told them, he had the Governor's repeated Orders to invite them to come and see him, and assured them of an hearty Welcome; and that they had moreover some important Matters to propose and transact with this Government.

THE Commissioners finding this to be the Case, and that these *Indians* were some of the most considerable Persons of the *Six Nations*, *Delawares*, *Shawonese*, with Deputies from the *Twightwees*, and *Owendaets*, met them in Council, in which the Commissioners declared the Contents of their Commission, acknowledged the Governor's Invitation, and bid them heartily welcome among their Brethren of *Pennsylvania*, to whom their Visit was extremely agreeable.—*Conrad Weiser* and *Andrew Montour* interpreting between the Commissioners and *Indians*, and several Magistrates, and others, of the principal Inhabitants of the County, favouring them with their Presence.

THE *Twightwees* and *Delawares* having had several of their great Men cut off by the *French* and their *Indians*, and all the Chiefs of the *Owendaets* being lately dead, it became necessary to condole their Loss; and no Business could be begun, agreeable to the *Indian* Customs, till the Condolances were passed; and as these could not be made, with the usual Ceremonies, for want of the Goods, which were not arrived, and it was uncertain when they would, the Commissioners were put to some Difficulties, and ordered the Interpreters to apply to *Scarrooyady*, an *Oneido* Chief, who had the Conduct of the Treaty in *Virginia*, and was a Person of great Weight in their Councils, and to ask his Opinion, whether the Condolances would be accepted by Belts and Strings, and Lists of the particular Goods intended to be given, with Assurances of their Delivery as soon as they should come. *Scarrooyady* was pleased with the Application; but frankly declared, that the *Indians* could not proceed to Business while the Blood remained on their Garments, and that the Condolances could not be accepted unless the Goods, intended to cover the Graves, were actually spread on the Ground before them. A Messenger was therefore forthwith sent to meet and hasten the Waggoners, since every Thing must stop till the Goods came.

IT was then agreed to confer with *Scarrooyady*, and some other of the Chiefs of the *Shawonese* and *Delawares*, on the State of Affairs at *Ohio*, and from them the Commissioners learned, in sundry Conferences, the following Particulars, *viz.*

"THAT when the Governor of *Pennsylvania's* Express arrived at *Ohio*, with the Account of the March of a large *French* Army to the Heads of *Ohio*, with Intent to take Possession of that Country, it alarmed the *Indians* so much, that the *Delawares*, at *Weningo*, an *Indian* Town, situate high up on *Ohio* River, went, agreeable to a Custom established among the *Indians*, and forbad, by a formal Notice, the Commander of that Armament, then advanced to the *Straits*, between Lake *Ontario* and Lake *Erie*, to continue his March, at least not to presume to come farther than *Niagara*. This had not however any Effect, but, notwithstanding this Notice, the *French* continued their March; which, being afterwards taken into Consideration by the Council, at *Logs-Town*, they ordered some of their principal *Indians* to give the *French* a second Notice to leave their Country, and return Home; who meeting them on a River running into Lake *Erie*, a little above *Weningo*, addressed the Commander in these Words:

The second Notice delivered to the Commander of the French *Army, then near* Weningo.

Father Onontio,

YOUR Children on *Ohio* are alarmed to hear of your coming so far this Way. We at first heard you came to destroy us; our Women left off planting, and our Warriors prepared for War. We have since heard you came to visit us as Friends, without Design to hurt us; but then we wondered you came with so strong a Body. If you have had any Cause of Complaint, you might have spoke to *Onas*, or *Corlaer* (meaning the Governors of *Pennsylvania*, and *New-York*) and not come to disturb us here. We have a Fire at *Logs-Town*, where are the *Delawares*, and *Shawonese*, and Brother *Onas;* you might have sent Deputies there, and said openly what you came about, if you had thought amiss of the *English* being there; and we invite you to do it now; before you proceed any further.

The French *Officer's Answer.*

Children,

I FIND you come to give me an Invitation to your Council Fire, with a Design, as I suppose, to call me to Account for coming here. I must let you know that my Heart is good to you; I mean no Hurt to you; I am come by the great King's Command, to do you, my Children, Good. You seem to think I carry my Hatchet under my Coat; I always carry it openly, not to strike you, but those that shall oppose me. I cannot come to your Council Fire, nor can I return, or stay here; I am so heavy a Body that the Stream will carry me down, and down I shall go, unless you pull off my Arm: But this I will tell you, I am commanded to build four strong Houses, *viz.* at *Weningo, Mohongialo Forks, Logs-Town,* and *Beaver Creek,* and this I will do. As to what concerns *Onas*, and *Assaragoa* (meaning the Governors of *Pennsylvania* and *Virginia*) I have spoke to them, and let them know they must go off the Land, and I shall speak to them again; if they will not hear me, it is their Fault, I will take them by the Arm, and throw them over the Hills. All the Land and Waters on this Side *Allegheny* Hills are mine, on the other Side theirs; this is agreed on between the two Crowns over the great Waters. I do not like your selling your Lands to the *English;* they shall draw you into no more foolish Bargains. I will take Care of your Lands for you, and of you. The *English* give you no Goods but for Land, we give you our Goods for nothing."

We were further told by *Scarrooyady*, that when the Answer to this Message was brought to *Logs-Town*, another Council was held, consisting of the *Six Nations*, *Delawares*, and *Shawonese*, who unanimously agreed to divide themselves into two Parties, one to go to *Virginia*, and *Pennsylvania*, with *Scarrooyady*, and the other to go with the *Half King* to the *French* Commander, who had it in Charge to make the following Declaration, as their third and last Notice.

The third Notice, delivered by the Half King *to the Commander of the* French *Forces.*

Father,

You say you cannot come to our Council Fire at *Logs-Town*, we therefore now come to you, to know what is in your Heart. You remember when you were tired with the War (meaning Queen *Anne*'s War) you of your own Accord sent for us, desiring to make Peace with us; when we came, you said to us, Children, we make a Council Fire for you; we want to talk with you, but we must first eat all with one Spoon out of this Silver Bowl, and all drink out of this Silver Cup; let us exchange Hatchets; let us bury our Hatchets in this bottomless Hole; and now we will make a plain Road to all your Countries, so clear, that *Onontio* may sit here and see you all eat and drink out of the Bowl and Cup, which he has provided for you. Upon this Application of yours we consented to make Peace; and when the Peace was concluded on both Sides, you made a solemn Declaration, saying, Whoever shall hereafter transgress this Peace, let the Transgressor be chastised with a Rod, even tho' it be I, your Father.

Now, Father, notwithstanding this solemn Declaration of yours, you have whipped several of your Children; you know best why. Of late you have chastised the *Twightwees* very severely, without telling us the Reason; and now you are come with a strong Band on our Land, and have, contrary to your Engagement, taken up the Hatchet without any previous Parley. These Things are a Breach of the Peace; they are contrary to your own Declarations: Therefore, now I come to forbid you. I will strike over all this Land with my Rod, let it hurt who it will. I tell you, in plain Words, you must go off this Land. You say you have a strong Body, a strong Neck, and a strong Voice, that when you speak all the *Indians* must hear you. It is true, you are a strong Body, and ours is but weak, yet we are not afraid of you. We forbid you to come any further; turn back to the Place from whence you came.

SCARROOYADY, who was the Speaker in these Conferences, when he had finished this Relation, gave his Reason for setting forth these three Messages to the *French* in so distinct a Manner; because, said he, the Great Being who lives above, has ordered us to send three Messages of Peace before we make War:—And as the *Half King* has, before this Time, delivered the third and last Message, we have nothing now to do but to strike the *French*.

THE Commissioners were likewise informed, by Mr. *Croghan*, that the *Ohio Indians* had received from the *Virginia* Government a large Number of Arms in the Spring, and that at their pressing Instances a suitable Quantity of Ammunition was ordered in the Treaty at *Winchester* to be lodged for them, in a Place of Security, on this Side the *Ohio*, which was committed to the Care of three Persons, *viz.* *Guest*, *William Trent*, and *Andrew Montour*, who were impowered to distribute them to the *Indians* as their Occasions and Behaviour should require. That all the Tribes settled at or near *Allegheny* would take their Measures from the Encouragement which these *Indians* should find in the Province of *Virginia*; and that the kind Intentions of this Government in the Appropriation of a large Sum of Money for the Use of these *Indians*, in case they should be distressed by their Enemies, and their Hunting and Planting prevented, were well known to them by the repeated Informations of *Andrew Montour* and the Traders.

CONRAD WEISER, to whom it was earnestly recommended by the Commissioners, to procure all the Information possible from the *Indians* of his Acquaintance, touching their Condition and Disposition, and the real Designs of the *French*, did likewise acquaint us, that all Persons at *Ohio* would have their Eyes on the Reception of those *Indians*, now at *Carlisle*, and judge of the Affection of this Province by their Treatment of them; and that as the intended Present was no Secret to those *Indians*, it was his Opinion, that the Whole should, at this Time, be distributed; for if any Thing can, such a generous Donation must needs attach the *Indians* entirely to the *English*.

THESE several Matters being taken into Consideration by the Commissioners, and the Governor having given them express Directions to accommodate themselves to the Circumstances of the *Indians*, as they should appear in examining them at the Place of Treaty, we were unanimously of Opinion, that an Addition should be made to the Goods bought at *Philadelphia*, in which a Regard should be had to such Articles as were omitted or supplied in less Quantities than was suitable to the present Wants of the *Indians*. On this resolution the Lists of Goods were examined, and an additional Quantity bought of *John Carson*, at the *Philadelphia* Price, and usual Rate of Carriage.

DURING these Consultations, it was rumoured that the *Half King* was returned to *Logs-Town*, and had received an unsatisfactory Answer, which was confirmed, but not in such Manner as could be positively relied on, by a Brother of *Andrew Montour*, and another Person who came directly from *Allegheny*. This alarmed the Commissioners, and made them willing to postpone Business till they should know the Certainty thereof, judging, that if the *Half King* was returned, he would certainly send a Messenger Express to *Carlisle*, with an Account of what was done by him; and from this the Commissioners might take their Measures in the Distribution of the Present.

A LETTER, wrote by *Taaf*, and *Callender*, two *Indian* Traders, dated the Twenty-eighth Day of *September*, from a Place situate a little on this Side *Allegheny* River, directed to *William Buchanan*, was given him the Morning of the first Day of *October*, and he immediately laid it before the Commissioners for their Perusal. In this Letter an Account is given, that the *Half King* was returned, and had been received in a very contemptuous Manner by the *French* Commander, who was then preparing with his Forces to come down the River; and that the *Half King*, on his Return, shed Tears, and had actually warned the *English* Traders not to pass the *Ohio*, nor to venture either their Persons or their Goods, for the *French* would certainly hurt them. On this News the Conferences with *Scarrooyady*, and the Chiefs of the *Six Nations*, *Delawares*, and *Shawonese*, were renewed, and the Letter read to them, at which they appeared greatly alarmed; but, after a short Pause, *Scarrooyady*, addressing himself to the *Delawares* and *Shawonese*, spoke in these Words:

Brethren and Cousins,

I LOOK on this Letter as if it had been a Message from the *Half King* himself: We may expect no other Account of the Result of his Journey.

However, I advise you to be still, and neither say nor do any Thing till we get Home, and I see my Friend and Brother the *Half King*, and then we shall know what is to be done.

THE Forms of the Condolances, which depend entirely on *Indian* Customs, were settled in Conferences with *Scarrooyady*, and *Cayanguileguoa*, a sensible *Indian*, of the *Mohock* Nation, and a Person intimate with and much consulted by *Scarrooyady*, in which it was agreed to take the *Six Nations* along with us in these Condolances; and accordingly the proper Belts and Strings were made ready, and *Scarrooyady* prepared himself to express the Sentiments of both in the *Indian* Manner. And as the Goods arrived this Morning before Break of Day, the several Sorts used on these Occasions were laid out; and the *Indians* were told that the Commissioners would speak to them at Eleven a Clock.

At a Meeting of the Commissioners, and Indians, *at* Carlisle, *the first Day of* October, 1753.

PRESENT,

RICHARD PETERS, ISAAC NORRIS, BENJAMIN FRANKLIN, Esquires, Commissioners.

The Deputies of the *Six Nations, Delawares, Shawonese, Twightwees,* and *Owendaets.*

CONRAD WEISER, ANDREW MONTOUR, Interpreters. JAMES WRIGHT, JOHN ARMSTRONG, Esquires, Members of Assembly.

The Magistrates, and several other Gentlemen and Freeholders of the County of *Cumberland.*

The SPEECH *of the Commissioners.*

Brethren, *Six Nations, Delawares, Shawonese, Twightwees,* and *Owendaets,*

THOUGH the City of *Philadelphia* be the Place where all *Indians* should go, who have Business to transact with this Government, yet at your Request, signified to Colonel *Fairfax,* at Winchester, and by him communicated to our Governor, by an Express to *Philadelphia,* he has been pleased on this particular Occasion to dispense with your coming there, and has done us the Honour to depute us to receive and treat with you at this Town, in his Place and Stead; this is set forth in his Commission, which we now produce to you, under the Great Seal of this Province, the authentick Sign and Testimony of all Acts of Government.

Brethren,

By this String we acquaint you, that the *Six Nations* do, at our Request, join with us in condoling the Losses you have of late sustained by the Deaths of several of your Chiefs and principal Men; and that *Scarrooyady* is to deliver for both what has been agreed to be said on this melancholy Occasion.

Here the Commissioners gave a String of Wampum.

Then Scarrooyady *spoke as follows:*

Brethren, the Twightwees *and* Shawonese,

It has pleased Him who is above, that we shall meet here To-day, and see one another; I and my Brother *Onas* join together to speak to you. As we know that your Seats at Home are bloody, we wipe away the Blood, and set your Seats in Order at your Council Fire, that you may sit and consult again in Peace and Comfort as formerly; that you may hold the antient Union, and strengthen it, and continue your old friendly Correspondence.

Here a String was given.

Brethren, Twightwees, *and* Shawonese,

We suppose that the Blood is now washed off. We jointly, with our Brother *Onas*, dig a Grave for your Warriors, killed in your Country; and we bury their Bones decently; wrapping them up in these Blankets; and with these we cover their Graves.

Here the Goods were given to the Twightwees, *and* Shawonese.

Brethren, Twightwees, *and* Shawonese,

I, and my Brother *Onas*, jointly condole with the Chiefs of your Towns, your Women and Children, for the Loss you have sustained. We partake of your Grief, and mix our Tears with yours. We wipe your Tears from your Eyes, that you may see the Sun, and that every Thing may become clear and pleasant to your Sight; and we desire you would mourn no more.

Here a Belt was given.

The same was said to the *Delawares, mutatis mutandis.*

And then he spoke to the *Owendaets,* in these Words:

Our Children, and Brethren, the Owendaets,

You have heard what I and my Brother *Onas* have jointly said to the

Twightwees, Shawonese, and *Delawares:* We now come to speak to you. We are informed that your good old wise Men are all dead, and you have no more left.

WE must let you know, that there was a Friendship established by our and your Grandfathers; and a mutual Council Fire was kindled. In this Friendship all those then under the Ground, who had not yet obtained Eyes or Faces (that is, those unborn) were included; and it was then mutually promised to tell the same to their Children, and Childrens Children: But so many great Men of your Nation have died in so short a Time, that none but Youths are left; and this makes us afraid, lest that Treaty, so solemnly established by your Ancestors, should be forgotten by you: We therefore now come to remind you of it, and renew it; we re-kindle the old Fire, and put on fresh Fuel.

Here a String was given.

THE other Speeches, of burying the Dead, *&c.* were the same as those to the *Twightwees,* &c.

AFTER each had been spoken to, *Scarrooyady* proceeded thus:

Brethren, Delawares, Shawonese, Twightwees, *and* Owendaets,

WE, the *English,* and *Six Nations,* do now exhort every one of you to do your utmost to preserve this Union and Friendship, which has so long and happily continued among us: Let us keep the Chain from rusting, and prevent every Thing that may hurt or break it, from what Quarter soever it may come.

THEN the Goods allotted for each Nation, as a Present of Condolance, were taken away by each, and the Council adjourn'd to the next Day.

At a Meeting of the Commissioners, and Indians, *at* Carlisle, *the 2d of* October, 1753.

PRESENT,

The Commissioners, The same *Indians* as Yesterday,

The Magistrates, and several Gentlemen of the County.

The SPEECH *of the Commissioners.*

Brethren, Six Nations, Delawares, Shawonese, Twightwees, *and* Owendaets,

NOW that your Hearts are eased of their Grief, and we behold one another with chearful Countenances, we let you know that the Governor, and good People of *Pennsylvania,* did not send us to receive you empty-handed; but put something into our Pockets, to be given to such as should favour us with this friendly Visit: These Goods we therefore request you would accept of, and divide amongst all that are of your Company, in such Proportions as shall be agreeable to you. You know how to do this better than we. What we principally desire, is, that you will consider this Present as a Token of our cordial Esteem for you; and use it with a Frugality becoming your Circumstances, which call at this Time for more than ordinary Care.

Brethren,

WITH Pleasure we behold here the Deputies of five different Nations, *viz.* the *United Six Nations*, the *Delawares*, the *Shawonese*, the *Twightwees*, and the *Owendaets*. Be pleased to cast your Eyes towards this Belt, whereon six Figures are delineated, holding one another by the Hands. This is a just Resemblance of our present Union: The five first Figures representing the five Nations, to which you belong, as the sixth does the Government of *Pennsylvania;* with whom you are linked in a close and firm Union. In whatever Part the Belt is broke, all the Wampum runs off, and renders the Whole of no Strength or Consistency. In like Manner, should you break Faith with one another, or with this Government, the Union is dissolved. We would therefore hereby place before you the Necessity of preserving your Faith entire to one another, as well as to this Government. Do not separate: Do not part on any Score. Let no Differences nor Jealousies subsist a Moment between Nation and Nation; but join all together as one Man, sincerely and heartily. We on our Part shall always perform our Engagements to every one of you. In Testimony whereof, we present you with this Belt.

Here the Belt was given.

Brethren,

WE have only this one Thing further to say at this Time: Whatever Answers you may have to give, or Business to transact with us, we desire you would use Dispatch; as it may be dangerous to you, and incommodious to us, to be kept long from our Homes, at this Season of the Year.

At a Meeting of the Commissioners, and Indians, *the 3d of* October, 1753.

PRESENT,

The Commissioners, The same *Indians* as before.

Several Gentlemen of the County.

Scarrooyady, Speaker.

Brother Onas,

WHAT we have now to say, I am going to speak, in Behalf of the *Twightwees, Shawonese, Delawares*, and *Owendaets*.

YOU have, like a true and affectionate Brother, comforted us in our Affliction. You have wiped away the Blood from our Seats, and set them again in order. You have wrapped up the Bones of our Warriors, and covered the Graves of our wise Men; and wiped the Tears from our Eyes, and the Eyes of our Women and Children: So that we now see the Sun, and all Things are become pleasant to our Sight. We shall not fail to acquaint our several Nations with your Kindness. We shall take Care that it be always remembered by us; and believe it will be attended with suitable Returns of Love and Affection.

Then one of the Twightwees *stood up, and spoke as follows:* (Scarrooyady *Interpreter.*)

Brother Onas,

THE *Outawas, Cheepaways*, and the *French*, have struck us.—The Stroke was heavy, and hard to be borne, for thereby we lost our King, and several of our Warriors; but the Loss our Brethren, the *English*, suffered, we grieve for most. The Love we have had for the *English*, from our first Knowledge of them, still continues in our Breasts; and we shall ever retain the same ardent Affection for them.—We cover the Graves of the *English* with this Beaver Blanket. We mourn for them more than for our own People.

Here he spread on the Floor some Beaver Skins, sewed together in the Form of a Large Blanket.

Then Scarrooyady *spoke as follows:*

Brother Onas,

I SPEAK now on Behalf of all the *Indians* present, in Answer to what you said when you gave us the Goods and Belt. What you have said to us Yesterday is very kind, and pleases us exceedingly. The Speech which accompanied the Belt, is particularly of great Moment. We will take the Belt home to *Ohio*, where there is a greater and wiser Council than us, and consider it, and return you a full Answer. We return you Thanks for the Present.

Gave a String.

Brother Onas,

LAST Spring, when you heard of the March of the *French* Army, you were so good as to send us Word, that we might be on our Guard: We thank you for this friendly Notice.

Brother Onas,

YOUR People not only trade with us in our Towns, but disperse themselves over a large and wide extended Country, in which reside many Nations: At one End live the *Twightwees*, and at the other End the *Caghnawagas*, and *Adirondacks;* these you must comprehend in your Chain of Friendship, they are, and will be, your Brethren, let *Onontio* say what he will.

Gave a String.

Brother Onas,

I DESIRE you would hear and take Notice of what I am about to say now. The Governor of *Virginia* desired Leave to build a strong House on *Ohio*, which came to the Ears of the Governor of *Canada;* and we suppose this caused him to invade our Country. We do not know his Intent; because he speaks with two Tongues. So soon as we know his Heart, we shall be able to know what to do; and shall speak accordingly to him. We desire that *Pennsylvania* and *Virginia* would at present forbear settling on our Lands, over the *Allegheny* Hills. We advise you rather to call your People back on this Side the Hills, lest Damage should be done, and you think ill of us. But to keep up our Correspondence with our Brother *Onas*, we will appoint some Place on the Hills, or near them; and we do appoint *George Croghan*, on our Part, and desire you to appoint another on your Part, by a formal Writing, under the Governor's Hand. Let none of your People settle beyond where they are now; nor on the *Juniata* Lands, till the Affair is settled between us and the *French*. At present, *George Croghan*'s House, at *Juniata*, may be the Place where any Thing may be sent to us. We desire a Commission may be given to the Person intrusted by the Government of *Pennsylvania;* and that he may be directed to warn People from settling the *Indian* Lands, and impowered to remove them.

Gave a Belt and String.

Brother Onas,

ALL we who are here desire you will hear what we are going to say, and regard it as a Matter of Moment: The *French* look on the great Number of your Traders at *Ohio* with Envy; they fear they shall lose their Trade. You have more Traders than are necessary; and they spread themselves over our wide Country, at such great Distances, that we cannot see them, or protect them. We desire you will call back the great Number of your Traders, and let only three Setts of Traders remain; and order these to stay in three Places, which we have appointed for their Residence, *viz. Logs-Town*, the Mouth of *Canawa*, and the Mouth of *Mohongely;* the *Indians* will then come to them, and buy their Goods in these Places, and no where else. We shall likewise look on them under our Care, and shall be accountable for them. We have settled this Point with *Virginia* in the same Manner.

Gave a String.

Brother Onas,

THE *English* Goods are sold at too dear a Rate to us. If only honest and sober Men were to deal with us, we think they might afford the Goods cheaper: We desire therefore, that you will take effectual Care hereafter, that none but such be suffered to come out to trade with us.

Gave a String.

Brother Onas,

YOUR Traders now bring scarce any Thing but Rum and Flour: They bring little Powder and Lead, or other valuable Goods. The Rum ruins us. We beg you would prevent its coming in such Quantities, by regulating the Traders. We never understood the Trade was to be for Whiskey and Flour. We desire it may be forbidden, and none sold in the *Indian* Country; but that if the *Indians* will have any, they may go among the Inhabitants, and deal with them for it. When these Whiskey Traders come, they bring thirty or forty Cags, and put them down before us, and make us drink; and get all the Skins that should go to pay the Debts we have contracted for Goods bought of the Fair Traders; and by this Means, we not only ruin ourselves, but them too. These wicked Whiskey Sellers, when they have once got the *Indians* in Liquor, make them sell their very Clothes from their Backs.—In short, if this Practice be continued, we must be inevitably ruined: We most earnestly therefore beseech you to remedy it.

A treble String.

Brother Onas,

I HAVE now done with generals; but have something to say for particular Nations.

THE *Shawonese* heard some News since they came here, which troubled their Minds; on which they addressed themselves to their Grandfathers, the *Delawares;* and said, Grandfathers, we will live and die with you, and the *Six Nations:* We, our Wives and Children; and Children yet unborn.

N. B. *This was occasioned by* Conrad Weiser*'s having told them in private Conversation, that while he was in the* Mohock *Country, he was informed, that the* French *intended to drive away the* Shawonese (*as well as the* English) *from* Ohio.

SCARROOYADY then proceeded, and said, I have something farther to say on Behalf of the *Shawonese.*

Brother Onas,

At the Beginning of the Summer, when the News was brought to us, of the Approach of the *French*, the *Shawonese* made this Speech to their Uncles, the *Delawares*, saying, "Uncles, you have often told us, that we were a sensible and discreet People; but we lost all our Sense and Wits, when we slipp'd out of your Arms; however, we are now in one another's Arms again, and hope we shall slip out no more. We remember, and are returned to our former Friendship, and hope it will always continue. In Testimony, whereof, we give you, our Uncles, a String of ten Rows."

The *Shawonese* likewise, at the same time, sent a Speech to the *Six Nations*, saying, "Our Brethren, the *English*, have treated us as People that had Wit: The *French* deceived us: But we now turn our Heads about, and are looking perpetually to the Country of the *Six Nations*, and our Brethren, the *English*, and desire you to make an Apology for us; and they gave eight Strings of Wampum." The *Delawares* and *Six Nations* do therefore give up these Strings to *Onas*, and recommend the *Shawonese* to him as a People who have seen their Error, and are their and our very good Friends.

Gave eight Strings.

Brother Onas,

Before I finish, I must tell you, we all earnestly request you will please to lay all our present Transactions before the Council of *Onondago*, that they may know we do nothing in the Dark. They may perhaps think of us, as if we did not know what we were doing; or wanted to conceal from them what we do with our Brethren; but it is otherwise; and therefore make them acquainted with all our Proceedings: This is what we have likewise desired of the *Virginians* when we treated with them at *Winchester*.

Brother Onas,

I forgot something which I must now say to you; it is to desire you would assist us with some Horses to carry our Goods; because you have given us more than we can carry ourselves. Our Women and young People present you with this Bundle of Skins, desiring some Spirits to make them chearful in their own Country; not to drink here.

Presented a Bundle of Skins.

Then he added:

The *Twightwees* intended to say something to you; but they have mislaid some Strings, which has put their Speeches into Disorder; these they will rectify, and speak to you in the Afternoon.

Then the Indians *withdrew.*

At a Meeting of the Commissioners and Indians *the 3d of* October, 1753. P. M.

PRESENT,

The Commissioners, The same *Indians* as before.

The Magistrates, and several Gentlemen of the County.

The Twightwees *speak by* Andrew Montour.

Brother Onas,

HEARKEN what I have to say to the *Six Nations, Delawares, Shawonese,* and *English.*

THE *French* have struck us; but tho' we have been hurt, it is but on one Side; the other Side is safe. Our Arm on that Side is entire; and with it we laid hold on our Pipe, and have brought it along with us, to shew you it is as good as ever: And we shall leave it with you, that it may be always ready for us and our Brethren to smoak in when we meet together.

Here he delivered over the Calumet, decorated with fine Feathers.

Brother Onas,

WE have a single Heart. We have but one Heart. Our Heart is green, and good, and sound; This Shell, painted green on its hollow Side, is a Resemblance of it.

THE Country beyond us, towards the Setting of the Sun, where the *French* live, is all in Darkness; we can see no Light there: But towards Sun-rising, where the *English* live, we see Light; and that is the Way we turn our Faces. Consider us as your fast Friends, and good Brethren.

Here he delivered a large Shell, painted green on the Concave-side, with a String of Wampum tied to it.

Brother Onas,

THIS Belt of Wampum was formerly given to the King of the *Piankashas,* one of our Tribes, by the *Six Nations;* that if at any Time any of our People should be killed, or any Attack made on them by their Enemies, this Belt should be sent with the News, and the *Six Nations* would believe it.

THE *Twightwees,* when they brought this Belt to the Lower *Shawonese* Town, addressed themselves to the *Shawonese, Six Nations, Delawares,* and then to the *English,* and said;

Brethren,

WE are an unhappy People: We have had some of our Brethren, the *English,* killed and taken Prisoners in our Towns. Perhaps our Brethren, the *English,* may think, or be told, that we were the Cause of their Death: We therefore apply to you the *Shawonese,* &c. to assure the *English* we were not. The Attack was so sudden, that it was not in our Power to save them. And we hope, when you deliver this Speech to the *English,* they will not be prejudiced against us, but look on us as their Brethren: Our Hearts are good towards them.

A large Belt of fourteen Rows.

Brethren,

ONE of our Kings, on his Death bed, delivered to his Son, the young Boy who sits next to me, these eight Strings of Wampum, and told him, Child, "I am in Friendship with the *Shawonese, Delawares, Six Nations,* and *English;* and I desire you, if by any Misfortune I should happen to die, or be killed by my Enemies, you would send this String to them, and they will receive you in Friendship in my Stead.

Delivers the Strings.

THE following is a Speech of the Wife of the *Piankasha* King, after her Husband's Death, addressed to the *Shawonese, Six Nations, Delawares,* and *English:* "Remember, Brethren, that my Husband took a fast Hold of the Chain of Friendship subsisting between your Nations: Therefore I now deliver up his Child into your Care and Protection, and desire you would take Care of him; and remember the Alliance his Father was in with you, and not forget his Friendship, but continue kind to his Child."

Gave four Strings black and white.

Brethren, Shawonese, Delawares, Six Nations, *and* English,

WE acquaint all our Brethren, that we have prepared this Beaver Blanket as a Seat for all our Brethren to sit on in Council. In the Middle of it we have painted a green Circle, which is the Colour and Resemblance of our Hearts; which we desire our Brethren may believe are sincere towards our Alliance with them.

Delivered a Beaver Blanket.

Then Scarrooyady *stood up and said:*

Brother Onas,

THE *Shawonese* and *Delawares* delivered this Speech to the *Six Nations,* and desired they would deliver it to the *English;* and now I deliver it on their Behalf.

Brethren,

WE acquaint you, that as the Wife of the *Piankasha* King delivered his Child to all the Nations, to be taken Care of, they desire that those Nations may be interceeded with, to take Care that the said Child may be placed in his Father's Seat, when he comes to be a Man, to rule their People. And the *Six Nations* now, in Behalf of the Whole, request, that this Petition may not be forgot by the *English,* but that they would see the Request fulfilled.

Gave four Strings.

THEN *Scarrooyady* desired the *Six Nations* Council might be made acquainted with all these Speeches: And added, that they had no more to say; but what they have said is from their Hearts.

At a Meeting of the Commissioners, and Indians, *the 4th of* October, 1753.

PRESENT,

The Commissioners, The same *Indians* as before.

The Gentlemen of the County.

The Commissioners, unwilling to lose any Time, prepared their Answers early this Morning, and sent for the Indians; *who having seated themselves, the following Speech was made to them:*

Brethren, Six Nations, Delawares, Shawonese, Twightwees, *and* Owendaets,

THE several Matters delivered by you Yesterday have been well considered; and we are now going to return you our Answers.

THE Concern expressed by the *Twightwees* for the Death and Imprisonment of the *English,* with their Professions of Love and Esteem, denotes a sincere and friendly Disposition, which entitles them to our Thanks, and the Continuance of our Friendship; this they may certainly depend on.

Brethren,

YOU have recommended to us the several Nations, who, you say, live in that great Extent of Country, over which our Traders travel to dispose of their Goods, and especially the *Twightwees, Adirondacks,* and *Caghnawagas,* who you say live at different Extremities, and have good Inclinations towards the *English.*—We believe you would not give them this Character unless they deserved it. Your Recommendations always will have a Weight with us, and will dispose us in Favour of them, agreeable to your Request.

Brethren,

THE several Articles which contain your Observations on the *Indian* Traders, and the loose straggling Manner in which that Trade is carried on, thro' Countries lying at great Distances from your Towns—Your Proposals to remedy this, by having named three Places for the Traders to reside in, under your Care and Protection, with a Request, that the Province would appoint the particular Persons to be concerned in this Trade, for whom they will be answerable—What you say about the vast Quantities of Rum, and its ill Effects, and that no more may be brought amongst you; all these have made a very strong Impression upon our Minds; and was it now in our Power to rectify these Disorders, and to put Matters on the Footing you propose, we would do it with great Pleasure: But these are Affairs which more immediately concern the Government; in these therefore, we shall imitate your Example, by laying them before the Governor, assuring you, that our heartiest Representations of the Necessity of these Regulations shall not be wanting, being convinced, that unless something effectual be speedily done in these Matters, the good People of this Province can no longer expect Safety or Profit in their Commerce, nor the Continuance of your Affection.

Brethren,

WE will send an Account to *Onondago* of all that has been transacted between us.

WE will assist you with Horses for the Carriage of the Goods given you.

WE grant your Women and young Men their Request for Rum, on Condition it be not delivered to them until you shall have passed the Mountains.

SCARROOYADY some Days ago desired us to give Orders for the Mending of your Guns, *&c.* and we did so; being obliged to send for a Gunsmith out of the Country, as no One of that Trade lived in the Town; who promised to come: But having broke his Word, it has not been in our Power to comply with this Request.

Here the String given with the Request was returned.

HAVING delivered our general Answer, we shall now proceed to give one to what was said by particular Nations, as well by the *Shawonese* in the Forenoon, as by the *Twightwees* in the Afternoon.

Brethren, Delawares, *and* Shawonese,

WE are glad to see you in such good Dispositions to each other. We entreat you to do every Thing you can to preserve the Continuance of this agreeable Harmony. The *Shawonese* may be assured we retain no Manner of Remembrance of their former Miscarriages: We are perfectly reconciled, and our Esteem for their Nation is the same as ever.

Gave a large String.

Brethren, Twightwees,

WE shall take your several Presents, Shells, Strings, Beaver Blanket, and Calumet Pipe, with us, and deliver them to the Governor; that these, and the several Things said at the Delivery of them, may remain in the Council Chamber, at *Philadelphia,* for our mutual Use and Remembrance, whenever it shall please the Great Being, who sits above, to bring us together in Council again.

Gave a long String.

Brethren,

WE desire you will send these two Strouds to the young King, as an Acknowledgment of our affectionate Remembrance of his Father's Love to us, and of our Good-will to him.

BE pleased to present to the Widow of the *Piankasha* King, our late hearty Friend, these Handkerchiefs, to wipe the Tears from her Eyes; and likewise give her Son these two Strouds to clothe him.

Here two Handkerchiefs and two Strouds were given.

Brethren, Twightwees,

WE assure you we entertain no hard Thoughts of you; nor in any wise impute to you the Misfortune that befel the *English* in your Town; it was the Chance of War: We were struck together; we fell together; and we lament your Loss equally with our own.

Brethren, Six Nations, Delawares, Shawonese, Twightwees, *and* Owendaets,

WE have now finished our Answers; and we hope they will be agreeable to you: Whatever we have said, has been with a hearty Good-will towards you; our Hearts have accompanied our Professions, and you will always find our Actions agreeable to them. Then the Commissioners were silent; and, after a Space of Time, renewed their Speeches to them.

Brethren, Six Nations, Delawares, Shawonese, Twightwees, *and* Owendaets,

WE have something to say to you, to which we entreat you will give your closest Attention, since it concerns both us and you very much.

Brethren,

WE have held a Council on the present Situation of your Affairs. We have Reason to think, from the Advices of *Taaf* and *Callender,* that it would be too great a Risque, considering the present Disorder Things are in at *Ohio,* to encrease the Quantity of Goods already given you: We therefore acquaint you, that, though the Governor has furnished us with a larger Present of Goods, to put into your publick Store-house, as a general Stock, for your Support and Service, and we did intend to have sent them along with you; we have, on this late disagreeable Piece of News, altered our Minds, and determined, that the Goods shall not be delivered till the Governor be made acquainted with your present Circumstances, and shall give his own Orders for the Disposal of them. And that they may lie ready for your Use, to be applied for, whenever the Delivery may be safe, seasonable, and likely to do you the most Service; we have committed them to the Care of your good Friend *George Croghan,* who is to transmit to the Governor, by Express, a true and faithful Account how your Matters are likely to turn out; and on the Governor's Order, and not otherwise, to put you into the Possession of them.

THIS we hope you will think a prudent Caution, and a Testimony of our Care for your real Good and Welfare.

Brethren,

WE have a Favour of a particular Nature to request from your Speaker, *Scarrooyady,* in which we expect your Concurrence, and joint Interest; and therefore make it to him in your Presence. Here the Commissioners applying to *Scarrooyady,* spoke as follows:

Respected Chief and Brother Scarrooyady,

WE have been informed by *Andrew Montour,* and *George Croghan,* that you did at *Winchester,* in publick Council, undertake to go to *Carolina,* to sollicit the Release of some Warriors of the *Shawonese* Nation, who are said to be detained in the publick Prison of *Charles-Town,* on Account of some Mischief committed by them, or their Companions, in the inhabited Part of that Province; and these two Persons, who are your very good Friends, have given it as their Opinion, if, after you know what has passed at *Ohio*, you shall now leave this Company of *Indians*, and not return with them to their Families, and assist in the Consultations with the *Half King*, and their other Chiefs, what Measures to take in this unhappy Situation of your Affairs, all may be irrecoverably lost at *Allegheny*, and the Loss with Justice be laid at your Door. You may, perhaps, be afraid to disoblige the *Shawonese*, as it was at their Instance you undertook this Journey; but we intend to speak to them, and have no Doubt of obtaining their Consent; convinc'd as we are, that the Release of these Prisoners will be sooner and more effectually procur'd by the joint Interposition of the Governors of *Pennsylvania* and *Virginia*, than by your personal Sollicitation; in as much as our Governor, to whom we shall very heartily recommend this Affair, can send, with greater Dispatch, his Letters to *Carolina*, than you can perform the Journey; for at this Season, Opportunities present every Day of sending by Sea to *Charles-Town;* and an Express by Land may be dispatched to Governor *Dunwiddie*, as soon as we return to *Philadelphia*.

Gave a String.

The *Shawonese* Chiefs expressing Dissatisfaction at this Endeavour of the Commissioners to stop *Scarrooyady*, it gave us some Trouble to satisfy them, and obtain their Consent; but at last it was effected; and when this was signified to *Scarrooyady*, he made this Answer.

Brother Onas,

I will take your Advice, and not go to *Virginia* at this Time,—but go Home, and do every Thing in my Power for the common Good. And since we are here now together, with a great deal of Pleasure I must acquaint you, that we have set a Horn on *Andrew Montour*'s Head, and that you may believe what he says to be true, between the *Six Nations* and you, they have made him one of their Counsellors, and a great Man among them, and love him dearly.

Scarrooyady *gave a large Belt to* Andrew Montour, *and the Commissioners agreed to it.*

After this Difficulty was got over, nothing else remained to be done; and as the Absence of these *Indians* was dangerous, the Commissioners put an End to the Treaty, and took their Leave of them, making private Presents at parting, to such of the Chiefs, and others, as were recommended by the Interpreters to their particular Notice.

Thus, may it please the Governor, we have given a full and just Account of all our Proceedings, and we hope our Conduct will meet with his Approbation. But, in Justice to these *Indians,* and the Promises we made them, we cannot close our Report, without taking Notice, That the Quantities of strong Liquors sold to these *Indians* in the Places of their Residence, and during their Hunting Seasons, from all Parts of the Counties over *Sasquehannah,* have encreased of late to an inconceivable Degree, so as to keep these poor *Indians* continually under the Force of Liquor, that they are hereby become dissolute, enfeebled and indolent when sober, and untractable and mischievous in their Liquor, always quarrelling, and often murdering one another: That the Traders are under no Bonds, nor give any Security for their Observance of the Laws, and their good Behaviour; and by their own Intemperance, unfair Dealings, and Irregularities, will, it is to be feared, entirely estrange the Affections of the *Indians* from the *English;* deprive them of their natural Strength and Activity, and oblige them either to abandon their Country, or submit to any Terms, be they ever so unreasonable, from the *French.* These Truths, may it please the Governor, are of so interesting a Nature, that we shall stand excused in recommending in the most earnest Manner, the deplorable State of these *Indians,* and the heavy Discouragements under which our Commerce with them at present labours, to the Governor's most serious Consideration, that some good and speedy Remedies may be provided, before it be too late.

RICHARD PETERS,

November 1, 1753. *ISAAC NORRIS,*

BENJ. FRANKLIN.